SOLUTION EQUILIBRIA

SOLUTION EQUILIBRIA

F. R. HARTLEY
Head of Department of Chemistry and Metallurgy
Royal Military College of Science, Shrivenham

C. BURGESS
Glaxo Operations UK Ltd.
Barnard Castle, County Durham

and

R. M. ALCOCK
Severn-Trent Water Authority, Birmingham

ELLIS HORWOOD LIMITED
Publishers   Chichester

Halsted Press: a division of
JOHN WILEY & SONS
New York - Chichester - Brisbane - Toronto

First published in 1980 by
ELLIS HORWOOD LIMITED
Market Cross House, Cooper Street, Chichester, West Sussex, PO19 1EB, England

The publisher's colophon is reproduced from James Gillison's drawing of the ancient Market Cross, Chichester.

Distributors:

Australia, New Zealand, South-east Asia:
Jacaranda-Wiley Ltd., Jacaranda Press,
JOHN WILEY & SONS INC.,
G.P.O. Box 859, Brisbane, Queensland 40001, Australia.

Canada:
JOHN WILEY & SONS CANADA LIMITED
22 Worcester Road, Rexdale, Ontario, Canada.

Europe, Africa:
JOHN WILEY & SONS LIMITED
Baffins Lane, Chichester, West Sussex, England.

North and South America and the rest of the world:
Halsted Press, a division of
JOHN WILEY & SONS
605 Third Avenue, New York, N.Y. 10016, U.S.A.

British Library Cataloguing in Publication Data
Hartley, Frank Robinson
Solution equilibria
1. Chemical equilibrium
2. Solution (Chemistry)
I. Title II. Burgess, C. III. Alcock, R. M.
541'.341   QD503   79–42956

ISBN 0–85312–148–6 (Ellis Horwood Ltd., Publishers, Library Edition)
ISBN 0–470–26880–8 (Halsted Press)

Typeset in Press Roman by Ellis Horwood Ltd.
Printed in Great Britain by W. & J. Mackay Ltd., Chatham

Table of Contents

Chapter 11 SECOND CASE STUDY: Leden and Non-linear Treatment of Potentiometric Data; The Silver(I)-Allylalcohol System

Chapter 12 THIRD CASE STUDY: Qualitative and Quantitative Analysis of Spectrophotometric Data; The Copper(II)-Ethylenediamine-Oxalate System

To

V.H., V.F.B., J.A.A., S.M.H., J.A.H., E.J.H., R.J.A.B.

Preface

Once upon a time, three chemists were interested in stability constants. The first was primarily an inorganic chemist investigating quantitative relationships between metals and ligands. The second was an analytical chemist interested in solution equilibria and spectrophotometry. The third was mathematically inclined with a penchant for computer model building. The result of this extraordinary three body collision catalysed by Dr. D. E. Rogers of the Chemistry Department, Southampton University, is this book.

It is some one hundred and fifteen years since Guldberg and Waage first set out the law of mass action, although solution equilibria studies were only really developed in the first half of the twentieth century. The pioneering work of the Bjerrums, Sillén and the Scandinavian school dominated this period. This work was brilliantly described by the Rossottis in their classic textbook *The Determination of Stability Constants* published in 1961. Since that time, two major developments have affected stability constant studies. Firstly, the advent of fast digital computers has enabled advanced mathematical treatment of large amounts of data to be carried out. Secondly, since the subject has 'come of age' many stability constants have been determined by chemists who are 'amateurs' in the sense that they do not devote all their professional lives to the determination of stability constants; rather they study the positions of equilibria they come across in the course of their chemical investigations.

This book has been written with four main purposes in mind. Firstly, to give an up-to-date account of the ways in which an equilibrium system may be studied. Secondly, to give sufficient experimental information so that the 'amateur' is able to choose a method suitable for his particular system and to avoid major pitfalls. Thirdly, to show how to turn apparently bewildering algebra into straightforward numerical results. Finally, to show the application of stability constants to major areas to scientific interest.

When writing any book today there is a problem with units. We have decided to use both SI and non-SI units, showing the latter in brackets. Some knowledge of matrix algebra is essential to the understanding of modern computational methods, and, recognising that not all readers will possess this, we have given a brief summary in Appendix I. Finally, there is the problem of symbols. The principal symbols used in more than one section of the book are listed on the bookmark and after the index.

Whilst writing this book we have been very conscious of how much we owe to our many friends and colleagues for their help in stimulating our efforts to understand the subject. Particular mention should be made of Dr. Rossotti who guided the first few steps of one of us in Oxford, and Dr. A. G. Fogg who did the same for another at Loughborough. All three of us are deeply appreciative of the many hours of discussion we spent during four very profitable years of collaboration with Dr. D. E. Rogers in Southampton. In particular we are grateful to our many colleagues at Southampton, especially Drs. Searle and Wagner who provided the data for the second and fourth case studies respectively and who read and commented on some of the early drafts of the manuscript. We thank Prof. Bjerrum for useful discussions and for allowing us to use his data in the third case study and Prof. Watters for the use of his data in the third case study as well as, in conjunction with the American Chemical Society, permitting us to develop Figure 12.1 from his original paper.

Finally, that this book ever reached completion is due to a number of people, to all of whom we owe our sincere thanks: Trish Abrams who deciphered our handwriting with remarkable patience, speed and accuracy in producing the typed manuscript; Ellis Horwood who agreed to publish; our wives and families who tolerated our absences; and Jenny who wined and dined us during our meetings together.

F. R. Hartley
C. Burgess
R. M. Alcock

CHAPTER 1

Fundamental Concepts

1.1 INTRODUCTION

There are two major areas of solution chemistry. The first of these, which forms the subject of the present book, is concerned with the chemical nature and concentration of each of the species present at equilibrium. The second concerns the rate and mechanism by which the species added to the solution come to equilibrium, and for this readers are referred to references [1–3]. These two aspects of solution chemistry are, of course, closely related. Consider a system

$$A + B \underset{k_r}{\overset{k_f}{\rightleftharpoons}} C + D \tag{1.1}$$

where k_f and k_r are the forward and reverse rate constants. The rate at which the reaction proceeds in a forward direction, which equals the rate of loss of A $(-dA/dt)$, is given by

$$-dA/dt = k_f\{A\}\{B\} \tag{1.2}$$

where $\{X\}$ is the activity of species X. In addition, the rate of the reverse reaction, which equals the rate of formation of A (dA/dt), is given by

$$dA/dt = k_r\{C\}\{D\} \tag{1.3}$$

At equilibrium the rates of the forward and reverse reactions are equal, and so

$$k_f\{A\}\{B\} = k_r\{C\}\{D\} \tag{1.4}$$

which may be rearranged to give

$$\frac{k_f}{k_r} = K^\ominus = \frac{\{C\}\{D\}}{\{A\}\{B\}} \tag{1.5}$$

where k_f/k_r, being a constant, is written as a single constant $K^\ominus$, and is known as an equilibrium constant. Equation (1.5) is known as Guldberg and Waage's relationship [4] and can be used as a basis for measuring equilibrium constants provided that the reaction takes place by a one-step mechanism [5]. Equilibrium constants that refer to the interaction of metal ions and ligands are commonly referred to as stability constants (see Section 1.5).

This book is concerned particularly with the evaluation of stability constants and hence the determination of the composition of a given solution. Before embarking on this let us look briefly at the applications of this information, which fall into two broad areas:

(i) Applications in other fields of chemistry

A knowledge of the nature and concentration of the species present in solution has many applications of which the following are some examples.

(a) It can be exploited in the medical field as in the treatment of Wilson's disease, which is an accumulation of copper in the liver, brain, and kidneys, with $Na_2CaEDTA$ (I); or in the use of cis-$[Pt(NH_3)_2Cl_2]$ for

$$
\begin{array}{l}
-OOC-CH_2 \\
\diagdown \\
N-CH_2-CH_2-N \\
\diagup \\
-OOC-CH_2
\end{array}
\qquad
\begin{array}{l}
CH_2-COO^- \\
\diagup \\
N \\
\diagdown \\
CH_2-COO^-
\end{array}
$$

I

treating certain forms of cancer; or in the administration of a buffered ferrous sulphate solution as an antidote to cyanide poisoning.

(b) It can be used in determining the role of metal ions in biological processes.

(c) The use of sodium thiosulphate in the developing of photographic films depends on its ability to dissolve silver halides and so remove them from the film emulsion as the stable water-soluble complex ion $[Ag(S_2O_3)_2]^{3-}$.

(d) The use of complexing agents, such as phosphates, as water softeners depends on their ability to form stable soluble complexes of metal ions, such as calcium, which would otherwise react with soap to form insoluble salts which appear as an objectionable scum.

(e) The field of analytical chemistry depends heavily on complexing agents both directly, as in complexometric (for example, EDTA) titrations and indirectly as indicators, masking agents, precipitants and reagents for redissolving precipitates.

These and further applications are considered in detail in Chapter 15.

(ii) *Applications to the theoretical understanding of inorganic chemistry*

Some insight into how and why species react can be gained from a study of the nature and stability of the species present in solution. This subject, which is still very much in its infancy, has led to a number of schemes for classifying Lewis acids and bases such as the class 'a'/class 'b' and 'hard and soft' approaches which are discussed in detail in Chapter 14.

1.2 SYSTEMATIC INVESTIGATION OF SOLUTION CHEMISTRY

The process by which the nature of the species present in a solution at equilibrium is systematically investigated can be divided into a number of steps:

(a) The nature of each of the species present in solution is first identified by using a mixture of 'chemical intuition' and a number of physico-chemical techniques which determine either the stoichiometry of the species present (that is, the values of m and n in $M_m L_n$) or the number of different species present. These form the subject matter of Chapter 2.

(b) Expressions relating the concentrations of the initial reactants and final products are set up. These expressions define the stability constants and form the subject matter of the present chapter.

(c) As many quantitative observations as possible are made on the solution, using one or more of the techniques outlined in Chapters 6–9.

(d) The errors inherent in these measurements are discussed in Chapter 4.

(e) The equilibrium concentrations of all the species present in solution are calculated. Linear methods for doing this (based on derived functions), most of which were developed before the days of modern digital computers, are described in Chapter 3. However, most of these methods are reliable only for simple systems, in particular mononuclear species with not more than three ligands (that is, $M_m L_n$ where $m = 1$ and $n \leqslant 3$). For more complex systems a non-linear data treatment using a digital computer must be used. This is described in Chapter 5.

Since the way in which one puts together the data obtained by following the scheme just outlined is complex, four case studies, in Chapters 10 to 13, describe the investigation of actual systems. Finally, having studied the equilibria present in a number of systems, it is sometimes possible to rationalise the data obtained and make predictions about other systems. This procedure is described in Chapter 14. Some of the applications of stability constants are described in Chapter 15.

1.3 COMPLEXES

Throughout this book we shall be concerned with the formation of complexes. What are complexes? They are compounds containing a central atom or ion, which is usually a metal but may be any electron acceptor (Lewis acid), and which is surrounded by several electron donor groups (Lewis bases) that are generally referred to as ligands. The complex, which may be either charged or neutral, tends to retain its identity even in solution, although of course both dissociation and replacement of the original ligands may occur. Since a number of different types of complex are referred to in the literature let us look at each of these in turn.

(i) *Inner- and outer-sphere complexes*

When a ligand bonds covalently to a metal the resulting complex is sometimes referred to as an **inner-sphere complex**. In such a complex the ligand occupies a clearly defined site within the coordination shell of the metal. An **outer-sphere complex** is formed when an inner-sphere complex is weakly linked through electrostatic, Van der Waals' or hydrogen-bonding to further groups. In general these groups do not occupy specific sites around the metal.

(ii) *Chelate complexes*

When a ligand such as EDTA, (I), or ethylenediamine, (II), which can potentially coordinate to a metal ion through more than one position acts as a multidentate ligand, the resulting complex is said to be a **chelate complex**. Chelate complexes,

$$NH_2 \diagup \overset{CH_2 \text{———} CH_2}{} \diagdown NH_2$$

II

considered in more detail in Chapter 14, are of particular importance because of their generally greater stability than the complexes of the corresponding unidentate ligands. This greater stability, known as the chelate effect (see Section 14.6), gives rise to their widespread applications in analytical chemistry, for example in complexometric titrations such as EDTA titrations. It is also responsible for the ligands which nature has chosen to surround metals in biological systems.

(iii) *Mononuclear and polynuclear complexes*

Mononuclear complexes have only one metal ion in each complex unit. Thus ML, ML_2, and ML_n are all **mononuclear** complexes. By contrast, complexes in which more than one metal ion is present, such as M_2L and M_mL_n ($m > 1$), are described as **polynuclear**. Polynuclear complexes are of particular importance in the hydrolysis of metal ions. For example, if alkali is added to a beryllium salt the polynuclear hydroxy-complexes $[Be_2(OH)]^{3+}$ and $[Be_3(OH)_3]^{3+}$ are formed in addition to the mononuclear $[Be(OH)_2]$.

1.4 STABILITY

Since, as we shall see in Section 1.5, the equilibrium constants that refer to the interaction of metals and ligands are widely referred to as stability constants, we must look carefully at what we mean by the word 'stability'. In practice there are two types of stability, namely *thermodynamic* and *kinetic*.

A system is said to be **thermodynamically stable** if its free energy is lower, that is, more negative, than the sum of the free energies of the products formed when it reacts (see Figure 1.1). When we determine free energies from equilibrium studies (see Section 1.10) we can use these to determine whether two of more species present in a mixture will react together and, if so, to what extent. Equilibrium studies alone cannot give any information about the reaction rate, because for a reaction to proceed, *two* criteria must be fulfilled:

(a) There must be a favourable free energy change.
(b) There must be a pathway of sufficiently low activation energy for it to occur at a measurable rate.

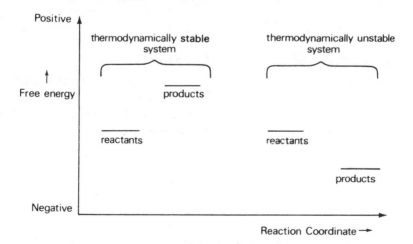

Figure 1.1 — The relation between free energy and thermodynamic stability.

If both criteria are met, the system is said to be **labile**. If there is no low activation pathway the reaction will not proceed, even it it is thermodynamically possible. A system in this state is said to be **inert**. This is illustrated in Figure 1.2.

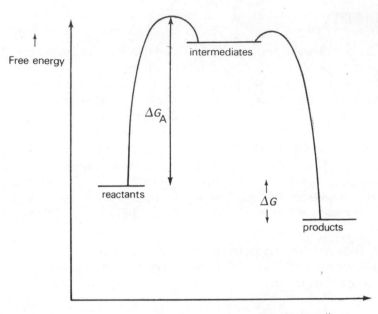

Figure 1.2 – The relation between the activation free energy (ΔG_A) and kinetic stability. If ΔG_A is too large, no reaction will occur even though ΔG is favourable.

1.5 THERMODYNAMIC STABILITY CONSTANTS

A fundamental concept in the study of solution equilibria is the equilibrium constant defined by Equation (1.5). There are two particular equilibrium constants that are commonly given special names. Thus when the Lewis acid is the proton, the inverse of the equilibrium constant for the reaction

$$H^+ + X^- \xrightleftharpoons{K^{\ominus}_{HX}} HX \qquad (1.6)$$

$$K^{\ominus}_a = 1/K^{\ominus}_{HX} = \{H^+\}\{X^-\}/\{HX\}$$

is known as the **acid dissociation constant** ($K^{\ominus}_a$) of the acid HX. The second special case is when the Lewis acid is a metal ion (M)† and the Lewis base is a ligand (L)†, then for the reaction

$$M + L \xrightleftharpoons{K^{\ominus}_{ML}} ML \qquad (1.7)$$

† Throughout this book charges are omitted for the sake of simplicity, except when discussing specific metal ions or ligands.

the equilibrium constant $K_{ML}^{\ominus}$ $(= \{ML\}/\{M\}\{L\})$ is known as a **stability constant**. Its inverse (that is, $1/K_{ML}^{\ominus} = \{M\}\{L\}/\{ML\}$) is known as an **instability constant** and was at one time widely favoured by Russian inorganic chemists.

In many cases more than one ligand can coordinate to a given metal ion. Niels Bjerrum first suggested in 1915 and later proved that the formation of complexes occurs in a stepwise manner so that ML is formed first, ML_2 second, and so on, and that in the general case it is not possible to form ML_n without first forming ML_{n-1}. Consider the case[‡] of the reaction of silver ions with ammonia in which only two complexes are formed,

$$Ag^+ + NH_3 \xrightarrow{\ K_1^{\ominus}\ } Ag(NH_3)^+ \qquad (1.8)$$

$$Ag(NH_3)^+ + NH_3 \xrightarrow{\ K_2^{\ominus}\ } Ag(NH_3)_2{}^+ \qquad (1.9)$$

$$K_1^{\ominus} = \{Ag(NH_3)^+\}/\{Ag^+\}\{NH_3\} \qquad (1.10)$$

$$K_2^{\ominus} = \{Ag(NH_3)_2{}^+\}/\{Ag(NH_3)^+\}\{NH_3\} \qquad (1.11)$$

$K_1^{\ominus}$ and $K_2^{\ominus}$ are known as **stepwise stability constants**. Since we are dealing with equilibrium systems we can quite easily consider the formation of $Ag(NH_3)_2{}^+$ from silver ions and ammonia.

$$Ag^+ + 2NH_3 \xrightarrow{\ \beta^{\ominus}\ } Ag(NH_3)_2{}^+. \qquad (1.12)$$

In such a case the stability constant is given the Greek letter β and is known as an **overall stability constant**.

$$\beta^{\ominus} = \{Ag(NH_3)_2{}^+\}/\{Ag^+\}\{NH_3\}^2 \qquad (1.13)$$

If more than two metal ligand complexes are formed, then several stability constants may be defined. In general,

$$K_n^{\ominus} = \{ML_n\}/\{ML_{n-1}\}\{L\} \qquad (1.14)$$

and the corresponding overall stability constants, $\beta_n^{\ominus}$, are given by

$$\beta_n^{\ominus} = \{ML_n\}/\{M\}\{L\}^n \qquad (1.15)$$

[‡] This system is considered further in Section 3.8.

There is, of course, a specific relationship between the overall stability constant $\beta_n^\ominus$ and the stepwise stability constants. In general

$$\beta_n^\ominus = K_1^\ominus \times K_2^\ominus \times K_3^\ominus \times \ldots K_n^\ominus \qquad (1.16)$$

which may be proved by writing down the expressions for $\beta_n^\ominus$ and $K_1^\ominus, K_2^\ominus \ldots K_n^\ominus$. We leave this as an exercise for the reader.

So far in this section we have totally ignored the solvent and have effectively considered that the reaction takes place in the gas phase. In solution a reaction that we might wish to write as in Equation $(1.7)^\dagger$ should strictly be written as

$$M(\text{solvent})_m + L(\text{solvent})_1 \rightleftharpoons ML(\text{solvent})_n + (m+1-n)\text{solvent} \qquad (1.17)$$

from which it is apparent that the solvation of all three species M, L, and ML will be crucial in determining the overall stability constant [6]. Many reactions have been studied in aqueous solution, and since in aqueous solution a metal ion will exist as $M(H_2O)_m^{n+}$ the reaction of metal ions and ligands in aqueous solution involves the displacement of coordinated water molecule by the ligand (Reaction (1.18), where 'aq' refers to non-specifically coordinated water).

$$M(H_2O)_m^{n+}.aq + L.aq \xrightarrow{\ K_{ML}^\ominus\ } ML(H_2O)_{m-1}^{n+}.aq + H_2O \qquad (1.18)$$

The equilibrium constant for this reaction, $K_{ML}^\ominus$, is given by

$$K_{ML}^\ominus = \frac{\{ML(H_2O)_{m-1}^{n+}\}\{H_2O\}}{\{M(H_2O)_m^{n+}\}\{L\}} \qquad (1.19)$$

The term $\{ML(H_2O)_{m-1}^{n+}\}/\{M(H_2O)^{n+}\}\{L\}$ is that usually referred to simply as the stability constant and is strictly known as the **conventional stability constant**. The whole of the right-hand side of Equation (1.19) is known as the **unitary part** of the stability constant. The term $\{H_2O\}$ is known as the **cratic part** of the stability constant [7] and for water at 25°C is 55.5 mol.l^{-1}. It is normally neglected, on the grounds that in most studies, which are made in dilute solution, the activity of the water is effectively constant so that the conventional stability constant is equal to $K_{ML}^\ominus/\{H_2O\}$ which is itself a constant. However, whilst conventional stability constants obtained in this way are adequate for comparing two ligands that coordinate through the same number of sites, they can be misleading when comparing two ligands that coordinate through different numbers of sites, for example, ammonia (NH_3) and ethylenediamine ($NH_2CH_2CH_2NH_2$).

† And will, in fact, often find written in this way in the literature.

1.6 STOICHIOMETRIC STABILITY CONSTANTS

So far we have defined all our equilibrium and stability constants in terms of the activities of the species present. However, in practice many analytical techniques yield concentrations rather than activities (see Section 6.1). Concentrations are, of course, related to activities by the expression

$$\{X\} = [X]\gamma_x \tag{1.20}$$

where $[X]$ = concentration of X and γ_x = activity coefficient of X. Activity coefficients are in general tedious and difficult to measure. They also depend very significantly on the nature and concentrations of the other species present in solution so that it is not possible to prepare universal tables of activity coefficients which could be consulted. Theoretical attempts at calculating activity coefficients, based on the Debye-Hückel approach and its extensions, are at best of only limited accuracy.

The most expedient solution to what is a very major problem is to rewrite the thermodynamic stability constant in terms of both concentrations and activity coefficients (Equation (1.21)).

$$K^\ominus = \frac{\{ML\}}{\{M\}\{L\}} = \frac{[ML]}{[M][L]} \times \frac{\gamma_{ML}}{\gamma_M \gamma_L} \tag{1.21}$$

If now it were possible to ensure that the term $\gamma_{ML}/\gamma_M \gamma_L$ remained constant (albeit at the expense of not knowing its absolute value) then K defined by Equation (1.22) would also be a constant.

$$K = [ML]/[M][L] \tag{1.22}$$

K is known as a **stoichiometric stability constant** whereas $K^\ominus$ is known as a **thermodynamic stability constant**. The term $\gamma_{ML}/\gamma_M \gamma_L$ in Equation (1.21) may be maintained effectively constant [8] by, (a) having a large excess of an inert background electrolyte present, that is an electrolyte which does not react with any of the metal, ligand, or metal-ligand species, and (b) using only low concentrations of metal and ligand so that any change in their concentrations as a result of their reaction together has a insignificant change on the overall ionic strength of the medium.

The ionic strength (μ) is normally defined by the equation $\mu = \frac{1}{2}\Sigma c_i z_i^2$, where c_i is the concentration and z_i is the charge of species i; accordingly ionic strength has the units of concentration (that is, mol.l^{-1}). However, it has recently been shown [9] that ionic strength should be defined by the equation $\mu = \frac{1}{2}\Sigma c_i |z_i|$. The two definitions are, of course, identical for univalent ions, but when significant concentrations of multivalent ions are present the latter should be used. It is generally possible to replace about 5% of the ions in the background electrolyte without appreciably altering the activity coefficients of the minor species present. Thus if, for example, a 2 mol.l^{-1} solution of sodium perchlorate is to be used as the background electrolyte, the upper limits of the concentrations of all the other ionic species present must not exceed 0.1 mol.l^{-1} (if these species are 1:1 electrolytes), 0.04 mol.l^{-1} (for 2:1 electrolytes), 0.025 mol.l^{-1} (for 2:2 electrolytes), 0.02 mol.l^{-1} (for 1:3 electrolytes), 0.015 mol.l^{-1} (for 2:3 electrolytes) and 0.011 mol.l^{-1} (for 3:3 electrolytes). For a 3 mol.l^{-1} background electrolyte the maximum permitted concentrations of the reacting species are increased to 0.14 mol.l^{-1} (for 1:1 electrolytes), 0.06 mol.l^{-1} (for 2:1 electrolytes), 0.036 mol.l^{-1} (for 2:2 electrolytes), 0.029 mol.l^{-1} (for 1:3 electrolytes), 0.022 mol.l^{-1} (for 2:3 electrolytes) and 0.016 mol.l^{-1} (for 3:3 electrolytes). This requirement to limit the concentrations of reacting metal ions and ligands will have important consequences when we come to choose a method for measuring stability constants, since it results in methods of low sensitivity being unattractive owing to the reduced reliability of their results. This point is taken up further in Chapter 9.

Since one of the principal applications of stability constant data is to compare one ligand with another or one metal ion with another, stoichiometric stability constants are usually as good as thermodynamic stability constants. However, in recording a stoichiometric stability constant it is essential to record not only the concentration of the background electrolyte but also its nature, since the activity coefficients depend on the electrolyte. Thus they may be different in 2 mol.l^{-1} $NaClO_4$ and 2 mol.l^{-1} KNO_3. Consequently, of course, in comparing stability constants, only data obtained under very similar conditions should be used unless the differences between the stability constants are large.

1.7 DETERMINATION OF THERMODYNAMIC STABILITY CONSTANTS

Occasionally it is possible to measure stoichiometric stability constants over a range of ionic strengths and to extrapolate to zero ionic strength, so obtaining thermodynamic stability constants. In doing this, care must be taken that the metal and ligand concentrations are sufficiently low that even at the lowest ionic strength there is enough inert background electrolyte present to make their contributions to the overall ionic strength constant. Ideally if thermodynamic stability constants must be obtained by extrapolation to zero ionic strength they should be obtained from measurements in two different ionic media, since agreement in the two media will ensure that no specific effects due to the background electrolytes are present. A number of techniques for extrapolating to zero ionic strength have been suggested, varying from plotting $\log K$ against the ionic strength (μ) itself, which is probably valid for uncharged ligands, through plotting $\log K$ against $\mu^{1/2}$ or $\mu^{1/3}$, to plotting complex functions such as the right-hand side of Equation (1.23) against μ or $\mu^{1/2}$. Equation (1.23) is obtained by combining an extended form of the Debye–Hückel equation (1.24) where a, A, B, and C are all constants, some or all of which may be treated as adjustable parameters, with Equation (1.21).

$$\log K^{\ominus} = \log K - \frac{A z_+ z_- \sqrt{\mu}}{1 + aB\sqrt{\mu}} - C\mu \tag{1.23}$$

$$-\log\gamma_{\pm} = \frac{A z_+ z_- \sqrt{\mu}}{1 + aB\sqrt{\mu}} - C\mu \tag{1.24}$$

None of these extrapolations is very reliable, as a survey of nine metal-ligand systems has shown [10], since each extrapolation gave a different value for the thermodynamic stability constant, and in the worst case the different extrapolations differed by over 400%! A plot of $\log K^{\ominus}$ for Equilibrium (1.25) against ionic strength emphasises the difficulties that any extrapolation is likely to yield (see Figure 1.3) [11].

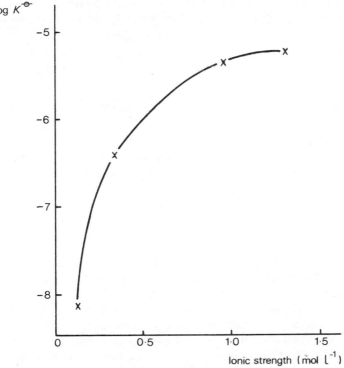

Figure 1.3 – Plot of $\log K^{\ominus}$ for Equilibrium (1.25) against ionic strength in the presence of potassium nitrate (data from reference [11]).

$$[AlA_2]^{5-} + 2H^+ \rightleftharpoons [AlA]^- + H_2A^{2-} \qquad (1.25)$$

(H$_2$A = catecholdisulphonic acid).

If thermodynamic stability constants are required they are best obtained by working in very dilute solution when all the activity coefficients are close to unity. Clearly this approach is limited to systems that have large stability constants. However, the third possible approach, namely to calculate the activity coefficients present in Equation (1.21), is unreliable [12] because of the limited accuracy of even the most extended forms of the Debye–Hückel relationship, such as that in Equation (1.24).

1.8 MEDIUM

Because of the difficulty of measuring activity coefficients most workers, led by the Scandinavian school, have preferred to ensure that they have been kept constant by using a high concentration of an inert background electrolyte. This in turn has resulted in most equilibrium studies being carried out in water or organic solvents, such as dioxane or ethyleneglycol, which dissolve appreciable quantities of a number of electrolytes. However, there are disadvantages in using polar solvents, and recently some workers have begun using non-polar solvents such as benzene and carbon tetrachloride. The disadvantages of polar solvents include:

(a) The incorporation of high solvation contributions into the overall thermodynamics of the interaction. These contributions are smaller in non-polar solvents and hence more closely cancel to zero.
(b) The greater difficulty of characterising the structure of the species in solution in the presence of a high concentration of a powerful nucleophile such as water.
(c) The insolubility of many non-polar ligands and their complexes in polar solvents such as water.

Clearly, non-polar solvents can only be used for metal complexes of low or zero overall charge and for neutral ligands such as ammonia or olefins. Where non-ionic species are present it is generally only necessary to work at low concentrations to ensure that the activity coefficients are constant, since for non-electrolytes activity coefficients tend to unity at low concentrations. What constitutes a sufficiently 'low' concentration depends very much on the nature of the solute and solvent. If both are non-polar and similar in structure, for example $SnCl_4$ and CCl_4, then 'low' can be as high as $1 \, mol.l^{-1}$, but as the polarity of the solute is increased the concentration needed to ensure unit activity coefficients decreases. However, almost all solutes exhibit unit activity coefficients (within experimental error) below about 10^{-3} mol.l^{-1}. The concentrations at which the approximation of considering activity coefficients to be unity ceases to be valid can be found be determining the concentration at which the vapour-pressure composition curve for the solution ceases to obey Raoult's Law [13, 14].

1.9 NATURE OF THE BACKGROUND ELECTROLYTE

As we have already mentioned, inert salts are often added to the medium to ensure that, in spite of the loss of free metal and free ligand and the formation of metal-ligand complexes, the ionic strength remains effectively constant throughout the reaction. The vital feature of the added background electrolyte is that it should take no part in the equilibrium being studied. Electrolytes that are commonly used are sodium salts such as the perchlorate or nitrate. For many years perchlorate ions were thought not to interact with metal ions at all, and therefore to be ideal as part of the background electrolyte. After the discovery that mercury(I), iron(II), and cerium(III) all complex with perchlorate [15], there was an immediate aversion to the use of perchlorate salts. However, it must be emphasised that any interaction between perchlorate ions and metal ions is the exception (albeit an important one) rather than the rule and that, except in special instances, perchlorate is usually more suitable than any other anion. Sodium chloride has been used as a background electrolyte, but its use is less common than the perchlorate or nitrate because chloride ions often form complexes with the metal ions under study. Potassium nitrate and chloride have also been used on occasions, but the perchlorate is unsuitable owing to its low solubility. In cases where the hydrogen ion concentration varies appreciably during the reaction, lithium salts are generally preferred because the small lithium cation more closely resembles the hydrogen ion than any other metal ion. Lithium salts are often useful in non-aqueous solvents such as ethers where they have a greater solubility than sodium or potassium salts.

We stated just now that the background electrolyte must take no part in the equilibrium being studied. However, it may take part in other equilibria present that are not being studied and indeed may well be chosen specifically for this. For example the equilibrium between allylammonium ions and tetrachloroplatinate(II) ions. (Reaction (1.26)) in aqueous solution was studied, using 1.9 mol.l^{-1} NaCl + 0.1 mol.l^{-1} HCl as the background electrolyte [16].

$$[PtCl_4]^{2-} + CH_2\text{=}CHCH_2NH_3^+ \rightleftharpoons \left[Cl_3Pt\text{—}\begin{matrix} CH_2 \\ \| \\ CHCH_2NH_3 \end{matrix} \right] + Cl^- \qquad (1.26)$$

The chloride was chosen to minimise Reaction (1.27) and the hydrogen ion to drive Equilibrium (1.28) to the right to prevent any significant quantity of free allylamine being present, since this would coordinate to platinum (II) through its nitrogen atom rather than through its double-bond. By forcing Equilibrium (1.27) to the left this equilibrium was minimised so enabling the position of the one remaining (1.26), to be determined more accurately.

$$[PtCl_4]^{2-} + H_2O \rightleftharpoons [PtCl_3(H_2O)]^- + Cl^- \qquad (1.27)$$

$$CH_2=CHCH_2NH_2 + H^+ \rightleftharpoons CH_2=CHCH_2NH_3^+ \qquad (1.28)$$

1.10 THERMODYNAMIC FUNCTIONS

Let us now turn to the evaluation of the free energy, enthalpy, and entropy changes corresponding to stability constants. Since most solution studies are carried out in open vessels we need only consider relationships that hold at constant pressure.

(i) Gibbs free energy
At constant pressure the Gibbs free energy change (ΔG) is related to the stability constant by Equation (1.29), where R is the gas constant and T is the absolute

$$\Delta G = -RT\ln K \qquad (1.29)$$

temperature. For an equilibrium such as (1.30) K is a dimensionless number, and so long as we express the concentrations of all four species A, B, C, and D in the

$$A + B \xrightleftharpoons{K} C + D \qquad (1.30)$$

same units, the resulting value of ΔG will have the units of RT, that is either $kJ.mol^{-1}$ or $kcal.mol^{-1}$. However, for Equilibrium (1.31),

$$A + B \xrightleftharpoons{K'} C \qquad (1.31)$$

K' has units of 1/concentration. It is therefore essential in this case that we express our concentration in the correct units. These are, of course, those pertaining to the standard state [17,18], and for a solution the units of concentration are $mol.l^{-1}$ at $25°C$ and 1 atmosphere pressure.

(ii) Enthalpy
The enthalpy change (ΔH) may be obtained in one of three ways:

(a) *The temperature dependence of the equilibrium constant*

At constant pressure,

$$\Delta G = \Delta H - T\Delta S \qquad (1.32)$$

where ΔS is the change in the entropy, and so from (1.29) and (1.32),

$$\ln K = \Delta S/R - \Delta H/RT \qquad (1.33)$$

It follows from (1.33) that IF ΔH and ΔS are temperature independent then a plot of $\ln K$ against $1/T$ should be a straight line of slope $-\Delta H/R$ and intercept $\Delta S/R$. In practice neither ΔH nor ΔS is strictly independent of temperature although they are both approximately so over a narrow range of temperature. The temperature dependences of ΔH and ΔS are given by,

$$\frac{\partial(\Delta H)}{\partial T} = \Delta C_p \qquad (1.34)$$

$$\frac{\partial(\Delta S)}{\partial T} = \frac{\Delta C_v}{T} \qquad (1.35)$$

where ΔC_p and ΔC_v are the differences in the thermal capacities of the products and reactants at constant pressure and constant volume respectively. The major difficulty inherent in using the temperature dependence of the stability constant to evaluate ΔH is now apparent: on the one hand one wants to use as wide a temperature range as possible in order to obtain the maximum precision in determining the slope of the $\ln K$ v $1/T$ plot, but on the other hand the temperature range that can be used is limited by the temperature dependence of ΔH itself. In general a compromise of about 30°C range of temperature is used. If the stability constants can be obtained to within ±3% then the resulting ΔH values have a precision of about $\pm 0.85\,\text{kJ.mol}^{-1}$ $(= 0.20\,\text{kcal.mol}^{-1})$.

Although it has been widely used in the past this approach, because of its limited accuracy, is not to be recommended if ΔH can be evaluated directly by either of the calorimetric methods in Sections (b) or (c) below. However, this is only possible in the case of systems that come to equilibrium rapidly; for kinetically inert systems the temperature dependence of the stability constant is the only method available for obtaining enthalpy data. In such cases the stability constants should, if possible, be evaluated from data based on activities rather than concentrations, because if the latter are used the temperature dependence of the activity coefficients of the species present will interfere.

(b) *Direct calorimetric measurement*

Direct calorimetric measurement [19] is always the method of choice
for determining the enthalpy change of a reaction if that reaction
occurs sufficiently rapidly to enable the heat absorbed or evolved to be
measured directly. With the more recent microcalorimeters reaction
times of up to 2 hours can be tolerated, although with less sophisticated
apparatus the reaction should be essentially complete within the time
of mixing. With suitable apparatus an accuracy of ±0.5% should be
obtainable (see Section 9.5(i)).

(c) *Thermometric titration calorimetry*

If instead of mixing all the metal and ligand together at the start of the
calorimetric experiment (as in method (b) above), the ligand is added
slowly and the temperature recorded as the addition proceeds, a
thermometric titration is carried out [20–22]. This is described in more
detail in Section 9.5(ii).

(iii) *Entropy*

Once ΔG and ΔH have been evaluated for a given reaction, ΔS can be obtained
from Equation (1.32).

REFERENCES

[1] Tobe, M. L. (1972). *Inorganic Reaction Mechanisms*. London: Nelson.
[2] Basolo, F. and Pearson, R. G. (1967). *Mechanisms of Inorganic Reactions*
     (2nd ed.) New York: Wiley.
[3] Wilkins, R. G. (1974). *The Study of Kinetics and Mechanism of Reactions
     of Transition Metal Complexes*. Boston: Allyn and Bacon.
[4] Guldberg, C. M. and Waage, P. (1879). *Z. prakt. Chem.*, **19**, 69.
[5] Horiuchi, J. (1957). *Z. phys. Chem. Frankfurt*, **12**, 321.
[6] Burgess, J. (1979). *Metal Ions in Solution*. Chichester: Ellis Horwood.
[7] Gurney, R. (1953). *Ionic Processes in Solution*. New York: McGraw-Hill.
[8] Biedermann, G. and Sillén, L. G. (1953). *Ark. Kemi.*, **5**, 425.
[9] Johansson, L. (1975). *Acta. Chem. Scand.*, **A29**, 365.
[10] Aditya, S., Nanda, R. K., and Das, R. C. (1966). *Z. phys. Chem. Frankfurt*,
     48, 126.
[11] Nasanen, R. (1957). *Acta. Chem. Scand.*, **11**, 1308.
[12] Rossotti, F. J. C. (1960). In *Modern Coordination Chemistry* (eds. Lewis,
     J. and Wilkins, R. G.) Chap. 1. New York: Interscience.
[13] Hildebrand, J. H. and Scott, R. L. (1950). *The Solubility of Non-Electro-
     lytes*. New York: Reinhold.
[14] Hildebrand, J. H. and Scott, R. L. (1962). *Regular Solutions*. Englewood
     Cliffs, N.J.: Prentice-Hall.

[15] Johansson, L. (1974). *Coord. Chem. Rev.*, **12**, 241.

[16] Denning, R. G., Hartley, F. R., and Venanzi, L. M. (1967). *J. Chem. Soc.*, (A), 324.

[17] Glasstone, S. (1960). *Textbook of Physical Chemistry* (2nd ed.) p. 827. London: Macmillan.

[18] Husain, D. (1978). *Chem. in Britain*, **14**, 465.

[19] Rossini, F. D. (ed. vol. 1) (1956) and Skinner, H. A. (ed. vol. 2) (1962). *Experimental Thermochemistry*. New York: Interscience.

[20] Christensen, J. J. and Izatt, R. M. (1968). In *Physical Methods in Advanced Inorganic Chemistry* (eds. Hill, H. A. O. and Day, P.) pp. 554–579. London: Interscience.

[21] Vaughan, G. A. (1973). *Thermometric and Enthalpimetric Titrimetry*. London: Van Nostrand Reinhold.

[22] Barthel, J. (1975). *Thermometric Titrations*, vol. 45 in *Chemical Analysis* (eds. Elving, P. J., Winefordner, J. D., and Kolthoff, I. M.). New York: Wiley-Interscience.

CHAPTER 2

The Number and Nature of Species in Solution

2.1 INTRODUCTION

Before an attempt is made to quantify the equilibrium condition of any solution reaction a clearly defined chemical model must be assumed. In order to do this, both the number and nature of the various chemical species in the solution should be known. A number of methods for determining these data are available and are the subject of this chapter. In many instances, however, it may not be possible to determine the number of chemical species and their formulae directly, and recourse must be made to chemical reasonableness and to statistical evaluation of the data, using various model systems. The latter approaches are dealt with in some detail in Chapter 5.

2.2 THE NUMBER OF SPECIES IN SOLUTION

In order to find the total number of species present in a solution at equilibrium, the technique employed must measure some physical parameter that is a function of the number of molecules of a given type. For this, each species should make its own unique contribution to the observable parameter through what is known as an intensive factor (see Section 6.1). The most widely used technique in this area is spectrophotometry. The role of spectrophotometry in the calculation of stability constants is discussed fully in Chapter 8.

In spectrophotometry we are concerned with the absorbance, A, which is a linear function of concentration of a given species at a specified wavelength, λ. The absorbance of a solution is given by Beer's Law, which may be expressed as in Equation (2.1).

$$\frac{A^{\lambda}_{obs}}{l} = \epsilon^{\lambda}_1 c_1 + \epsilon^{\lambda}_2 c_2 + \ldots \epsilon^{\lambda}_n c_n \qquad (2.1)$$

where $\dfrac{A^{\lambda}_{obs}}{l}$ = the observed absorbance per unit path length at wavelength λ,

$\epsilon_1^\lambda, \epsilon_2^\lambda, \epsilon_n^\lambda$ = the molar absorptivities of species 1, 2, and n at wavelength λ, and

c_1, c_2 and c_n are their respective concentrations.

More will be said of the basis for this equation and the practical determination of A_{obs}^λ in Chapter 8. The important feature of Equation (2.1) is the linear dependence of A_{obs}^λ on the concentrations of the various species present. Obviously if a species present has an ϵ^λ value of zero, that is, it does not absorb in the spectral region chosen, then it does not influence A_{obs}^λ.

It is usual in solution equilibrium studies to use constant ionic backgrounds such as sodium perchlorate (see Section 1.5) and to adjust equilibria with solutions of strong mineral acids and alkalies. These species do not absorb appreciably in the spectral region usually studied of 200 and 800 nm. This

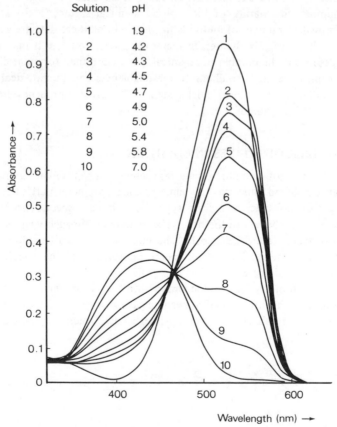

Figure 2.1 – pH dependence of methyl red absorption spectrum.

spectral region is within the capabilities of the most modern u.v.-visible spectro-photometers. The majority of solution equilibria of interest to the analytical or inorganic chemist involve metal ligand systems which exhibit pronounced and characteristic absorption in this region.

In the simplest case, the u.v.-visible spectrum is recorded for a number of solutions containing a constant amount of the metal but with increasing ligand concentrations. The spectra are superimposed and the presence of any spectrally invariant points produced by intersection noted (for example, spectra 2 to 10 in Figure 2.1). These points are known as isosbestic points. The presence of one or more such points has been assumed to indicate the presence of two species, which differ in their ratio of metal to ligand, in equilibrium. This assumption is dangerous for two reasons:

(a) More than two absorbing species may have identical molar absorptivities.

(b) Three or more absorbing species all of which have different molar absorptivities may be linked in a 'pseudo-two-component' system. This occurs in the sodium tetrachoropalladate(II)–sodium chloride system and is described in Chapter 13.

Therefore the existence of an isosbestic point can only be taken to indicate the presence of at least two independent species [1–3]. Hence the isosbestic technique must be supplemented by other methods to define reliably the number of species present.

Let us consider a series of solutions numbered 1 to j. Each has had its absorbance measured at a number of different wavelengths 1 to i. The data set may then be laid out in the form of a matrix,

$$
\begin{matrix}
a_{11} & a_{21} & a_{31} & \cdots & a_{i1} \\
a_{12} & a_{22} & a_{32} & \cdots & a_{i2} \\
a_{13} & a_{23} & a_{33} & \cdots & a_{i3} \\
\vdots & \vdots & \vdots & & \vdots \\
a_{1j} & a_{2j} & a_{3j} & \cdots & a_{ij}
\end{matrix}
\qquad (2.2)
$$

where a_{ij} represents the absorbance of solution j at wavelength i and is said to be an element of the matrix **A** as represented by Matrix (2.2). The rank of this matrix is the order of the largest non-zero determinant that can be obtained from the elements of this matrix. Readers who are unfamiliar with matrix algebra should consult Appendix I for basic details and references for further reading.

Since the determinant of **A** equals zero if its rows and columns are linearly dependent, the rank R is equal to the number of linearly independent columns of **A**. That is to say, the rank is equal to the number of absorbing species in solution. The condition that may be easily tested graphically is that each determinant of **A** that has a rank of $R + 1$ must be zero.

2.3 GRAPHICAL METHODS FOR DETERMINING THE NUMBER OF SPECIES IN SOLUTION

Graphical methods can be applied to systems where the total number of absorbing species is less than or equal to three. It must be remembered that the matrix analysis approach is valid only if Beer's Law (Equation (2.1)) is obeyed. Deviations from linearity will cause spurious results. This aspect is discussed more fully in Section 8.2. Graphical procedures have been developed for two types of condition [4].

(i) *Graphical procedure when no restraint is placed upon the stoichiometry of the solutions examined*

One, two, and three species tests are summarised in Table 2.1. For example, let us take the acid base equilibria absorbance data for methyl red obtained by Wallace and Katz [5] (Table 2.2). A similar series of pH dependent spectra are shown in Figure 2.1. There is an isosbestic point at 465 nm and only the spectrum

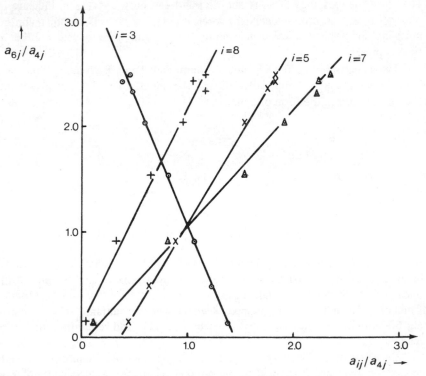

Figure 2.2 – Two-species plot for the methyl red data in Table 2.2.

Table 2.1 – Graphical functions for species testing of solution absorbance data in which there is no restriction of stoichiometry.

Number of species to be tested for	Absorbance plotting functions		Notes and results for valid test
	y-axis	x-axis	
1	a_{mj}	a_{ij}	For all values where $i \neq m$, and m is usually a wavelength of maximum absorbance. A series of straight lines are produced passing through the origin.
2	$\dfrac{a_{mj}}{a_{nj}}$	$\dfrac{a_{ij}}{a_{nj}}$	For all values where $i \neq m \neq n$, and m is usually a wavelength of maximum absorbance. A series of straight lines passing through the origin are produced. A one-species test can sometimes produce a set of straight lines with this function, but they do not pass through the origin.
3	$\dfrac{(a_{mx} a_{ij}) - (a_{my} a_{ix})}{(a_{mx} a_{iz}) - (a_{mz} a_{ix})}$	$\dfrac{(a_{mx} a_{ij}) - (a_{mj} a_{ix})}{(a_{mx} a_{iz}) - (a_{mz} a_{ix})}$	For values where $i \neq m$ and $j \neq x, y$ or z, and m is usually a wavelength of maximum absorbance; x, y and z are arbitrary but fixed solution numbers. A family of straight lines will result with a common point of intersection.

Table 2.2 – Acid-base equilibria absorbance data for methyl red (data from reference [5]).

Solution number (j)	Wavelength number (i)								Approx. pH
	1	2	3	4	5	6	7	8	
1	0.017	0.058	0.167	0.420	0.770	1.015	0.935	0.443	2.2
2	0.045	0.080	0.180	0.402	0.735	0.990	0.940	0.480	3.0
3	0.062	0.100	0.187	0.395	0.690	0.922	0.875	0.462	3.4
4	0.110	0.152	0.222	0.365	0.565	0.742	0.702	0.342	3.8
5	0.197	0.238	0.282	0.342	0.437	0.528	0.488	0.235	4.6
6	0.278	0.320	0.330	0.310	0.278	0.282	0.255	0.108	5.4
7	0.332	0.372	0.368	0.300	0.192	0.147	0.118	0.049	6.2
8	0.377	0.417	0.400	0.292	0.131	0.051	0.032	0.015	6.6

of the solution of lowest pH does not pass through it. One could presume on the basis of the presence of one isosbestic point and a red-yellow colour change that two species were present. However, the result of plotting a_{6j}/a_{4j} against a_{ij}/a_{4j} for the two-species test in Table 2.1, does not yield the expected family of straight lines passing through the origin (see Figure 2.2).

Choosing x, y, and z to be 1, 2, and 8 respectively and m equal to 4, a three-species test can be carried out.

The function for the y-axis becomes

$$\frac{(a_{41}\, a_{i2}) - (a_{42}\, a_{i1})}{(a_{41}\, a_{i8}) - (a_{48}\, a_{i1})} \tag{2.3}$$

and for the x-axis

$$\frac{(a_{41}\, a_{ij}) - (a_{4j}\, a_{i1})}{(a_{48}\, a_{i8}) - (a_{48}\, a_{i1})} \tag{2.4}$$

The y-axis function is a function of i and independent of j. The x-axis function requires solution for each j value in question. The values that j can have are 3, 4, 5, 6, and 7. The ensuing plots are shown in Figure 2.3. A family of straight

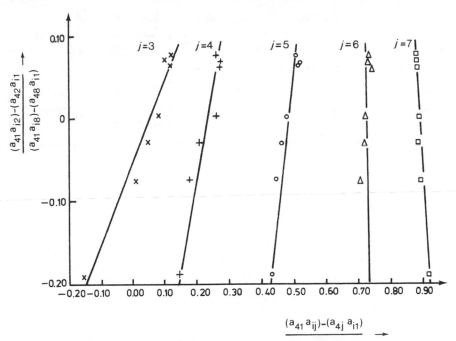

Figure 2.3 – Three-species plot for the methyl red data in Table 2.2.

lines is observed which is consistent with three absorbing species. However, more scatter is observed than might reasonably be expected from the spectrophotometric measurements. For more complicated systems, computational methods for finding the rank of the matrix have to be resorted to (see Section 2.4).

(ii) *Graphical procedure for restricted stoichiometries*

If either the sum of the concentrations of the absorbing species or the sum of the reactant concentrations is held constant, the plotting functions for the two- or three-species tests given in Table 2.1 can be simplified. These are listed in Table 2.3. An example of the application of the three-species test of Table 2.3 is described in Section 12.2.

Table 2.3 – Graphical functions for species testing of solution absorbance data under conditions of restricted stoichiometry.

Number of species to be tested for	Absorbance plotting functions		Notes and results for valid test
	y-axis	x-axis	
2	$a_{ij} - a_{ij'}$	$a_{i'j} - a_{i'j'}$	For $i \neq i'$ and $j \neq j'$, a family of straight lines passing through the origin.
3	$\dfrac{(a_{bj} - a_{bj'})}{(a_{ij} - a_{ij'})}$	$\dfrac{(a_{cj} - a_{cj'})}{(a_{ij} - a_{ij'})}$	For $i \neq b \neq c$ and $j \neq j'$, a straight line or a series of straight lines.

2.4 COMPUTATIONAL METHODS FOR DETERMINING THE NUMBER OF SPECIES IN SOLUTION

For equilibria involving three or more absorbing species, it is usually necessary to use computational methods to determine the rank of the matrix [5-11]. The best method is briefly as follows. The absorbance matrix A is reduced by a series of elementary operations to an equivalent reduced matrix in which the largest elements are on the leading diagonal and all elements below this are zero [5]. This process is called triangularisation of the A matrix. The rank of the matrix is given by the number of non-zero elements on this diagonal. However, the main problem is deciding what 'zero' is, as in real systems random errors cause non-zero diagonal elements to occur. This may be overcome by reducing an error matrix E containing expected error values by the same process. The values of the corresponding elements of A and E can be compared, and the criterion used is that the element of the A matrix is non-zero if it is greater than three times the corresponding element in the E matrix [6]. If a range of E values are used, the variation of the rank found with error provides insight into the reliance one can place on the number of species found. A computer program TRIANG has been written to do this calculation and is listed in Appendix II [12].

Let us illustrate the use of TRIANG by considering the methyl red data in Table 2.2. The authors estimated the expected error to be 0.003 absorbance units. Table 2.4 gives the output from TRIANG for these data. The number of species was found to be three, confirming the graphical evidence. If, however, the elements of the absorbance matrix E are reduced to 0.002 or 0.001, four species are indicated, whereas if the elements are increased up to 0.010 absorbance units the number of species indicated remains at three. Hence it is unlikely that there are more than three absorbing species in this system.

Sometimes, the spectrophotometric measurement is subject to much greater errors in unfavourable circumstances. For example, the reaction between hafnium(IV) and chloranilic acid in 3M perchloric acid was studied spectrophotometrically in the region 260 nm to 360 nm. Twelve solutions were measured at 21 wavelengths [6]. The number of species found for a given error matrix element is shown in Figure 2.4. The data obtained for chloranilic acid in 3M perchloric acid under the same conditions is given also in Figure 2.4. Only one species is expected in the 3M perchloric acid/chloranilic acid system, that is the undissociated acid. This result is achieved only if the value taken for the error matrix is greater than 0.010. The correct number of species present in the hafnium(IV)-3M perchloric acid–chloranilic acid is thought to be three, although to obtain this the value for the error matrix element must be $0.014 < e_{ij} < 0.045$. A significant part of this large error was known to be due to solution make-up rather than to purely photometric sources. In addition hafnium(IV) is known to produce hydrolysis or polynuclear species at almost any pH in aqueous media.

Table 2.4 – Reproduction sample output from program TRIANG for the methyl red data in Table 2.2.

THE ABSORBANCE MATRIX A

0.017000	0.045000	0.062000	0.110000	0.197000	0.278000	0.332000	0.377000
0.058000	0.080000	0.100000	0.152000	0.238000	0.320000	0.372000	0.417000
0.167000	0.180000	0.187000	0.222000	0.282000	0.330000	0.368000	0.400000
0.420000	0.402000	0.395000	0.365000	0.342000	0.310000	0.300000	0.292000
0.770000	0.735000	0.690000	0.565000	0.437000	0.278000	0.192000	0.131000
1.015000	0.990000	0.922000	0.742000	0.528000	0.282000	0.147000	0.051000
0.935000	0.940000	0.875000	0.702000	0.488000	0.255000	0.118000	0.032000
0.443000	0.480000	0.462000	0.342000	0.235000	0.108000	0.049000	0.015000

THE ERROR MATRIX E

0.003000	0.003000	0.003000	0.003000	0.003000	0.003000	0.003000	0.003000
0.003000	0.003000	0.003000	0.003000	0.003000	0.003000	0.003000	0.003000
0.003000	0.003000	0.003000	0.003000	0.003000	0.003000	0.003000	0.003000
0.003000	0.003000	0.003000	0.003000	0.003000	0.003000	0.003000	0.003000
0.003000	0.003000	0.003000	0.003000	0.003000	0.003000	0.003000	0.003000
0.003000	0.003000	0.003000	0.003000	0.003000	0.003000	0.003000	0.003000
0.003000	0.003000	0.003000	0.003000	0.003000	0.003000	0.003000	0.003000
0.003000	0.003000	0.003000	0.003000	0.003000	0.003000	0.003000	0.003000

THE REDUCED ABSORBANCE MATRIX

1.015000	0.051000	0.922000	0.742000	0.528000	0.282000	0.990000	0.147000
0.000000	0.414086	0.047314	0.109600	0.207829	0.303886	0.023429	0.363600
0.000000	0.000000	0.050420	0.020073	0.008196	-.009753	0.048322	-.008785
0.000000	0.000000	0.000000	-.015686	-.007170	-.006903	-.005265	-.003480
0.000000	0.000000	0.000000	0.000000	-.006450	-.004823	-.006348	0.000523
0.000000	0.000000	0.000000	0.000000	0.000000	0.005275	0.003168	-.003296
0.000000	0.000000	0.000000	0.000000	0.000000	0.000000	0.005672	-.004498
0.000000	0.000000	0.000000	0.000000	0.000000	0.000000	0.000000	0.004322

THE REDUCED ERROR MATRIX

0.003000	0.003000	0.003000	0.003000	0.003000	0.003000	0.003000	0.003000
0.003015	0.003850	0.003024	0.003041	0.003088	0.003152	0.003019	0.003202
0.003761	0.003876	0.003910	0.003641	0.003458	0.003321	0.003957	0.003287
0.004954	0.004047	0.006077	0.005833	0.004816	0.004356	0.006310	0.004233
0.003691	0.005070	0.004683	0.006457	0.006840	0.006595	0.006944	0.005065
0.005649	0.004091	0.007912	0.011327	0.000292	0.011739	0.011792	0.007196
0.003119	0.000067	0.004422	0.004050	0.005436	0.019693	0.017245	0.013388
0.003001	0.000011	0.004102	0.004777	0.005346	0.007207	0.027071	0.020393

NUMBER OF SPECIES = 3

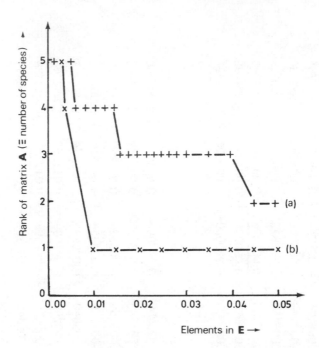

Figure 2.4 — Matrix rank analysis of the hafnium(IV)–perchloric acid–chloranilic acid system: (a) hafnium(IV) - perchloric acid - chloranilic acid, (b) perchloric–chloranilic acid only.

2.5 THE NATURE OF SPECIES IN SOLUTION

(i) *Molar ratio method*

Having determined the number of species present in the solution, the next problem is to find their stoichiometry. The simplest approach is to use the molar ratio method [13,14]. In this method, if the reaction produces a change in absorption spectra, the absorbance at a suitable wavelength of a series of solutions of constant metal concentration containing varying amounts of ligand is taken. Ideally two straight lines are obtained on plotting the observed absorbance against the ligand to metal ratio (Figure 2.5). The point of intersection corresponds to the stoichiometric ratio on interpolation to the x-axis. In practice, however, this approach can yield quite incorrect results [15] unless the following criteria apply:

(a) Metal and ligand react to from only one complex,

(b) the stability constant K is sufficiently large to produce a clear-cut point of intersection, and

(c) other complexing species such as buffers or masking agents are present to constant but excess concentration.

These conditions are rarely satisified in real systems, and consequently the usefulness of the method is severely limited. Regrettably, one still encounters its indiscriminate use in the literature.

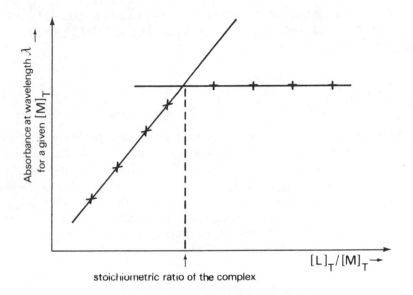

Figure 2.5 – Idealised molar ratio digram.

(ii) *Method of continuous variations (Job's Method)*

A better approach is the method of continuous variations. This is popularly attributed to Job [16] but the principles had been established by Ostromisslensky [17] and Denison [18]. Consider the formation of a complex ML_n described by Equation (2.6).

$$M + nL \xrightarrow{\beta_n} ML_n \qquad\qquad (2.5)$$

A series of solutions are prepared such that the sum of total metal and total ligand molar concentrations is a constant.

Hence

$$[M]_T + [L]_T = C \qquad\qquad (2.6)$$

Three mass balance equations may now be written

$$[M] = C(1-x) - [ML_n] \qquad\qquad (2.7)$$

$$[L] = Cx - n[ML_n] \qquad (2.8)$$

and $\qquad [ML_n] = \beta_n [M] [L]^n \qquad (2.9)$

where x is the mole fraction of the ligand. Taking first differentials of Equations (2.8) and (2.9), followed by elimination of [M], [L], and [ML_n], yields a value for x, x_{max}, which is dependent only on n.

$$n = \frac{x_{max}}{1 - x_{max}} \qquad (2.10)$$

If the absorbance of a solution at a given wavelength is plotted against mole fraction of ligand x a plot such as that in Figure 2.6 can result. The x_{max} value obtained for a maximum value of A_{obs}^{λ} is 0.5, which, from Equation (2.10), is indicative of a 1:1 complex. If x_{max} had been at 0.67 or 0.75, these values would have corresponded to 1:2 or 1:3 stoichiometries. However, the plot shown in Figure 2.6 is somewhat skew owing to the fact that both the metal and the ligand absorb appreciably at the chosen wavelength, λ. Equation (2.1) can be rewritten in terms of Equation (2.5)

$$\frac{A_{obs}^{\lambda}}{l} = \epsilon_1^{\lambda} [M] + \epsilon_2^{\lambda} [L] + \epsilon_3^{\lambda} [ML_n] \qquad (2.11)$$

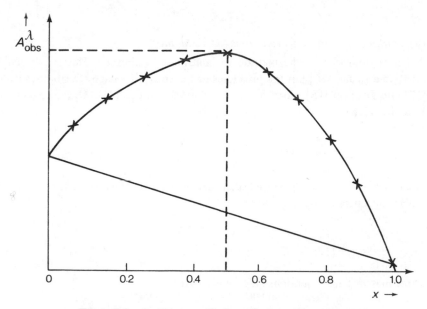

Figure 2.6 – Continuous variations plot for a 1:1 complex.

where ϵ_1^λ, ϵ_2^λ, and ϵ_3^λ are the molar absorptivities of the metal, ligand, and complex respectively. The theoretical absorbance due to the ligand and metal alone if there were no reaction between them can be written as A_{theo}^λ.

$$\frac{A_{theo}^\lambda}{l} = \epsilon_1^\lambda [M] + \epsilon_2^\lambda [L] \tag{2.12}$$

For unit path length and remembering Equations (2.7) and (2.8) we get

$$A_{obs}^\lambda = \epsilon_1^\lambda C(1-x) - \epsilon_1^\lambda C[ML_n] + \epsilon_2^\lambda Cx - \epsilon_2^\lambda n [ML_n] + \epsilon_3^\lambda [ML_n] \tag{2.13}$$

and $\qquad A_{theo}^\lambda = \epsilon_1^\lambda C(1-x) + \epsilon_2^\lambda Cx \tag{2.14}$

Hence a corrected absorbance function, Y_{calc}^λ, can be defined as the difference between A_{obs}^λ and A_{theo}^λ.

Subtracting Equation (2.14) from Equation (2.13),

$$Y_{calc}^\lambda = A_{obs}^\lambda - A_{theo}^\lambda = \epsilon_3^\lambda [ML_n] - \epsilon_1^\lambda [ML_n] - n\epsilon_2^\lambda [ML_n] \tag{2.15}$$

hence the Y_{calc}^λ value is independent of C and a function of $[ML_n]$ only. Usually the ligand does not absorb in the region of interest, and Equation (2.15) reduces to:

$$Y_{calc}^\lambda = \epsilon_3^\lambda [ML_n] - \epsilon_1^\lambda [ML_n] \tag{2.16}$$

Hence if $\epsilon_3^\lambda > \epsilon_1^\lambda$ then when $[ML_n]$ is a maximum Y_{calc}^λ will be at a maximum, or if $\epsilon_3^\lambda < \epsilon_1^\lambda$ then Y_{calc}^λ will be at a minimum.

An example of a 1:1 complex formation system is given in the copper(II)-ethylenediamine-oxalate case study, (Section 12.2) where typical Y_{calc}^λ plots are shown in Figure 12.2. In this instance both 'metal' and 'ligand' absorb strongly, and allowance has to be made for both in Equation (2.14). Prediction of whether Y_{calc}^λ will show a positive or negative maximum is more difficult as three molar absorptivities are involved. The convention y_{ij} is used in this example for Y_{calc}^λ, indicating the calculated value for solution j at wavelength i.

However, there are a number of inherent assumptions made in the theory of continuous variations [19]. These are that

(a) Each of the reactant species corresponds to one stoichiometry. In other words, the reactants do not participate in other equilibria such as ion-association or protonation, in addition to the reaction specified.

(b) The law of mass action is valid in terms of concentration. That is to say, the activity coefficients are effectively constant.

(c) There is only one complex formed.

It is usually possible to ensure reasonable experimental compliance with the first two conditions. The latter is usually not complied with by uni- or bi-dentate ligands and transition metals. Erroneous results can occur if the range of wavelengths studied is too narrow.

Let us consider the nickel(II)–ethylenediamine system, chosen as a case study in Chapter 10. The solutions of nickel(II) and ethylenediamine are 0.4 mol.l^{-1} and 1 mol.l^{-1} with respect to perchlorate ions. If these solutions and their mixtures are protected from carbon dioxide absorption, then conditions (a) and (b) are closely approximated to. A series of solutions ranging from $x_{en} = 0$ to $x_{en} = 1$ are made up and absorbance measurements made at seven wavelengths between 530 nm and 650 nm in 10 mm path length cells. The results are given in Table 2.5. In this spectral region nickel(II) shows appreciable absorption but ethylendiamine does not. Equation (2.16) is therefore valid. Equation (2.14) becomes

$$A^{\lambda}_{theo} = \epsilon^{\lambda}_1 C(1 - x_{en}) \tag{2.17}$$

This is readily solved, as when $x_{en} = 0$

$$A^{\lambda}_{obs} = \epsilon^{\lambda}_1 C \tag{2.18}$$

Table 2.5 – Method for continuous variations, raw absorbance data for the nickel(II)–ethylenediamine system.

| x_i | Absorbance at λ (nm) | | | | | | | x_{en} |
	530	550	570	590	610	630	650	
0.0	0.000	0.000	0.000	0.000	0.000	0.000	0.000	1.0
0.1	0.289	0.290	0.233	0.165	0.106	0.060	0.046	0.9
0.2	0.619	0.600	0.495	0.360	0.245	0.160	0.120	0.8
0.3	0.600	0.720	0.713	0.600	0.470	0.350	0.267	0.7
0.4	0.438	0.583	0.697	0.735	0.708	0.621	0.515	0.6
0.5	0.342	0.467	0.620	0.770	0.810	0.780	0.674	0.5
0.6	0.258	0.363	0.520	0.680	0.783	0.805	0.740	0.4
0.7	0.190	0.273	0.412	0.569	0.693	0.770	0.752	0.3
0.8	0.136	0.198	0.312	0.460	0.600	0.723	0.758	0.2
0.9	0.095	0.138	0.226	0.350	0.505	0.655	0.767	0.1
1.0	0.065	0.085	0.140	0.243	0.410	0.638	0.778	0.0

The corrected absorbance for a wavelength i and solution number j corresponding to $x_{en} = 0.1$ to 0.9, y_{ij} can now be calculated from A^λ_{obs}, and A^λ_{theo} calculated from Equation (2.18). The results are given in Table 2.6 and plotted in Figure 2.7. It is immediately apparent that the value of x_{max} found is extremely wavelength dependent, and maxima corresponding to the 1:1, 1:2, and 1:3 complexes are all observed. This arises because nickel(II) has a maximum co-ordination number of six and accordingly reacts with ethylenediamine to form three complexes of stoichiometry 1:1, 1:2, and 1:3 respectively. Each complex has a different absorption spectrum, and if a suitable range of wavelengths is chosen then it is possible to find wavelengths at which each complex dominates the resulting Job plot. Thus the plots at 630 nm and 650 nm are dominated by the 1:1 complex, between 570 nm and 590 nm it is the 1:2 complex that is the predominant absorbing species, and at 530 nm it is the 1:3 complex that is the strongest absorber.

Analysis of the data in Table 2.6 using TRIANG (Section 2.4) indicated the presence of four species for all values of e_{ij} between 0.001 and 0.010 corresponding to Ni^{2+}, $[Ni(en)]^{2+}$, $[Ni(en)_2]^{2+}$ and $[Ni(en)_3]^{2+}$, thus confirming the findings of the method of continuous variations. It is readily apparent that even if a sufficiently large number of wavelengths are studied, it is increasingly difficult to distinguish x_{max} values when three or more species are present. In such situations reliance should be placed on the number of species determined by matrix rank analysis, and with the knowledge of the reactants present a chemically reasonable model can be formulated.

Table 2.6 — Method of continuous variations — corrected absorbance data for the nickel(II)–ethylenediamine system.

(j)	x_{Ni}	Absorbance for wavelength i (nm)							x_{en}
		530	550	570	590	610	630	650	
9	0.1	0.283	0.282	0.219	0.082	0.065	−0.004	−0.032	0.9
8	0.2	0.606	0.583	0.467	0.311	0.163	0.032	−0.036	0.8
7	0.3	0.581	0.695	0.671	0.527	0.347	0.159	0.034	0.7
6	0.4	0.412	0.549	0.641	0.638	0.554	0.366	0.204	0.6
5	0.5	0.310	0.425	0.550	0.649	0.605	0.461	0.285	0.5
4	0.6	0.219	0.312	0.436	0.534	0.537	0.442	0.273	0.4
3	0.7	0.145	0.214	0.314	0.399	0.406	0.323	0.207	0.3
2	0.8	0.084	0.131	0.200	0.266	0.272	0.213	0.136	0.2
1	0.9	0.036	0.061	0.100	0.131	0.136	0.081	0.067	0.1

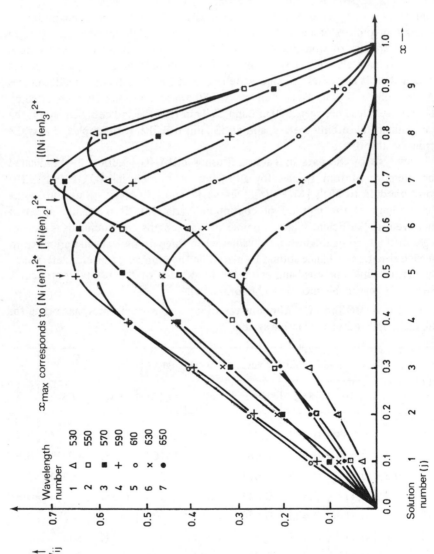

Figure 2.7 — Continuous variations method plots for the nickel (II)–ethylenediamine system.

2.6 CONCLUSION

It has been shown how, through a variety of mathematical techniques, the total number of observable species and some knowledge of their stoichiometries may be obtained. On this basis a chemical model for the equilibrium system can be proposed. Once we have our equilibrium system, we can now explore the ways of calculating stability constants, using a variety of algebraic techniques. This is the subject for Chapter 3.

REFERENCES

[1] Nowicka-Jankowska, T. (1971). *J. Inorg. Nucl. Chem.*, **33**, 2043.
[2] Chylewski, Ch. (1971). *Angew. Chem. Int. Edn.*, **10**, 195.
[3] Brynestad, J. and Smith, G. P. (1968). *J. Phys. Chem.*, **72**, 296.
[4] Coleman, J. S., Varga, L. P., and Mastin, S. H. (1970). *Inorg. Chem.*, **9**, 1015.
[5] Wallace, R. M. and Katz, S. M. (1964). *J. Phys. Chem.*, **68**, 3890.
[6] Varga, L. P. and Veatch, F. C. (1967). *Anal. Chem.*, **39**, 1101.
[7] Wallace, R. M. (1960). *J. Phys. Chem.*, **64**, 899.
[8] Ainsworth, S. (1961). *J. Phys. Chem.*, **65**, 1968.
[9] Ainsworth, S. (1963). *J. Phys. Chem.*, **67**, 1613.
[10] Katakis, D. (1965). *Anal. Chem.*, **37**, 876.
[11] Hugus, Z. Z. and El.Awady, A. A. (1971). *J. Phys. Chem.*, **75**, 2954.
[12] Alcock, R. M. (1976). Ph.D. thesis, University of Southampton.
[13] Yoe, J. H. and Jones, A. L. (1944). *Ind. Eng. Chem. Anal. Ed.*, **16**, 111.
[14] Momoki, K., Sekino, J., Sato, H., and Yamaguchi, N. (1969). *Anal. Chem.*, **41**, 1286.
[15] Budesinsky, B. W. (1974). *Talanta.*, **21**, 323.
[16] Job, P. (1928). *Ann. Chim.*, **9**, 113.
[17] Ostromisslensky, I. (1911). *Ber.*, **44**, 268.
[18] Denison, R. B. (1921). *Trans. Farad. Soc.*, **8**, 20 and 35.
[19] Woldbye, F. (1955). *Acta. Chem. Scand.*, **9**, 299.

CHAPTER 3

Treatment of Data: Derived Functions

3.1 INTRODUCTION

In order to evalute the stability constant, K, for a simple system such as

$$M + L \xrightleftharpoons{K} ML \qquad (3.1)$$

it is, in theory, only necessary to prepare a single solution containing a known total amount of metal ion, $[M]_T$, and ligand, $[L]_T$, and measure one of the three remaining unknown concentrations. These are the free metal ion concentration, $[M]$, the free ligand concentration, $[L]$, and the metal-ligand complex concentration, $[ML]$. In practice, however, one would prepare a whole series of solutions contining a wide range of $[M]_T$ and $[L]_T$ values and measure the chosen experimental observable for each solution. This excess of data allows us to do two things. (i) Firstly, it enables us to check the validity of the chemical model chosen. That is to say, to confirm that our system as defined by Equation (3.1) is correct and that any other chemically reasonable species such as M_2L, ML_2, or ML_3 are absent. If our initial model is incorrect this will be reflected in a value for K which is dependent on $[L]_T$ (and/or $[M]_T$) together with poor agreement between measured and calculated values for the observable. This last point will be discussed further in Chapter 5. Methods available for determination of the total number of species present in the solution were described in Chapter 2. (ii) Secondly, having a large number of values of both the stability constant, K, and the experimental variable at our disposal, estimates of the precision of K and the overall consistency of the data set can be made. Such information is vital if we are to evaluate the reliability of the stability constant, especially if it is necessary to use it to calculate thermodynamic parameters. More will be said of this particular aspect in Chapter 5.

To take full advantage of the large amount of data obtained, a number of ingenious and subtle algebraic dodges have been developed. They are collectively known as **secondary concentration variables**, and undoubtedly many of them were developed because computers, which can readily assimilate large quantities of data, arrived relatively late on the scene. However, some of these, designed primarily to facilitate the manual handling of data, greatly facilitate computer calculations as well.

3.2 SECONDARY CONCENTRATION VARIABLES

As we have seen in Chapter 1, it is possible to define a series of stability constants for the successive formation of mononuclear complexes involving two species. In order to evelute these stability constants, it is necessary to find a relationship between them and the experimentally determined variables ($[M]$, $[L]$, etc.). This relationship is often established via the definition of secondary concentration variables. It is from these variables that the stability constants are calculated. In this chapter, we shall derive three of these functions and show some of the ways of proceeding from these to the stability constants themselves.

(i) *The complex formation function, $\bar{n}$.*

Let us consider a metal ion, M, and a ligand, L, interacting in a solution of constant ionic strength. The equilibria present are:

$$M + L \overset{K_1}{\rightleftharpoons} ML$$

$$M + L \overset{K_2}{\rightleftharpoons} ML_2 \tag{3.2}$$

$$ML_{n-1} + L \overset{K_n}{\rightleftharpoons} ML_n$$

The maximum value of n, written N, will be a function of both the maximum coordination number of the metal ion and the multidentism of the ligand. Having defined our system we can now write mass balance equations for both the total metal ion, and total ligand concentrations:

$$[M]_T = [M] + [ML] + [ML_2] + \dots [ML_n] \tag{3.3}$$

$$[L]_T = [L] + [ML] + 2[ML_2] + \dots n[ML_n] \tag{3.4}$$

A function, $\bar{n}$, defined as the average number of ligands, L, attached to the metal, M, may be written

$$\bar{n} = \frac{\text{total bound ligand}}{\text{total metal}} = \frac{[L]_T - [L]}{[M]_T} \tag{3.5}$$

Substituting Equations (3.3) and (3.4) in (3.5) yields

$$\bar{n} = \frac{[ML] + 2[ML_2] + \ldots n[ML_n]}{[M] + [ML] + [ML_2] \ldots [ML_n]} \tag{3.6}$$

In summation terms Equation (3.6) becomes

$$\bar{n} = \frac{\sum_{n=1}^{n=N} n[ML_n]}{[M] + \sum_{n=1}^{n=N} [ML_n]} \tag{3.7}$$

where N is the maximum coordination number for the metal if L is a monodentate ligand. Inspection of Equation (3.7) shows that it will not help a great deal in evaluating $\bar{n}$, as $[ML_n]$ and $[M]$ are not in general readily obtainable as experimental observables. As we have seen in Section 1.5, K_n is defined by

$$K_n = \frac{[ML_n]}{[ML_{n-1}][L]} \tag{3.8}$$

and β_n as

$$\beta_n = \frac{[ML_n]}{[M][L]^n} \tag{3.9}$$

In addition, $\beta_n = K_1 K_2 K_3 \ldots K_n$ \hfill (3.10)

and, on substituting Equation (3.8) into (3.6) gives

$$\bar{n} = \frac{K_1[M][L] + 2K_1 K_2[M][L]^2 + \ldots + nK_1 K_2 \ldots K_n[M][L]^n}{[M] + K_1[M][L] + K_1 K_2[M][L]^2 + \ldots + K_1 K_2 \ldots K_n[M][L]^n} \tag{3.11}$$

and after dividing through by [M] and remembering Equation (3.10)

$$\bar{n} = \frac{\beta_1[L] + 2\beta_2[L]^2 + \ldots n\beta_n[L]^n}{1 + \beta_1[L] + \beta_2[L]^2 \ldots \beta_n[L]^n} \tag{3.12}$$

which may be more conveniently written in summation terms

$$\bar{n} = \frac{\displaystyle\sum_{n=1}^{n=N} n\beta_n[\text{L}]^n}{1 + \displaystyle\sum_{n=1}^{n=N} \beta_n[\text{L}]^n} \equiv \frac{\displaystyle\sum_{n=0}^{n=N} n\beta_n[\text{L}]^n}{\displaystyle\sum_{n=0}^{n=N} \beta_n[\text{L}]^n} \tag{3.13}$$

It is immediately apparent from Equation (3.13) that $\bar{n}$ is solely dependent on the free ligand concentration, [L], and is independent of $[\text{M}]_\text{T}$, $[\text{L}]_\text{T}$, and the free metal ion concentration [M]. The complex formation function, $\bar{n}$, first introduced by Niels Bjerrum and later developed by Jannik Bjerrum [1,2], is the starting point for many of the methods used in the calculation of stability constants (see Section 3.6).

(ii) *The degree of formation, α_c*
For any individual component of the system, a variable α_c can be defined such that

$$\alpha_c = \frac{[\text{ML}_c]}{[\text{M}]_\text{T}} \quad \text{for } c = 0, 1, 2 \ldots N \tag{3.14}$$

This variable α_c is the partial mole fraction of the component ML_c. The degree of formation of the system as a whole may be considered, and another variable, α_T, can be defined

$$\alpha_\text{T} = \sum_{c=1}^{c=N} \alpha_c \tag{3.15}$$

Hence, α_T is the fraction of total metal bound to ligand in the form of a complex. By an analogous procedure to that used to derive Equation (3.13) we leave it as an exercise for the student to show that:

$$\alpha_c = \frac{\displaystyle\sum_{c=1}^{c=N} \beta_c[\text{L}]^c}{1 + \displaystyle\sum_{c=1}^{c=N} \beta_c[\text{L}]^c} \equiv \frac{\displaystyle\sum_{c=1}^{c=N} \beta_c[\text{L}]^c}{\displaystyle\sum_{c=0}^{c=N} \beta_c[\text{L}]^c} \tag{3.16}$$

One interesting solution to Equation (3.14) is when $c = 0$ and hence

$$\alpha_0 = \frac{[\text{M}]}{[\text{M}]_\text{T}} \tag{3.17}$$

This function, α_0, gives the species distribution for the free metal ion in the solution. When no complex formation takes place then α_0 is unity because $[M]_T = [M]$. Hence it is possible to plot a series of component distribution curves ($N + 1$ of them) of α_c versus $[M]_T$ or $[L]_T$, and this is clearly shown in Figure 12.7. The α_c function is used in a recent atlas of metal-ligand equilibria in aqueous solution to show at a glance the relative proportions of each of the species present in solution [3].

(iii) *The degree of complex formation, ϕ*

A third secondary concentration variable, ϕ, is defined as:

$$\phi = \frac{[M]_T}{[M]} = 1 + \sum_{n=1}^{n=N} \beta_n [L]^n \tag{3.18}$$

This function finds an application in the methods of Leden and Froneaus, as will be seen later (Section 3.7).

At this stage it is valuable to summarise the definitions of the three secondary concentration variables that we have met so far. This, together with experimental data that must be available to use each of them, is given in Table 3.1.

Table 3.1 – Summary of the secondary concentration variables, $\bar{n}$, α_c, and ϕ.

Variable	Title	Definition	Experimental observables required
$\bar{n}$	complex formation function	$([L]_T - [L])/[M]_T$	$[M]_T, [L]_T, [L]$
α_c	degree of formation	$[ML_c]/[M]_T$	$[M]_T, [L]_T, [L]$
ϕ	degree of complex formation	$[M]_T/[M]$	$[M]_T, [M]$

3.3 INTER-RELATIONSHIPS BETWEEN $\bar{n}$, α_c, and ϕ

A number of inter-relationships exist between these three secondary concentration variables which can sometimes be useful. From Equations (3.17) and (3.18), by substitution we get

$$\alpha_c = \frac{\beta_c [L]^c}{\phi} \tag{3.19}$$

and differentiating Equation (3.18) with respect to $[L]$

$$\frac{\partial \phi}{\partial [L]} = \sum_{n=1}^{n=N} n\beta_n [L]^{n-1} \tag{3.20}$$

Substituting in Equation (3.20) for Equation (3.13) and rearranging, we obtain:

$$\bar{n} = \frac{\partial \log \phi}{\partial \log [L]} \tag{3.21}$$

From Equation (3.21) it is possible to find $\bar{n}$ from graphical differentiation of a plot of $\log\phi$ versus $\log[L]$. That is to say, the tangent at any point on the curve will yield $\bar{n}$. Taking logarithms of Equation (3.19)

$$\log\phi = \log\beta_c + c\log[L] - \log\alpha_c \tag{3.22}$$

Differentiating this equation with respect to [L] and substituting for Equation (3.21) we get

$$\bar{n} = n - \frac{\partial \log\alpha_n}{\partial \log[L]} \tag{3.23}$$

This important equation clearly shows that when α_n reaches a maximum value so that the differential term in Equation (3.23) becomes zero, $\bar{n}$ will be equal to n. The observant reader will on deriving Equations (3.22) and (3.23) find c in place of n. However, as c only differs from n in that it can assume a value of zero, n is used in preference, as when $c = 0$, $\bar{n}$ is also zero.

Of these three secondary concentration variables, $\bar{n}$ is the most widely used in the calculation of stability constants. There are numerous methods that utilize $\bar{n}$ values, and some of these are outlined in Section 3.6. The ϕ function finds application in both Leden's and Froneaus' methods, but these are less commonly used for a variety of reasons discussed in Sections 3.7 and 3.8.

3.4 STEPWISE FORMATION OF COMPLEXES

Before progressing to calculation methods, one important feature has still to be discussed; that is the fundamental assumption that complex formation is a stepwise process. If this is true then the ratios of the various stability constants could in theory be predicted by statistical considerations. The experimental ratios will of course be dependent on electronic and steric factors in addition to a simple statistical effect. For a series of complexes, ML_n, where L is a unidentate ligand, it is usual to assume that:

(a) all possible coordination sites (N) are identical;

(b) the tendency of a complex ML_n to lose a ligand, L, is proportional to the number of ligand occupied sites (n); and

(c) the tendency for a complex ML_n to take up another ligand is proportional to the number of vacant sites ($N - n$).

Hence the N consecutive stability constants $K_1, K_2, \ldots K_N$ will be predicted to be proportional to $\dfrac{N}{1}, \dfrac{N-1}{2}, \ldots \dfrac{(N-n+1)}{n}, \dfrac{N-n}{n+1}, \ldots \dfrac{2}{N-1}, \dfrac{1}{N}$ respectively, so that the ratio between successive constants due to statistical effects will be given by

$$\frac{K_n}{K_{n+1}} = \frac{(N-n+1)(n+1)}{(N-n)n} = f_n \qquad (3.24)$$

Generally speaking it is usually more convenient to quote the logarithmic ratios of stability constants, and another parameter $S_{n,\,n+1}$ is defined as

$$S_{n,\,n+1} = \log K_n - \log K_{n+1} = \log f_n \qquad (3.25)$$

As can be expected, if multidentate ligands are used the ratios differ considerably. For example, taking $N = 6$ and assuming octahedral geometry, the ratios $K_1 : K_2 : K_3$ for a bidentate ligand will be $12 : \frac{5}{2} : \frac{4}{15}$. It is always useful to examine a series of successive stability constants to see any unusual ligand effects on the overall stability constant, β_n. This is discussed further in Section 14.4. To take account of the importance of the ratio of successive stability constants on the approximations that can be made in the course of their calculation, Jannik Bjerrum introduced the concept of a spreading factor x.

3.5 INFLUENCE OF THE SPREADING FACTOR, x, ON THE FORMATION FUNCTION, $\bar{n}$

The spreading factor, x, is defined by:

$$\frac{K_n}{K_{n+1}} = f_n x^2 \qquad (3.26)$$

It should be noted that if $x = 1$ Equation (3.26) reverts to the statistical model, Equation (3.24). Assuming that (3.26) is valid, the successive constants K_n can be expressed as a function of the average constant $\bar{K}$ such that the greatest possible symmetry is obtained.

$$K_n = \left\{ \frac{N-n+1}{n} \right\} \bar{K} x^{(N+1-2n)} \qquad (3.27)$$

where $\quad \bar{K} = \left\{ \dfrac{1}{[L]} \right\}_{\text{at } \bar{n} = N/2}$ (3.28)

For $N = 2$, Equation (3.27) reduces to:

$$K_1 = 2x\bar{K}$$ (3.29)

$$K_2 = \frac{1}{2x} \bar{K}$$ (3.30)

Substituting these relationships in Equation (3.12), we obtain

$$\bar{n} = \frac{2x\bar{K}[L] + 2\bar{K}^2[L]^2}{1 + 2x\bar{K}[L] + \bar{K}^2[L]^2}$$ (3.31)

If we take $\bar{K} = 1$, and a range of [L] values between 10^{-3} and 10^3, the effect of x, the spreading factor, can clearly be seen from Figure 3.1. Thus if $x > 100$ the two complexes are clearly formed in separate steps. As x decreases, the two steps become less pronounced and gradually distributed until when $x < 2$ only a single step is discernible. If $x = 0$, the uptake of the two ligands appears to occur in a single step.

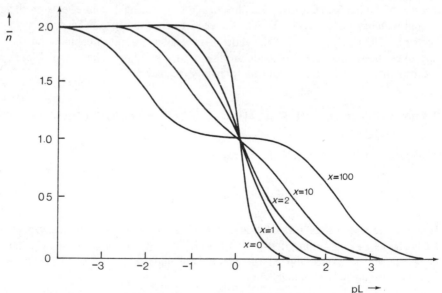

Figure 3.1 — Plot of the formation function, $\bar{n}$, against minus the logarithm of the free ligand concentration, pL, for varying values of the spreading factor, x.

3.6 CALCULATION OF STABILITY CONSTANTS BASED ON THE COMPLEX FORMATION FUNCTION, $\bar{n}$

Most stability constant calculations based on Bjerrum's $\bar{n}$ function essentially involve a plot of $\bar{n}$ against free ligand concentration. Such plots can be prepared by three main methods:

(a) If the free ligand concentration is measured directly, for example by an electrode reversible to that ligand, then knowing the total concentrations of metal and ligand present, $\bar{n}$ can be calculated from Equation (3.5) and a plot of $\bar{n}$ against [L] prepared. This method cannot be used for very weak complexes or when the total metal concentration is very low, since in either case $[L]_T - [L]$ will be close to zero and hence $\bar{n}$ will also be close to zero.

(b) Rearrangement of Equation (3.5) gives

$$[L]_T = \bar{n}[M]_T + [L] \tag{3.32}$$

so that if a series of solutions could be prepared in which $\bar{n}$ and [L] were constant although unknown, a plot of $[L]_T$ against $[M]_T$ would be a straight line of slope $\bar{n}$ and intercept [L]. Such a series of solutions are known as 'corresponding solutions'. Since $\bar{n}$ is shown in Equations (3.12) and (3.13) to be a function of [L] only, it is apparent that if we could establish that [L] was constant, albeit of unknown value, for a set of solutions, $\bar{n}$ would also necessarily be constant. There are many ways of determining the correspondence of solutions; measurements of absorbance or e.m.f. are frequently used. Thus a series of solutions of different total metal and total ligand concentrations are prepared. A parameter (for example, e.m.f. or absorbance) is measured, and the total metal and total ligand concentrations of strictly corresponding solutions are determined by interpolation. A series of plots of $[M]_T$ against $[L]_T$ are prepared yielding a series of values of $\bar{n}$ and [L] that can then be used for subsequent evaluation of stability constants. The method of corresponding solutions can be used only when $[L]_T - [L]$ is significantly greater than zero and less than $[L]_T$. This method is particularly useful when dealing with spectrophotometric data (see Section 8.5).

(c) By following some property that is proportional to α_c, such as the e.m.f. of a metal ion reversible electrode or the distribution of a metal ion between two immiscible solvents, $\bar{n}$ can be evaluated from Equation (3.23). This approach can be used even when $[L]_T - [L]$ is close to zero and is therefore of value when low total metal concentrations are present.

Having prepared a plot of $\bar{n}$ against the free ligand concentration it is possible to use it to determine stability constants. Consider the case when $N = 2$. Equation (3.6) then reduces to

$$\bar{n} = \frac{[\text{ML}] + 2[\text{ML}_2]}{[\text{M}] + [\text{ML}] + [\text{ML}_2]} = \frac{K_1[\text{L}] + 2K_1K_2[\text{L}]^2}{1 + K_1[\text{L}] + K_1K_2[\text{L}]^2} \tag{3.33}$$

If the ratio of K_1/K_2 is of the order of 10^4 (that is, $x \geqslant 100$) then at any free ligand concentration only two metal containing species are present in appreciable amounts. Thus when the average number of ligands per metal atom ($\bar{n}$) is 0.5, only the species M and ML will be present in significant quantities. Hence at $\bar{n} = 0.5$ Equation (3.33) can be reduced to

$$\bar{n} = \tfrac{1}{2} = \frac{[\text{ML}]}{[\text{M}] + [\text{ML}]} = \frac{K_1[\text{L}]}{1 + K_1[\text{L}]} \tag{3.34}$$

whence clearly at $\bar{n} = 0.5$, $K_1 = 1/[\text{L}]$. It can further be shown that so long as K_n/K_{n+1} is large, K_n can be obtained from the value of $[\text{L}]$ corresponding to $\bar{n} = n - \tfrac{1}{2}$, that is

$$K_n = \left\{\frac{1}{[\text{L}]}\right\}_{\text{at } \bar{n}=n-\frac{1}{2}} \tag{3.35}$$

This relationship is easily seen if it is realised that at the points $\bar{n} = n - \tfrac{1}{2}$, $[\text{ML}_{n-1}] = [\text{ML}_n]$ by inspection of Equation (3.8). Using Equation (3.35) it is only possible to obtain a single value of K_n. This is not only undesirable as it gives no indication of the reliability of K_n; it is also a very inefficient use of the available data. Given the aforementioned criteria, it can be shown that the ratio of the concentration of two consecutive complexes is given by:

$$\frac{[\text{ML}_n]}{[\text{ML}_{n+1}]} = \frac{\bar{n} + 1 - n}{n - \bar{n}} \quad \text{if } n > \bar{n} > n - 1 \tag{3.36}$$

Substitution of Equation (3.36) into Equation (3.8) yields

$$K_n = \left\{\frac{(\bar{n} + 1 - n)}{n - \bar{n}}\right\}\frac{1}{[\text{L}]} \tag{3.37}$$

Hence for a system where $N = 2$, Equation (3.37) becomes

$$K_1 = \frac{\bar{n}}{(1 - \bar{n})}\left\{\frac{1}{[\text{L}]}\right\}; \quad K_2 = \frac{(\bar{n} - 1)}{(2 - \bar{n})}\left\{\frac{1}{[\text{L}]}\right\} \tag{3.38}$$

$$\text{for } 1 > \bar{n} > 0 \qquad\qquad \text{for } 2 > \bar{n} > 1$$

From Equation (3.38), K_n can be evaluated at all points between $\bar{n} = n$ and $\bar{n} = n-1$. An alternative approach is to find the slope of the formation function curve, that is the plot of $\bar{n}$ against [L].

This is given by

$$\delta = \frac{-\partial\bar{n}}{\partial ln[L]} = -0.4343 \frac{\partial\bar{n}}{\partial pL} \tag{3.39}$$

This leads directly to Equation (3.40) by differentiating Equation (3.33) with respect to free ligand concentration

$$\delta = \frac{2x\bar{K}[L] + 4\bar{K}^2[L]^2 + 2x\bar{K}^3[L]^3}{(1 + 2x\bar{K}[L] + \bar{K}^2[L]^2)^2} \tag{3.40}$$

At the midpoint of the formation curve, that is, $\bar{n} = N/2$, then $\bar{K}[L] = 1$ and the slope at this point, Δ, is given by

$$\Delta = \frac{1}{1+x} \tag{3.41}$$

Equation (3.41) is obtained directly from (3.40) by substitution of $\bar{K}[L] = 1$.

Up until now we have only considered examples where x is large. If x is not large the values of K_n that we calculate are only approximate. The half integral values can be corrected by a successive approximation procedure. If Equation (3.13) is rewritten

$$\bar{n} + (\bar{n}-1)[L]K_1 + (\bar{n}-2)[L]^2 K_1 K_2 + \dots (\bar{n}-N)[L]^N K_1 K_2 \dots K_n = 0 \tag{3.42}$$

Solving this equation for K_n we get

$$K_n = \left\{ \frac{\displaystyle\sum_{i=0}^{i=n-1} \frac{\bar{n} - n + 1 + i}{[L]^i K_1 K_2 K_3 \dots K_{n-1} \dots K_{n-i}}}{\displaystyle\sum_{i=0}^{i=N-n} (n - \bar{n} + i)[L]^i K_{n+1} K_{n+2} \dots K_{n+i}} \right\} \frac{1}{[L]} \tag{3.43}$$

where i is an integer and can have all values between 0 and $N-n$. Substituting $\bar{n} = n - \frac{1}{2}$ in Equation (3.43)

$$K_n = \left(\frac{1}{[L]}\right)_{\text{at } \bar{n}=n-\frac{1}{2}}$$

$$\left\{\frac{1 + \displaystyle\sum_{i=1}^{i=n-1} \frac{1 + 2i}{[L]^i_{\text{at } \bar{n}=n-\frac{1}{2}} K_1 K_2 K_3 \ldots K_{n-1} \ldots K_{n-i}}}{1 + \displaystyle\sum_{i=1}^{i=N-n} (1 + 2i)\,([L]^i)_{\text{at } \bar{n}=n-\frac{1}{2}}\, K_{n+1} K_{n+2} \ldots K_{n+i}}\right\}$$

$$(3.44)$$

This somewhat cumbersome equation is a convergence formula. We can use the half integral values of $\bar{n}$ to obtain K_n (Equation (3.35)) as the starting point. Equation (3.44) is best thought of as

$$K_n^* = K_n C \tag{3.45}$$

where K_n^* is the better approximation of K_n and C is a correction factor tending towards a constant value. The success of the method depends on the magnitude of the spreading factor, x. If $x \leqslant 1$ then this method of calculation yields only approximate values. More complex methods exist for getting better estimates of K_n by successive approximation. The reader is directed to references [4] and [5] for a more complete discussion, and to Section 10.4(ii) where an application is given.

Nearly all the variants we have used up to now have been concerned with the half integral values of the formation function. However, unlike them, the integral values of $\bar{n}$ have a clearly defined chemical meaning in that they are independent of the ratios of the stability constants.

(i) *Graphical methods based on* $\bar{n}$

Graphical methods are popular as they make use of all the data. Two forms of linear treatment are available when $N = 2$, namely extrapolation and elimination. For $N = 2$ Equation (3.12) can be arranged to give

$$\bar{n} = (1 - \bar{n})[L]K_1 + (2 - \bar{n})[L]^2 K_1 K_2 \tag{3.46}$$

which on division by $\bar{n}$ and further rearranging becomes

$$\frac{(1 - \bar{n})}{(2 - \bar{n})[L]} = \left\{\frac{\bar{n}}{(2 - \bar{n})[L]^2}\right\}\frac{1}{K_1} - K_2 \tag{3.47}$$

If the left-hand side of Equation (3.47) is plotted against $\bar{n}/(2-\bar{n})[L]^2$ a straight line results. An interesting point to note is that whilst the y-intercept gives $-K_2$ and the slope $1/K_1$, the x intercept gives $K_1 K_2$ which is a useful check on the consistency of the data. The reader should verify this latter point by equating the left-hand side of Equation (3.47) to zero and then solving for $K_1 K_2$.

Another method of approach is to take Equation (3.46) and divide by $\bar{n}$ without rearranging:

$$1 = \frac{(1-\bar{n})}{n}\,[L]\,K_1 + \frac{(2-\bar{n})}{\bar{n}}\,[L]^2\,K_1\,K_2 \qquad (3.48)$$

This equation takes the form of

$$f_1 x + f_2 y = 1 \qquad (3.49)$$

where f_1 and f_2 are functions of $\bar{n}$ and $[L]$, whilst x and y are K_1 and $K_1 K_2$ respectively. This type of equation can be solved graphically by plotting $1/f_1$ against $1/f_2$, the point of intersection yielding K_1 and $K_1 K_2$ by inspection. This method is known as elimination. The sharpness of the point of intersection gives an indication of the order of the experimental error in the data set.

Up till now we have only considered systems where $N \leqslant 2$ and hence linear methods apply. If we consider systems for $N \geqslant 3$ then rearrangement of Equation (3.13) gives:

$$\sum_{n=0}^{n=N} (\bar{n}-n)\beta_n[L]^n = 0 \qquad (3.50)$$

and this can be rearranged into the form:

$$\frac{N-\bar{n}}{N-1-\bar{n}}\,[L] = \frac{\beta_{N-1}}{\beta_N} + \frac{\beta_{N-2}}{\beta_n[L]} + \sum_{n=0}^{n=N-3} \frac{\bar{n}-n}{N-1-\bar{n}}\,\frac{\beta_n}{\beta_N}\,[L]^{n-N+1} \qquad (3.51)$$

Although this somewhat alarming equation is non-linear, a plot of the left-hand side against $(\bar{n} - N + 2)/(N - 1 - n)[L]$ will have an intercept β_{N-1}/β_N and a limiting slope of β_{N-2}/β_N as $[L]$ tends to zero. Hence all the values of the various K values (via β's) can be found. It should be stressed, however, that with an approach of this type errors will accumulate as we calculate K_1 to K_n.

(ii) *Numerical methods based on $\bar{n}$*

Equations like (3.13), which are non-linear with respect to the observables, may be solved provided that the number of data points is greater than or equal to the number of unknowns. This type of calculation is best carried out on a computer using non-linear least-squares refinement techniques as described in Chapter 5. However, many systems of interest involve multidentate ligands which for octahedral complexes means that $N \leqslant 3$. To illustrate the principle we can rewrite Equation (3.42) for $N = 3$ in terms of β_n.

$$\bar{n} = (1 - \bar{n})[L]\beta_1 + (2 - \bar{n})[L]^2\beta_2 + (3 - \bar{n})[L]^3\beta_3 \tag{3.52}$$

which is solvable if we have three sets of data, enabling Equation (3.52) to be written in the form (3.53) where the subscripts 1, 2, and 3 refer to each separate set of data.

$$[\beta_1 \beta_2 \beta_3] \begin{bmatrix} (1 - \bar{n})[L]_1 & (1 - \bar{n})[L]_2 & (1 - \bar{n})[L]_3 \\ (2 - \bar{n})[L]_1^2 & (2 - \bar{n})[L]_2^2 & (2 - \bar{n})[L]_3^2 \\ (3 - \bar{n})[L]_1^3 & (3 - \bar{n})[L]_2^3 & (3 - \bar{n})[L]_3^3 \end{bmatrix} = \begin{bmatrix} \bar{n}_1 \\ \bar{n}_2 \\ \bar{n}_3 \end{bmatrix} \tag{3.53}$$

In matrix notation† this is represented by

$$B\,A = C \tag{3.54}$$

which on solving for B yields

$$B = C\,A^{-1} \tag{3.55}$$

Thus B can be found by inverting the **A** matrix and premultiplying by the column vector C. There is a simple method due to Block and McIntyre [6] for solving Equation (3.55), which is based on Crammer's Rule for determinants. It can easily be done on a small electronic calculator in an hour or so. If we rewrite Equation (3.13),

$$\bar{n} = \sum_{i=1}^{i=n} (i - \bar{n})[L]^i \beta_i \tag{3.56}$$

and substitute J_n for $(n - \bar{n})[L]^n$ we get:

$$\bar{n} = \sum_{i=1}^{i=n} J_i \beta_i \tag{3.57}$$

† Appendix I briefly introduces matrix algebra for those readers unfamiliar with this topic.

By defining a series of functions J_n, L_n and M_{np} as in Table 3.2 it is possible, for $N = 3$, to derive the equations listed in Table 3.3 for the stability constants, K_1, K_2 and K_3. An example of the application of this procedure is given in section 10.4(iii). For the method to be successful, three criteria must be met:

(a) the experimental data must be good, as even small errors can yield erroneous or negative answers;

(b) the $\bar{n}$ values chosen should lie ideally in the following ranges:

$$0.2 < \bar{n}_1 < 0.8$$
$$1.2 < \bar{n}_2 < 1.8$$
$$2.2 < \bar{n}_3 < 2.8$$

and (c) the value for N must be known.

Table 3.2 — Functions necessary for the Block and McIntyre solution of Equation (3.55) for $N = 3$. $\bar{n}_i$ and $[L]_i$ are pairs of experimental values, $n = 1$, 2, or 3, $p = 3$, and $n \neq p$.

$$
\begin{aligned}
J_n &= (n - \bar{n}_1)[L]_1^n & L_n''' &= \bar{n}_2 J_n'' - \bar{n}_3 J_n' \\
J_n' &= (n - \bar{n}_2)[L]_2^n & M_{np}' &= J_n J_p' - J_n' J_p \\
J_n'' &= (n - \bar{n}_3)[L]_3^n & M_{np}'' &= J_n J_p'' - J_n'' J_p \\
L_n' &= \bar{n}_1 J_n' - \bar{n}_2 J_n & M_{np}''' &= J_n' J_p'' - J_n'' J_p' \\
L_n'' &= \bar{n}_1 J_n'' - \bar{n}_3 J_n
\end{aligned}
$$

3.7 CALCULATION OF STABILITY CONSTANTS BASED ON THE DEGREE OF COMPLEX FORMATION ϕ

(i) *Leden's method*

Leden [7] defined a function, $F(L)$ such that

$$F(L) = \frac{\phi - 1}{[L]} = \frac{[M]_T - [M]}{[M][L]} \tag{3.58}$$

which, incorporating Equation (3.18), can be rewritten:

$$F(L) = \beta_1 + \sum_{i=2}^{i=N} \beta_i [L]^{i-1} \tag{3.59}$$

Table 3.3 – Equations for the stability constants K_1, K_2, and K_3 according to Block and McIntyre's solution of Equation (3.55). The functions J_n, L_n and M_{np} are given in Table 3.2.

Maximum number of ligands per metal (N)	Equilibrium constant	Equation number
1	$K_1 = \dfrac{\bar{n}}{J_1}$	1
2	$K_1 = \dfrac{(n_1 J_2' - \bar{n}_2 J_2)}{(J_1 J_2' - J_1' J_2)}$	2
	$K_2 = \dfrac{(\bar{n}_2 J_1 - \bar{n}_1 J_1')}{(\bar{n}_1 J_2' - \bar{n}_2 J_2)}$	3
3	$K_1 = \dfrac{(L_3'' M_{23}' - L_3' M_{23}'')}{(M_{13}'' M_{23}' - M_{13}' M_{23}'')}$	4
	$K_1 = \dfrac{(L_3' M_{23}''' - L_3''' M_{23}')}{(M_{13}' M_{23}''' - L_3''' M_{23}')}$	5
	$K_1 = \dfrac{(L_3'' M_{23}' - L_3''' M_{13}'')}{(M_{13}'' M_{23}''' - M_{13}''' M_{23}'')}$	6
	$K_2 = \dfrac{(L_3'' M_{13}' - L_3' M_{13}'')}{(L_3' M_{23}'' - L_3'' M_{23}')}$	7
	$K_2 = \dfrac{(L_3' M_{13}''' - L_3''' M_{13}')}{(L_3''' M_{23}' - L_3' M_{23}''')}$	8
	$K_2 = \dfrac{(L_1' L_3'' - L_1'' L_3')}{(L_2'' L_3' - L_2' L_3'')}$	9
	$K_2 = \dfrac{(L_1''' L_3' - L_1' L_3''')}{(L_2' L_3''' - L_2''' L_3')}$	10
	$K_2 = \dfrac{(L_3'' M_{13}''' - L_3' M_{13}'')}{(L_3''' M_{23}'' - L_3'' M_{23}''')}$	11
	$K_3 = \dfrac{(L_1'' L_2' - L_1' L_2'')}{(L_1' L_3'' - L_1'' L_3')}$	12
	$K_3 = \dfrac{(L_1' L_2''' - L_1''' L_2')}{(L_1''' L_3' - L_1' L_3''')}$	13
	$K_3 = \dfrac{(L_1'' L_2''' - L_1''' L_2')}{(L_1''' L_3'' - L_2'' L_3''')}$	14

If $N = 2$ this becomes:

$$F(L) = \beta_1 + \beta_2[L] \tag{3.60}$$

If $F(L)$ is plotted against $[L]$ a straight line graph results having an intercept of β_1 and slope β_2. For systems where $N \geqslant 3$ the relationship is no longer linear, and β_1 has to be found by extrapolation to zero free ligand concentration either by hand or better by computer curve-fitting techniques. Having found β_1 by this method, a new function can be defined

$$G(L) = \frac{F(L) - \beta_1}{[L]} = \beta_2 + \sum_{i=3}^{i=N} \beta_i[L]^{i-1} \tag{3.61}$$

and hence β_2 can be evaluated. This procedure can be continued until β_n is found. Unfortunately, like all graphical extrapolation methods, the errors in β_n accumulate as n increases. This method has another disadvantage in that generally speaking both $[L]$ and $[M]$ have to be known. However, it is possible to get round this for systems where $N = 2$ and $K_1 \gg K_2$ by defining a new secondary concentration variable, $\bar{v}$, as:

$$\bar{v} = \frac{[L]_T - [L]}{[M]_T - [M]} \tag{3.62}$$

$\bar{v}$ is the 'average number of ligands per metal ion', and since $N = 2$ and $K_1 \gg K_2$, $\bar{v}$ will be only slightly greater than unity. Thus by putting $\bar{v} = 1$ it is possible to obtain a first estimate of the free ligand concentration from Equation (3.62). Since $[L]_T - [L]$ represents the bound ligand, that is,

$$[L]_T - [L] = [ML] + 2[ML_2] \tag{3.63}$$

and $[M]_T - [M]$ represents the complexed metal, that is,

$$[M]_T - [M] = [ML] + [ML_2] \tag{3.64}$$

it follows that

$$\bar{v} = \frac{[ML] + 2[ML_2]}{[ML] + [ML_2]} \tag{3.65}$$

which, multiplying the first terms by $1/[M][L]$ and the second terms by $[ML][L]/[ML][L]^2[M]$ (equivalent to $1/[M][L]$) becomes

$$\bar{v} = \left\{ \frac{[ML]}{[M][L]} + \frac{2[ML_2][ML][L]}{[ML][L]^2[M]} \right\} \Big/ \left\{ \frac{[ML]}{[M][L]} + \frac{[ML_2][ML][L]}{[ML][L]^2[M]} \right\} \quad (3.66)$$

which on tidying up yields

$$\bar{v} = \frac{\beta_1 + 2\beta_2[L]}{\beta_1 + \beta_2[L]} \quad (3.67)$$

Equation (3.67) can be used to derive first estimates of β_1 and β_2 from the first estimate of the free ligand concentration. The first estimates of β_1, β_2, and the free ligand concentration are then used to obtain a first improved value of $F(L)$ through Equation (3.58) which from (3.60) gives first improved values of β_1 and β_2. This iterative approach is continued until no significant change occurs between cycles. Thus by measuring only a single experimental variable, [M], Leden's method enables two stability constants β_1 and β_2 to be evaluated. This technique is illustrated in the second case study (Chapter 11) for the formation of complexes between silver(I) and allyl alcohol in aqueous solution. From Chapter 11 it is apparent that iteration does not need to be continued through many cycles – in Chapter 11 the second cycle gives essentially the same result as the first.

(ii) *Froneaus' method*

In contrast to Leden, Froneaus [8] used ϕ directly as his starting function

$$X(L) = \phi = 1 + \sum_{i=1}^{i=N} \beta_i[L]^i \quad (3.68)$$

This is identical with Equation (3.18). The differential form of this equation, (3.21), on rearrangement gives

$$\ln X(L) = \int_0^L \frac{\bar{n}}{[L]} \, d[L] \quad (3.69)$$

Graphical integration of the right-hand side of Equation (3.69) yields the desired function and requires a knowledge of only one experimental variable [L]. From here the method proceeds similarly to Leden's method, as a simple interrelationship exists:

$$X(L) = F(L)[L] + 1 \quad (3.70)$$

However, there is no simple relation between either of these functions and $\bar{n}$.

3.8 COMPARISON OF THE VARIOUS METHODS OF CALCULATING STABILITY CONSTANTS

The reader will no doubt by now be asking the question 'What method do I use, and which will give me the best answer'? So far we have omitted description of the various advanced numerical methods now available on large computers; these have been left for Chapter 5. As the reader will appreciate, the methods described so far in this chapter will only cope satisfactorily with systems where $N \leqslant 3$. All three methods described in Sections 3.6 and 3.7 give unique solutions for the various K_n values, and any differences in magnitude between them are due solely to errors inherent in the experimental data [9], or non-rigorous data treatment, that is, least-squares fit to curves with correlated errors. Leden's method is more limited in its applicability as it generally requires two experimental variables. Froneaus' method has inherent difficulties owing to uncertainties being introduced by graphical integration. The same may be said of Bjerrum's method if $\bar{n}$ is obtained. Froneaus' method has the advantages that it can be applied to mixed ligand complexes [8] and is more flexible than either of the other two methods in that it is capable of coping with polynuclear species.

All these procedures have a common fault in that as n increases, K_n becomes more prone to error. This is particularly true of non-linear extrapolation methods. Rossotti and Rossotti [5] have emphasised that unless there are large differences between successive K values, it is very difficult, if not impossible, to estimate

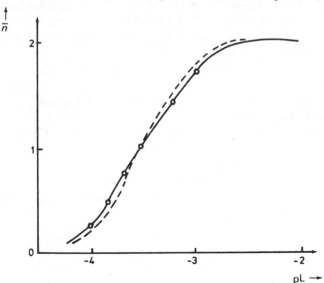

Figure 3.2 — Formation curve for the silver (I)-ammonia system.
———— Bjerrum's values [2] $\beta_1 = 1580, \beta_2 = 1.07 \times 10^7$;
– – – – Calculated values assuming β_1 is negligible and $\beta_2 = 10^7$;
  O Experimental points.

the errors. In addition, if the existence of a complex can only be inferred by assuming that $K_n \leqslant K_{n+1}$ then this should be viewed with great suspicion. In such cases the complex contains only a very small amount of the total metal present, $[M]_T$, even at the optimum $[L]$ concentration. Furthermore, plots of $\bar{n}$ against pL are remarkably insensitive to small changes in K_n unless the experimental data is extremely good. This point has been clearly illustrated [10] for the silver(I)-ammonia system using Bjerrum's original data [2]. As can be seen from Figure 3.2, the formation curves calculated from $\beta_1 = 1580$ and $\beta_2 = 1.07 \times 10^7$, and from the assumption that β_1 is negigible and $\beta_2 = 10^7$, are very similar. If the experimental data had been only slightly less accurate, no real evidence for the formation of the intermediate complex $[Ag(NH_3)]^+$ could be presented.

In conclusion, it can be said that whilst nearly all the methods are very useful for mononuclear systems where $N \leqslant 3$, the only really satisfactory methods for more complex systems are iterative non-linear least-squares refinement techniques carried out on a large volume of data on high-speed digital computers. These are described in Chapter 5.

REFERENCES

[1] Bjerrum, N. (1921). *Z. Anorg. Allgem. Chem.*, **119**, 179.

[2] Bjerrum, J. (1941). *Metal Ammine Formation in Aqueous Solution* (reprinted 1957). Copenhagen: P. Haase and Son.

[3] Kragten, J. (1978). *Atlas of Metal-Ligand Equilibria in Aqueous Solution*, Chichester: Ellis Horwood.

[4] Beck, M. T. (1970). *Chemistry of Complex Equilibria.* London: Van Nostrand.

[5] Rossotti, F. J. C. and Rossotti, H. (1961). *The Determination of Stability Constants.* McGraw-Hill.

[6] Block, B. P. and McIntyre, G. H. *J. Amer. Chem. Soc.*, (1953) **75**, 5667; (1955) **77**, 6723.

[7] Leden, I. (1941). *Z. Physik. Chem.*, **A188**, 160.

[8] Froneaus, S. (1950). *Acta. Chem. Scand.*, **4**, 72.

[9] Sullivan, J. C. and Hindman, J. C. (1952). *J. Amer. Chem. Soc.*, **74**, 6091.

[10] Wormser, Y. (1954). *Bull. Soc. Chim. France*, 387.

CHAPTER 4

Treatment of Data:
Linear Methods, Errors and Statistics

4.1 INTRODUCTION

When a series of measurements of a single quantity are made it is found imposs-ible in practice to obtain exactly the same value at every observation. By this is meant that every observation has a limited precision, and the value of any parameter cannot reliably be quoted to an infinite number of decimal places. One cause of this is the occurrence of random errors, the magnitude of which determine the precision of the result.

Stability constants are not directly measureable but must be calculated from an observed response function of a fixed, but experimentally adjustable, variable. Since the response data are subject to random error and indeed may be subject to systematic errors if we have not controlled the experiment well, the stability constants will be calculated with limited precision. However, it is important to have an estimate of the precision of any calculated constants, as it will indicate the reliability of the value obtained and in turn the efficiency of the experiment.

In addition we need to have an idea of how good our mathematical model is in describing the data, otherwise the presence of further species in solution may be overlooked and inaccurate stability constants will be evaluated.

4.2 MODEL BUILDING

Any experiment in science attempts to find some functional form for the way quantities in nature are related. That is, we try to build up a mathematical model. This mathematical model may be an assumed one, in which case we need some measure of how good the model is in describing our data, or it may be derived from first principles and then tested experimentally. The model may be approximate, which may still be acceptable, especially initially, and may then be refined or modified in the light of futher experimental observations.

The typical experiment consists of fixing one group of variables, called independent variables, at known values and then making observations of another dependent variable. In stability constant work the independent variables might be temperature, ionic strength, or the concentration of one or more components, and the dependent variable the e.m.f. or absorbance of the solution. We then calculate, or estimate, the parameters of interest from the assumed functional form relating the dependent to the independent variables. Examples of this would be the calculation of stability constants from measurement of the complex formation function $\bar{n}$, or the degree of complex formation ϕ as described in Chapter 3. Note that the calculations still have to be done in terms of an assumed model. That is, an assumed number of stability constants such as n in Equation (3.13), although qualitative data should already have given us a good idea of what this model is likely to be (Chapter 2).

The parameters for our model are calculated by fitting them to the experimental data. This may be done either graphically or by a mathematical procedure, such as that of least-squares. This latter method calculates the values of the parameters such that the sum of the squares of the residuals is a minimum. A residual is the difference between the observed and calculated data points at each fixed value of the independent variable. It is the most widely used data handling technique because, given some assumptions about the nature of the statistical population from which the data sample is drawn, the calculated parameters have certain desirable properties [1-3]. That is, the least-squares estimators of the parameters are unbiased, minimum variance estimators of the true values. In addition the method of least-squares allows us both to obtain estimates of the errors in the parameters of interest and to estimate the 'goodness of fit' of the assumed model, that is, it allows us to test alternative hypotheses. Of course, different hypotheses can be tested by fitting different models graphically 'by eye', but this method can never be as objective as the least-squares calculation procedure.

In the next sections we shall briefly consider basic statistical concepts of error and experimental precision and accuracy before outlining the theory of least-squares and the way in which error estimates for the calculated constants can be obtained. In addition we shall indicate methods by which models can be built up and hypotheses tested.

4.3 RANDOM ERRORS

Random or observational errors are assumed to follow a Gaussian or normal distribution [4,5], expressed mathematically as:

$$f(r_x) = \frac{1}{\sqrt{2}\sigma_x} e^{-r_x^2/2\sigma_x^2} \tag{4.1}$$

where r_x is the residual of x or observed value−true value, σ_x^2 is the variance of x, and σ_x is the standard deviation.

The probability of observing the ith residual, p_i, in the region r_{xi} to $r_{xi} + dr_{xi}$ is:

$$p_i = \frac{1}{\sqrt{2}\sigma_x} \left(e^{-r_{xi}^2/2\sigma_x^2} \right) dr_{xi} \tag{4.2}$$

Now the probability of obtaining a given set of n observations, P, is the product of the probabilities of each of the ith measurements.

$$P = \prod_{i=1}^{i=n} p_i = \left(\frac{\partial r_{xi}}{\sqrt{2}\sigma_x} \right)^n e^{-(1/2\sigma_x^2)\Sigma r_{xi}^2} \tag{4.3}$$

Based on the statistical principle of maximum likelihood [1] this probability becomes a maximum when the sum of the squares residuals is a minimum.

$$\sum_{i=1}^{n} r_{xi}^2 = \text{minimum} \tag{4.4}$$

Hence the origin of the term 'least-squares' is apparent.

The discussion so far has assumed that the measurements of x have all come from the same population distribution, that is, the variance of the residuals are equal. If this is not so, Equation (4.2) should be rewritten as:

$$p_i = \frac{1}{\sqrt{2}\sigma_{xi}} \left(e^{-r_{xi}^2/2\sigma_{xi}^2} \right) dr \tag{4.5}$$

and Equation (4.3) becomes

$$P = \prod_{i=1}^{i=n} p_i = \left(\frac{\partial r_{xi}}{\sqrt{2}} \right)^n \left(\frac{1}{\sigma_{x_1} \sigma_{x_2} \cdots \sigma_{xn}} \right) e^{-\frac{1}{2}\Sigma(r_{xi}^2/\sigma_{xi}^2)} \tag{4.6}$$

and the least-squares principle gives:

$$\sum_{i=1}^{i=n} \left(\frac{r_{xi}^2}{\sigma_{xi}^2} \right) = \text{minimum} \tag{4.7}$$

A quantity inversely proportional to the variance is termed the weight of an observation. Hence:

$$w_{xi} = \frac{\sigma_o^2}{\sigma_{xi}^2} \tag{4.8}$$

where σ_0^2 is known as the variance of an observation of unit weight. In practice σ_0^2 will often have the value of unity. The quantity now to be minimised is the sum of the weighted squares of the residuals.

$$\sum_{i=1}^{i=n} w_{xi} r_{xi}^2 = \text{minimum} \tag{4.9}$$

Thus those residuals arising from observations of greater precision, or smaller variance, are given more importance in the determination of the best estimate of x, which intuitively seems a reasonable thing to do. In practice we cannot know the true value of x, but the principle of least-squares attempts to adjust the estimate of x according to Equation (4.9). Generally the experimental data are a function of the parameter x so that r_{xi} in Equation (4.9) is defined as:

$$r_{xi} = [f(x_i) - f(\bar{x})] \tag{4.10}$$

and $\bar{x}$ is the least-squares estimator of the true value of the parameter.

4.4 SYSTEMATIC ERRORS
Before going on to derive equations for the least-squares estimation of the parameters of a model it is important to consider the problem of systematic errors. Systematic errors are caused by the limitations of the apparatus, or experimenter!, and introduce bias [5] into the data resulting in inaccurate parameters. Thus it is possible to obtain high precision with poor accuracy, as indicated diagrammatically in Figure 4.1.

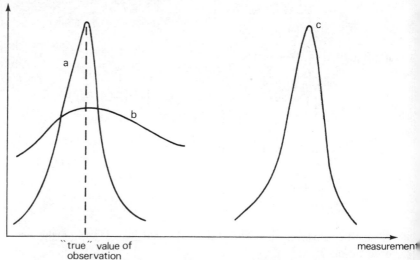

Figure 4.1 – Diagrammatic representation of types of experimental error: (a) high precision, high accuracy; (b) low precision, high accuracy (due to large random errors); (c) high precision, poor accuracy (due to systematic errors).

Therefore, before any least-squares adjustment of data are carried out, it is important to take account of, or reduce to a negligible value, any source of systematic error. If a systematic error is overlooked in an experiment the residuals in a least-squares adjustment to a function become distorted from their original distribution. The least-squares method then becomes meaningless because the sum of the weighted squares of the residuals has a different relationship to the new distribution with bias error superimposed.

A simple example of this can be given by considering the determination of a molar absorptivity, ϵ, of a compound using Beer's law:

$$A = \epsilon cl \tag{4.11}$$

where A = absorbance, ϵ = molar absorptivity, c = molar concentration of the solute and, l = path length in centimetres. Now usually the two spectrophotometric cells in which the experiment is carried out do not have exactly the same absorbance characteristics as discussed in Section 8.3. In this situation Equation (4.11) can be written more strictly as:

$$A = \epsilon cl + p \tag{4.12}$$

where p is a constant which allows for the absorbance difference of the cells. One could determine p by filling both cells with solvent ($c = 0$) and measuring the absorbance obtained. This value could then be subtracted from each concentration absorbance measurement A, and a least-squares adjustment carried out on $A - p$ and c as observations:

$$(A - p) = \epsilon cl \tag{4.13}$$

However, this would be incorrect in principle because p is not known exactly but is only estimated from a single reading. The least-squares solution of Equation (4.13), in which the curve is forced to pass through the origin, distorts the residuals of the original observations, as can be seen from Figure 4.2.

The use of the least-squares solution here is statistically incorrect since the residuals using Equation (4.13) are not only larger than those using Equation (4.12) but are not randomly distributed about the least-squares estimate of the function. The correct procedure is therefore to use Equation (4.12) and treat the source of systematic error, the absorbance blank p, as an extra parameter to be determined [5]. In this example the desired result is relatively easy to achieve, but this is not always so. Nevertheless all possible sources of systematic error should be properly taken account of in order to correctly treat the data.

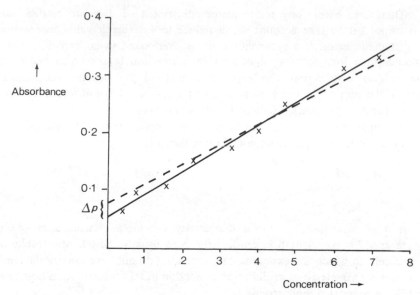

Figure 4.2 – Graph of Absorbance versus Concentration: x represent the original data points, the solid line is the least-squares fit to Equation (4.12), the broken line is least-squares fit to Equation (4.13); Δp = difference between direct observation of p and least-squares estimate of p using Equation (4.12).

4.5 LINEAR LEAST-SQUARES

A commonly occurring task in chemistry, and particularly in stability constant work where only two complexes are formed, is to assume a linear model and fit a response function y to the functional form:

$$y = px + q \tag{4.14}$$

in order to evaluate the parameters p and q. An example of a linear equation is (3.47) where the formation function $\bar{n}$ is used to calculate two stability constants, but note the restrictions on the application of least-squares analysis discussed in Section 4.6. If this linear relationship were true and all the experimental measurements were without error, then all the points $(x_1, y_1), (x_2, y_2) \ldots (x_n, y_n)$ when plotted on a Cartesian graph would lie exactly on a straight line. In practice this will not be so, since one and sometimes both x and y will contain random errors and the problem will be to find the 'best' line through the points, that is, the line that gives the 'best' estimate of p and q.

To obtain the best line according to simple least-squares theory, it is a fundamental assumption that the precision with which the independent, or experimentally adjustable, variable x can be measured is much greater than the dependent variable, y. Corresponding to each value of x_i there is a true value of the response variable y_i' such that a set of residuals can be defined as:

$$r_1 = y_1 - y_1' = y_1 - px_1 - q$$
$$r_2 = y_2 - y_2' = y_2 - px_2 - q$$

$$\vdots \qquad\qquad\qquad\qquad\qquad (4.15)$$

$$r_n = y_n - y_n' = y_n - px_n - q$$

The sum to be minimised is S, the sum of squares of these residuals:

$$S = \sum_{i=1}^{i=n} r_i^2$$

$$S = \sum_{i=1}^{i=n} (y_i - px_i - q)^2 \qquad\qquad (4.16)$$

Differentiating with respect to p and q gives two equations:

$$\frac{\partial S}{\partial p} = -2 \sum_{i=1}^{i=n} x_i(y_i - px_i - q)$$

$$\frac{\partial S}{\partial q} = -2 \sum_{i=1}^{i=n} (y_i - px_i - q) \qquad\qquad (4.17)$$

For a minimum, Equations (4.17) are set to zero, and these give Equations (4.18), called the normal equations:

$$\sum_{i=1}^{i=n} x_i y_i - q \sum_{i=1}^{i=n} x_i - p \sum_{i=1}^{i=n} x_i^2 = 0$$

$$\sum_{i=1}^{i=n} y_i - nq - p \sum_{i=1}^{i=n} x_i = 0 \qquad\qquad (4.18)$$

Solving for p and q and leaving out the subscripts to the summation signs yields:

$$p = \frac{n\Sigma xy - \Sigma x \Sigma y}{n\Sigma x^2 - (\Sigma x)^2} \qquad q = \frac{\Sigma x^2 \Sigma y - \Sigma x \Sigma y}{n\Sigma x^2 - (\Sigma x)^2} \qquad (4.19)$$

For one or two sets of data these two expressions can easily be evaluated with an electronic calculator, but for more data a computer program is a useful thing to have. Most computer installations have library routines for linear regression, which removes most of the effort involved in developing a program.

A major advantage of a least-squares analysis of data is that estimates of the precision of the parameters are available. Since the errors in p and q have been assumed to derive from errors in y, the standard deviation of p and q are estimated by:

$$\sigma_p = \left(\frac{\sigma_y}{(n-2)[n\Sigma x^2 - (\Sigma x)^2]}\right)^{\frac{1}{2}} \qquad \sigma_q = \left(\frac{\sigma_y \Sigma x^2}{(n-2)[n\Sigma x^2 - (\Sigma x)^2]}\right)^{\frac{1}{2}}$$

(4.20)

where σ_y is given by:

$$\sigma_y{}^2 = n\Sigma y^2 - (\Sigma y)^2 - \frac{[n\Sigma xy - \Sigma x \Sigma y]^2}{[n\Sigma x^2 - (\Sigma x)^2]}$$

(4.21)

The factor $n-2$ in Equation (4.20) arises from the fact that no estimate of the precision of a value for the slope of a straight line, the parameter p, would be available from a line drawn between two points. $n-2$ is defined as the number of degrees of freedom [2] of the estimates of the standard deviations in the parameters.

4.6 LIMITATIONS OF LINEAR LEAST-SQUARES

Chapter 3 describes linear equations, derived from the general case for that when only two complexes are present, for calculating the stability constants. Examples are Equation (3.47) using the complex formation function $\bar{n}$, and Equation (3.58) using the degree of complex formation, ϕ. Unfortunately, these equations have often had linear least-squares statistics applied to them for calculating the stability constants. This is particularly so for the Leden method (see Section 3.7(i)) where the constants are evaluated in an iterative cycle.

These equations do not conform to the conditions necessary for the simple linear least-squares procedure to be valid [6] and erroneous stability constants may be calculated, for the following reasons:

(a) The independent variable, the x-coordinate, is not exact and cannot be considered error free.
(b) Since both the independent and dependent variables, the x- and y-coordinates, are complex functions of the same quantity, [L], the errors are correlated.

(c) The errors in these complex functions forming the x- and y-coordinates may vary considerably throughout the experiment, and very careful weighting is necessary to allow for this.

Rigorous statistics have been developed for this situation [7,8] and they should therefore be used.

The linear equations of Chapter 3 are perhaps more useful for graphical representation of the data, as no more objective criterion than the eye is used for deciding on the values of the stability constants in any case.

4.7 LINEAR LEAST-SQUARES – GENERALISED MATRIX APPROACH

The matrix approach to linear least-squares theory is outlined for the general case where more than two parameters are to be estimated. This provides the basis for the more advanced computer based data treatment methods described in Chapter 5.

Suppose we have n experimental observations $o_1, o_2 \ldots o_n$ having associated random errors $e_1, e_2 \ldots e_n$ which depend linearly on m unknowns $x_1, x_2 \ldots x_m$, then n equations arise of the type:

$$o_i = b_{ii}x_1 + \ldots b_{im}x_m + e_i \tag{4.22}$$

which can be expressed in matrix notation as,

$$O = \mathbf{B} X + E \tag{4.23}$$

If a vector $\widehat{X}$ represents the 'best fit' values of X to the regression equation, then a vector of residuals can be defined by:

$$V = O - \mathbf{B}\,\widehat{X} \tag{4.24}$$

The quantity to be minimised is again the sum of the squares of the residuals given by:

$$S = \tilde{V} V \tag{4.25}$$

where $\tilde{V}$ is the transpose of V.

If the variances of the residuals are not equal, a weighting matrix can be introduced so that:

$$S = \tilde{V} \mathbf{W} V \tag{4.26}$$

$\mathbf{W}$ is the inverse of the matrix $\mathbf{M}$, termed the moment matrix [1], and contains the variances of the residuals, σ_{ii}^2, as diagonal elements and the co-variances σ_{ij}

as off-diagonal elements. Often the absolute values of these quantities are not known, but they may be known to within a constant scale factor σ_o^2, the variance of the observation of unit weight. Hence, we need only know the relative magnitudes of σ_{ii}^2 and σ_{ij}. Usually the σ_{ij} are arranged experimentally to be zero, or nearly zero, in which case **W** is a diagonal matrix. All off-diagonals are zero. Substituting Equation (4.24) into (4.26)

$$S = (O - B \, \widehat{X})\tilde{} \; W(O - B \, \widehat{X}) \tag{4.27}$$

Since $(B \, \widehat{X})\tilde{} = \widetilde{X} \, \widetilde{B}$ then:

$$S = \widetilde{O} \, W \, O + \widetilde{X} \, \widetilde{B} \, W \, B \, \widehat{X} - \widetilde{O} \, W \, B \, \widehat{X} - \widetilde{X} \, \widetilde{B} \, W \, O \tag{4.28}$$

Also $\widetilde{O} \, W \, B \, \widehat{X} = O \, W \, \widetilde{B} \, \widetilde{X}$, therefore:

$$S = \widetilde{O} \, W \, O + \widetilde{X} \, \widetilde{B} \, W \, B \, \widehat{X} - 2\widetilde{X} \, \widetilde{B} \, W \, O \tag{4.29}$$

Differentiating with respect to each of the parameters X in turn and equating to zero:

$$\partial S = 2(\partial \widetilde{X})(\widetilde{B} \, W \, B \, \widehat{X} - \widetilde{B} \, W \, O) \tag{4.30}$$

Therefore:

$$(\widetilde{B} \, W \, B)\widehat{X} = \widetilde{B} \, W \, O \tag{4.31}$$

and the least-squares estimates of the parameters $\widehat{X}$ are given by:

$$\widehat{X} = (\widetilde{B} \, W \, B)^{-1} \, \widetilde{B} \, W \, O \tag{4.32}$$

It can also be shown [1] that estimates of the variances of the parameters are avialable from:

$$T = \sigma_o^2 (\widetilde{B} \, W \, B)^{-1} \tag{4.33}$$

where σ_o^2 is the variance of an observation of unit weight. The matrix **T** contains the variance of the parameters X (σ_{ii}^2) on the diagonal and the covariances (σ_{ij}) on the off-diagonals. Since σ_o^2 will rarely be available it is estimated from:

$$\sigma^2 = \frac{\widetilde{V} \, W \, V}{n - m} \tag{4.34}$$

where $n - m$ is the number of degrees of freedom of σ^2. This is the number of experimental observations minus the number of parameters evaluated by the calculations. This last equation, as is all the foregoing, is only true assuming our chemical model is adequate. This being so the least-squares estimate of the parameters $\widehat{X}$, are the minimum variance estimate of the true values of X whatever the form of the distribution. Assuming a normal distribution of errors has occurred, however, it is possible to test the adequacy of the model using the standard statistical F- and t-tests [1,2,4]. This is termed hypothesis testing.

4.8 HYPOTHESIS TESTING

When a particular physical model has been fitted to an observed data set, and the stability constants calculated, it is important to be able to judge the adequacy of the postulated model. This can be done by comparing the estimate of the variance, σ^2, obtained from evaluation of the parameters with a prior estimate of the variance σ_p^2, in an F-test [4]. This prior estimate may have been obtained in one of three ways:

(a) It may be obtained from a separate experiment.
(b) It can be taken from previous experience of the variation of the variable.
(c) It may be estimated from repeat observations of a given value of the variable.

The last source is known as a 'pure error' estimate of the variance [2]. The procedure is then to compare the ratio:

$$F = \frac{\sigma^2}{\sigma_p^2} \tag{4.35}$$

The appropriate value of F, at the significance level desired and with the degrees of freedom associated with σ^2 and σ_p^2, that would be obtained by chance is then found from an F-distribution table. These tables are found in most university or college statistics textbooks. If the value of F calculated from Equation (4.35) is less than that from the table, the fit can be assumed satisfactory, at the chosen significance level. If it is larger, the model should be modified, for example, in stability constant work by the addition or deletion of another likely species, or the data examined for bias errors. If qualitative work on the number of species present has been done beforehand as described in Chapter 2, the latter is the most likely course. If no estimate of σ_p^2 is available, then the F-test cannot be applied at all, and recourse must be made to an examination of the residuals. If the signs of the residuals do not appear to change randomly, but show alternating sequences of positive and negative deviations, then it is likely that a poor fit was obtained. Hypothesis testing in this manner is one of the great advantages of a calculation procedure involving least-squares over graphical treatments.

This is especially true of the more advanced non-linear data treatments now common in stability constant work which are described in Chapter 5. Every effort should therefore be made to obtain an estimate of σ_p^2 for the dependent variable being used to calculate the stability constants.

4.9 GEOMETRY OF LINEAR LEAST-SQUARES − THE ERROR ELLIPSE

We will briefly consider here a pictorial representation of the variance-covariance matrix, T, as it is useful in future discussions in Chapter 5 on non-linear estimation and problems of error surfaces and convergence. A geometric interpretation of this matrix, Equation (4.33), is given by consideration of the quadratic form [1]:

$$S = (\widehat{X} - X)^{\sim} [\sigma^2(\widetilde{B} W B)]^{-1} (\widehat{X} - X) \tag{4.36}$$

This is in fact an equation of a hyperellipsoid centred at the point $X = \widehat{X}$ in the n-dimensional parameter space. In the linear case under consideration the probability distribution function for the errors in the parameters is a function of S, so that this ellipsoid is one of constant probability which defines a confidence contour [1,2]. A confidence contour defines the boundary of a region in parameter space wherein the true values of the parameters are expected to lie with a given percentage confidence level. Reference [4] should be consulted for the calculation of confidence intervals of individual parameters by means of the F- (variance known) or t-distribution tables† (variance unknown and estimated from the data). This ellipsoid can be represented for a two-parameter problem by Figure 4.3.

The standard deviations of the parameters as given by Equation (4.33) are the projections of the error ellipse onto the parameter axes. These values take into account the correlation of the parameters, represented here by the fact that the major axes of the ellipse are not parallel to the parameter axes. If the axes were parallel to the coordinate axes, the half lengths of the major axes would give estimates of the standard deviations. Separate confidence intervals for each parameter may be calculated using the formula:

$$X \pm t_{(n-m,\alpha)}(\widetilde{B} W B \sigma^2)^{\frac{1}{2}} \tag{4.37}$$

where $t_{(n-m,\alpha)}$ is the appropriate percentage point of the t-distribution at the significance level desired, α, and $n - m$ degrees of freedom. Such confidence

---

† The percentage points of the t-distribution function are another statistical function which may be used to evaluate the adequacy of an experimental model under certain circumstances. See the description of the F-test in Section 4.8.

intervals are only appropriate for specifying ranges for the individual parameters irrespective of the value of the other parameter. Thus it is erroneous to interpret these intervals jointly, or it could be incorrectly thought that the rectangles which they define are joint confidence regions. For example point R in Figure 4.3 could be regarded as representing possible values for the two parameters, but the true joint confidence region defined by the data shows that such values are not reasonable.

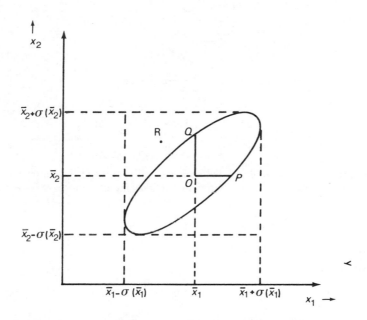

Figure 4.3 — Error ellipse $(S = 1)$ for two correlated parameters; OP and OQ are the conditional standard deviations.

Actual confidence contours of different probabilities are calculated from the values of the parameters that satisfy:

$$(X - \hat{X})^{\sim} \tilde{B} W B (X - \hat{X}) = mF_{(\alpha,m,n-m)}\sigma^2 \qquad (4.38)$$

where σ^2 is an independent estimate of error variance, obtained from Equation (4.34), and $F_{(\alpha,m,n-m)}$ is the α percentage point of the F-distribution with m and $n - m$ degrees of freedom. Figure 4.4 gives an example of confidence regions so calculated for a hypothetical linear problem. A full discussion of the geometry of both linear and non-linear least-squares is given in Chapter 10 of Reference [2].

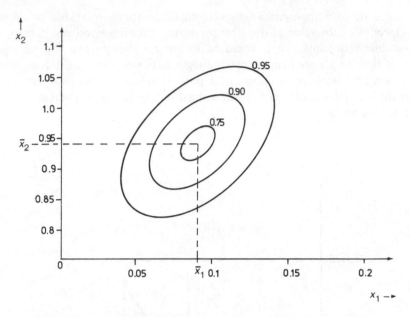

Figure 4.4 – Confidence contours; the region enclosed by the 0.95 contour has a 95% probability that it contains the true parameter values $\widehat{X}$.

REFERENCES

[1] Hamilton, W. C. (1964). *Statistics in Physical Science*. N.Y.: Ronald Press Co.

[2] Draper, N. R. and Smith, H. (1966). *Applied Regression Analysis*. John Wiley and Sons Inc.

[3] Box, G. E. P. (1960). *Anal. N.Y. Acad. Sci.*, **86**, 792.

[4] Barford, N. C. (1967). *Experimental Measurements: Precision, Error and Truth*. Addison-Wesley Publishing Co. Inc.

[5] Wentworth, W. E. (1965). *J. Chem. Ed.*, **42**, 96.

[6] Rossotti, F. J. C., Rossotti, H. S., and Whewell, R. J. (1971). *J. Inorg. Nucl. Chem.*, **33**, 2051.

[7] York, D. (1966). *Can. J. Phys.*, **44**, 1074.

[8] York, D. (1969). *Earth and Planetary Sci. Lett.*, **5**, 320.

CHAPTER 5

Treatment of Data: Non-Linear Parameter Estimation

5.1 INTRODUCTION

Most of the classical calculations and graphical methods for the evaluation of stability constants in solution described in Chapter 3 were developed during the early history of the subject before the advent of digital computers. At that time the systems studied were, no doubt deliberately, comparatively simple, and thus these methods often manipulated the data into a form suitable for linear graphical representation [1]. As the subject has progressed there has been increasing emphasis on more complex systems, particularly in the area of attempting to understand the coordinating role of metal ions in biological and catalytic systems. Alongside this has grown up the general availability of the digital computer. Thus it is noteworthy that over the past 10 to 15 years non-linear estimation procedures have been increasingly applied to the calculation of stability constants. In these procedures iterative algorithms are used to evaluate the parameters in question, usually directly from the observed values of the dependent variable. Most of these mathematical methods have been known for many years but have been difficult or impossible to apply except in the simplest of cases. Computers have now brought these calculation procedures within the grasp of most chemists and have enabled systems that could not be dealt with graphically, to be investigated. Two reviews of the computer calculation of stability constants have been given [2,3].

5.2 LIMITATIONS OF GRAPHICAL METHODS

Modern calculation methods, as well as being the only ones capable of dealing with complex systems, also overcome some of the limitations of graphical methods. These may be listed as follows:

(a) It is difficult to obtain reliable estimates of the errors in the parameters.
(b) It may be difficult to decide whether the parameters give a reasonable fit to the experimental observables. Thus testing different hypotheses (chemical models) presents difficulties.

(c) In some complicated cases only a portion of the data may be used in evaluating a particular parameter, for example, by extrapolating to some point. In this case the precision of the parameter becomes limited.

(d) Considerable effort may be expended in arriving at justifiable assumptions for manipulating the equations into a form that can conveniently be plotted.

(e) For a large number of determinations, graphical solutions may be much more time-consuming compared with the task of preparing the input data for a computer program.

Despite these points, it is true that non-linear least-squares programs require initial estimates of the parameters for refinement, and graphical procedures may be used for obtaining these initial approximations. Indeed, graphical representations are useful as visual summaries and have often been recommended after the least-squares analysis has been carried out [2,4–8]. This is particularly helpful in the analysis of spectrophotometric data, when calculated spectra can be plotted out, either by hand or machine. Chemical knowledge and experience can then be applied as a final check that the calculated parameters are reasonable. Also patterns in the residuals, which are the difference between the observed and calculated values of the dependent variable, are more easily seen if the calculated and observed curves formed by measurement of the dependent variable are plotted out. The residuals should always be printed out for examination.

5.3 LEAST-SQUARES – EXTENSION TO NON-LINEAR CASE

To extend least-squares theory to the non-linear case, that is the situation where the dependent variables are non-linear functions of the independent variables, we take Equation (4.22) and express the dependent variables (observables) o_i as a function f_i of the m unknowns by a Taylor series expansion [9]. Thus if the initial estimates of the parameter values are $(x_1^o \ldots x_m^o)$, then the observables are expressed about this point in parameter space by:

$$o_i = f_i(x_1^o \ldots x_m^o) + \left(\frac{\partial f_i}{\partial x_1}\right)_o (x_1 - x_1^o) + \ldots \left(\frac{\partial f_i}{\partial x_m}\right)_o (x_m - x_m^o) \qquad (5.1)$$

that is

$$o_i = f_i(x_1^o \ldots x_m^o) + \sum_{j=1}^{j=m} \left(\frac{\partial f_i}{\partial x_j}\right)_o \Delta x_j \qquad (5.2)$$

where terms higher than first order have been neglected. Therefore the change in the observables Δo_i, on making the corrections Δx_j are given by:

$$\Delta o_i = o_i - f_i(x_1^o \ldots x_m^o) = \sum_{j=1}^{j=m} \left(\frac{\partial f_i}{\partial x_j} \right)_o \Delta x_j \qquad (5.3)$$

which can be expressed in matrix notation as:

$$O = \mathbf{B} X \qquad (5.4)$$

The problem has been linearised with O, $\mathbf{B}$ and X containing elements Δo_i, $\partial f_i/\partial x_j$ and Δx_j respectively. Assuming errors in each experimental observable as before and working through the mathematics [10,11] then gives the same equation as previously (4.32) for the estimates of the parameters $\widehat{X}$. In this case, however, $\widehat{X}$ does not give the least-squares estimates of the parameters in one iteration, but merely the correction vector ΔX which (theoretically) produces a lower sum of squares of the errors. This is because the Taylor expansion is not strictly valid, that is, $\partial f_i/\partial x_j$ varies with x_j. In this way a vector of improved values of the parameters is generated which is used as the estimate for the next calculation, so that if the function is well behaved and the starting vector X^o is not too far from the final values, the process will converge to the least-squares estimates in a finite number of iterations.

It is this iterative method that has been incorporated in a number of computer-based algorithms for the calculation and refinement of stability constants [5,11–16]. It has become a very large field, and some of the programs available, problems encountered, approximations made and their effects on experimental design are discussed in the next sections. Firstly, a note will ensue on model building and hypothesis testing in the non-linear situation.

5.4 HYPOTHESIS TESTING

It is possible to use the theory developed for the linear case to calculate an internal estimate of the variance, σ^2, the standard deviations of the parameters, and to test hypotheses with F- and t-tests. However, it is an overriding premise that these calculations are approximate. The extent of approximation depends on the degree of non-linearity of the function, but quite often this may not be too severe in the region of the minimum [10]. Even with a normal distribution of experimental errors for the non-linear model, $\widehat{X}$ is no longer normally distributed and Equation (4.34) does not give a truly unbiased estimate of σ^2. It is the probability level at which the F-test is applied which then becomes approximate rather than the calculations themselves.

Another quantity which has been used [15] in non-linear estimation situations is the Hamilton R-factor [17]. In this procedure the R-factor defined by:

$$R = \left[\frac{\sum\limits_{i=1}^{i=n} w_i \left(o_i^{\text{calc}} - o_i^{\text{obs}} \right)^2}{\sum\limits_{i=1}^{i=n} w_i \left(o_i^{\text{obs}} \right)^2} \right]^{\frac{1}{2}} \tag{5.5}$$

is compared with R_{lim} calculated from:

$$R_{\text{lim}} = \left[\frac{\sum\limits_{i=1}^{i=n} w_i e_i^2}{\sum\limits_{i=1}^{i=n} w_i \left(o_i^{\text{obs}} \right)^2} \right]^{\frac{1}{2}} \tag{5.6}$$

where e_i is the residual in the ith equation calculated from estimates of the errors in all the experimental quantities using error propagation rules [18], o_i^{calc} and o_i^{obs} are the calculated and observed values of the response variable respectively, and w_i are the appropriate weighting factors. A satisfactory fit is assumed if $R < R_{\text{lim}}$.

To test alternative hypotheses the R-factor ratio test can be applied. If, for example, a particular hypothesis H_o gave an R-factor R_o and an alternative hypothesis H_1 a value R_1, then H_1 can be rejected at the α-significance level if:

$$\frac{R_1}{R_o} > R_{(m, n-m, \alpha)} \tag{5.7}$$

where m is the number of unknown parameters that have been refined and $n - m$ is the number of degrees of freedom of the least-squares adjustment. The value of $R_{(m, n-m, \alpha)}$ is found from statistical tables [17].

5.5 GEOMETRY OF NON-LINEAR LEAST-SQUARES

Equation (4.38) can be applied to the non-linear case and yields reasonably good approximations to confidence contours when the problem is sufficiently near linear to ensure validity of the whole procedure. It is probably better to calculate true confidence contours in the non-linear case, using Equation (5.8).

$$S = \widehat{S} + m\sigma^2 F_{(\alpha, m, n-m)} \tag{5.8}$$

where $\hat{S}$ is the value of the sum of the squares of the errors at the least-squares estimate of X and S is that at some other value of X that satisfies the equation. Here, it is only the probability level of this equation that is approximate [10].

Equation (5.8) is difficult to compute because it is necessary to find the locus of all the parameter sets $(x_1 \ldots x_m)$ that yield the same residual sum of squares of errors [19]. However, it can give a useful picture of the conditioning (shape) of the error surface and the extent of parameter correlation. The contours do not turn out to be regular ellipsoids as in Figure 4.4, but may be narrow and attenuated [20-22] or even banana shaped [23] as in Figure 5.1. It is this parameter surface, or space when $m > 2$, that in fact determines the ease and rapidity with which the minimum variance estimates of the parameters are found, and consequently, which modification of the basic iterative least-squares algorithm is best used. Note that if this space is multidimensional, that is, $m > 2$, then sections in various 'directions' through parameter space can still be drawn by holding the appropriate parameters constant.

Readers interested in the problem of exact confidence regions in non-linear estimation should consult References [24-26].

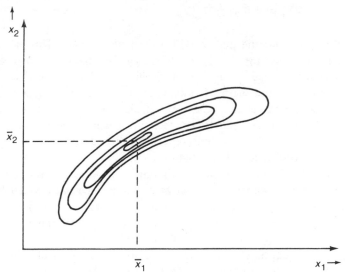

Figure 5.1 — A hypothetical error surface generated by the sum of the squares of the error contours for a non-linear problem.

5.6 ILL-CONDITIONING OF THE NORMAL EQUATIONS — CONVERGENCE

The most commonly used method of non-linear least-squares parameter estimation in the field of stability constant calculations is the already outlined Gauss-Newton method [27], in which the function to be fitted is expanded as a Taylor series and truncated at the first-order term [4,11,12,16,27–30]. Occasionally the second-order terms have been taken into account (the Newton-Rapheson approach) in an effort to obtain more efficient convergence properties, but there are conflicting reports [15,31] regarding its efficacy in so doing. Another method that has been commonly applied (though perhaps less often recently) is the 'pit-mapping' approach of Sillén and co-workers [7,21,32–34]. In this method, the error square sum S for an initial set of stability constants K is calculated and the S is recalculated with each K_i in turn incremented by a given step h_i. Using each of the S values from $\frac{1}{2}(n + 1)(n + 2)$ systematically chosen points, where n is the number of stability constants being adjusted, the coefficients of a second degree (parabolic) surface are found and hence the minimum K_o of the surface evaluated. This set of values is then used for the start of the next iteration. These two methods have their merits, and are claimed [7,31] to have advantages over each other, but the main problem encountered by these and other programs in the field [35,36] is the reliability of convergence.

The reason for this can be seen by considering again the equation for obtaining the correction vector to the parameters, viz:

$$\Delta X = (\tilde{B} W B)^{-1} \tilde{B} W O \qquad (5.9)$$

To solve this equation, the matrix $\tilde{B} W B$ must be inverted. This can only be achieved if the determinant of this matrix is non-zero, because if it is zero, the matrix is singular and has no inverse. However, if the determinant is not zero, but very small, then the matrix is said to be ill-conditioned. This effect has often been reported in stability constant calculations [37–39]. Indeed readers familiar with force constant refinement techniques will be aware that it occurs in this field [40–42]. It has also been reported in fitting equations to chromatograms [43] and in optical lens design [44–47].

The physical effect of this ill-conditioning is manifest by the sum of the squares of the errors, S, undergoing haphazard and, in some cases, wild oscillation [46] instead of steady convergence to a minimum value. This is due to the parameter surface in many practical situations, considering for the moment only three dimensions, being a narrow, elongated bent valley analogous to Figure 5.1. The use of Equation (5.9) results in a rapid oscillation of direction across the narrow valley owing to the poor Taylor series approximation, particularly when the parameter starting values are far from the minimum, resulting in 'overshoot'. This is why the importance of good initial estimates of the parameters has often been emphasised in stability constant calculations [11,16]. This requirement is probably no longer necessary nowadays as modern algorithms will converge from almost any reasonable set of starting values for the constants, albeit at the expense of more computer time. Some of these algorithms will be briefly discussed in the next section, but before doing so a note will be made on the possibility of converging to a so-called 'false minimum'.

The often mentioned problem of 'false minima' has in our experience been overemphasised and in any case can be obviated by beginning the iterative process from several widely different sets of parameter starting values. If two or more minima did exist with any real system it would mean that two or more parameters were highly correlated, and better data is required to obtain separate estimates of their values (see Section 5.8).

5.7 NON-LINEAR LEAST-SQUARES ALGORITHMS

The simplest algorithm for function minimisation, the function being the sum of the squares of the errors as calculated by the equation relating the dependent to the independent variables, does not use Equation (5.9) but proceeds by the method of steepest descent. This is conceptually the simplest to envisage, as the parameters are adjusted in proportion to the magnitude of the derivatives evaluated at the particular point in parameter space currently occupied. The direction of movement is always ensured to be such that progress down the 'slope' is made [48]. However, the major disadvantage of this type of method is that after initial rapid progress, further minimisation is painfully slow [10,22,44]. This is only to be expected, since after initial movement down the steep sides of the 'valley', further minimisation is a slow crawl along the 'valley floor'. For this reason this method is not recommended for stability constant calculations.

Mention should also briefly be made here of the grid and pattern search methods of function minimisation and of simplex optimisation [49]. Rarely used in least-squares problems and still more rarely used in stability constant calculations, these methods are not particularly efficient. They do not involve the calculation of derivatives but rely on evaluating the values of the objective function (the sum of the squares of the residuals) at several chosen points. These points may be random or situated along coordinate directions. The values so obtained are then examined, using various strategies to decide on the next direction of search.

By far the most commonly used non-linear least-squares algorithms for the calculation of stability constants are those based on Equation (5.9), which are the Gauss-Newton-Rapheson methods. These methods fall into two main headings which describe the manner in which a decrease in the sum of squares, S, is ensured on each iteration.

- (a) Scaling or optimisation of the corrections is carried out subsequent to the calculations, so as to bring about the maximum decrease in S for the given iteration. This ensures ultimate convergence.
- (b) A modification is made to the equations, prior to the calculation of the corrections, which tries to ensure that convergence will eventually be achieved.

An example of type (a) is the shift optimisation method [50]. It has been used [4,8,15,31,51] in the stability constant field, and the procedure is to calculate the objective function, S, from the parameters with zero, one half, and the full correction (as calculated from Equation (5.9)) applied. A paraboloid surface is assumed for this quantity as a function of the correction vector ΔX. The minimum is then given by adding the fraction u of the correction vector calculated from:

$$u = \tfrac{1}{2} + \tfrac{1}{4}\left[\frac{S_0 - S_1}{S_1 - 2S_{\frac{1}{2}} - S_0}\right] \tag{5.10}$$

The effect of this procedure is to scale down any large corrections calculated as a result of any ill-conditioning of the normal equations. It has been extended by other workers [52] but is perhaps not as efficient as the algorithms of type (b) in view of the extra function evaluations required on each iteration.

Two extremely useful methods of type (b) which have recently been applied [35,37,53,54] to stability constant calculations are those of Marquardt [55] and Fletcher-Powell [56]. The former is also known as 'damped' least-squares and is essentially a rediscovery of an older idea by Levenberg [57], wherein the sum of the squares of the corrections to the parameters is minimised along with the sum of the squares of the residuals. Marquardt arrived at his algorithm by noting that, at any given point on the parameter surface, there will generally be two directions in which a reduction in S will be brought about. These are the Taylor series direction V (here V defines a vector if it is a column matrix) and the steepest descent direction D, also a vector. In many actual systems investigated it was found [55] that the angle between V and D was often between $80°$ and $90°$, so this method attempts to compromise between the two directions. This is achieved by solving the equation:

$$(\tilde{B} W B + \omega I) X = \tilde{B} W E \tag{5.11}$$

where X is the best vector of parameter corrections and I is the identity matrix. This equation is identical to Equation (5.9) except that the quantity ω has been added to the diagonal elements of $\tilde{B} W B$. For this to be meaningful $\tilde{B} W B$ must be normalised so that the diagonal elements are unity. When ω equals 0, X equals V, the Taylor series direction. As ω increases, X swings towards the steepest descent direction D. The strategy followed by the algorithm is to increase ω within iterations until a reduction in S is obtained, but between iterations to attempt to reduce ω to ensure second order convergence. Another reason for the success of this algorithm can be seen from the fact that the determinant of $\tilde{B} W B$ cannot now be zero, or nearly zero, if a constant is added to the diagonal elements in this way. Thus the problem of near singularity and ill-conditioning has been removed, ensuring convergence.

The Fletcher-Powell algorithm is essentially a modified version of the Newton-Rapheson method wherein the second-order terms are taken into account in the calculations. In this procedure, however, the matrix of second derivatives are not calculated directly but are initially approximated by the identity matrix I. This matrix is successively updated with information from each iteration until an approximation to the inverse of the matrix G is obtained, where the elements of G are given by:

$$g_{ij} = \frac{\partial^2 S}{\partial x_i \partial x_j} \tag{5.12}$$

The initial iterations are thus in the steepest descent direction, when we are likely to be far from the minimum, but then the algorithm gradually swings round to the second-order Taylor series direction near the minimum. This is another method, therefore, of avoiding convergence difficulties.

Which, then, is the best algorithm to use for stability constant calculations? This is not an easy question to answer as the problem of parameter estimation by non-linear least-squares is complex. Traditionally, though, two methods with only two exceptions [35,36] have been applied in this field, either Gauss-Newton with or without Hartley's shift optimisation procedure [50], or the method of Sillén [7], which is basically a modified Newton-Rapheson method. Various workers have commented on the deficiencies in the convergence properties of these algorithms [2,29,31,35,58] and on the subsequent need for good initial estimates of the parameters [2,7,29,32]. However, the authors believe that insufficient attention has been paid by workers in the stability constant field to methods used in other areas. Thus optical lens designers have been using algorithms based on Marquardt's 'damped' least-squares with considerable success for some years [44-47,60,61]. These problems have much in common with stability constant calculations in that there are many parameters to be estimated, which may be correlated to some degree. The familiar problems of large 'overshifts' and poor convergence properties were encountered [44] prior to the adoption of Marquardt's algorithm. This method has also been used successfully on other practical problems such as force constant refinements [62,63] and the fitting of equations to chromatograms [43]. Computational comparisons have been made between various algorithms for function minimisation using benchmark [64] and practical problems [65]. It would appear from these that the methods of Marquardt and Fletcher-Powell are currently the best available, with perhaps the former being slightly to be more recommended owing to its wide practical success so far. This is particularly true if the damping factor is not applied and adjusted empirically, but is specifically calculated for each iteration [66], or for each parameter at each iteration [61, 67].

5.8 PARAMETER CORRELATION

Information about the conditioning of the parameter surface is contained in the matrix of the normal equations. As well as the standard deviations of the parameters obtainable from the diagonal elements of the matrix, quantities known as correlation coefficients can be obtained from the off-diagonal elements.

$$z_{ij} = \frac{b_{ij}}{(b_{ii}b_{jj})^{\frac{1}{2}}} \qquad (5.13)$$

where b_{ij} is the appropriate off-diagonal element of the matrix $(\tilde{B} W B)^{-1}$. In matrix terms the correlation coefficient matrix C is given by:

$$C = H^{-\frac{1}{2}} (\tilde{B} W B)^{-1} H^{-\frac{1}{2}} \qquad (5.14)$$

where H is a diagonal matrix whose diagonal elements are the diagonal elements of $(\tilde{B} W B)^{-1}$, that is, the b_{ii}. These coefficients have values between 0 and 1 and provide a measure of the linear dependence of one parameter on another [17], the remaining parameters being held constant. Values close to unity mean that the parameters are not separately defined by the data but that only a linear combination of them can be estimated from the data. This is important because this means it is possible to have a good fit to the data even with one parameter erroneously estimated, as the error in this parameter can be offset by an appropriate change in the other [11].

Significant parameter correlation ($z_{ij} > 0.9$) has often been reported in the literature, particularly in spectrophotometric work [5,11,12]. The reason for this is that band overlaps in electronic spectra occur to a greater or lesser degree, and through possible adjustment of the molar absorptivities, give rise to pairwise parameter correlation. Therefore any non-linear least-squares program should calculate the correlation coefficients on the final iteration, as well as standard deviations in the parameters, so that any deficiency in the data defining the parameters will be apparent. In one investigation into pH-dependent solution equilibria [11], the recommended procedure was to plot out theoretical titration curves with the parameters set at their calculated values, and then to replot them with each parameter altered in turn by a small amount. Adjustment of correlated parameters often gave rise to titration curves that were significantly different from the 'best' calculated curve at given ligand concentrations. This procedure indicates at what ligand concentrations and/or wavelengths further data should be obtained to better define the system. Correlation coefficients can be reduced by this method. This will have a beneficial effect on the iteration to the minimum. Highly correlated parameters indicate the parameter surface is a shallow 'pit', and so reduction of the correlation coefficients improves the conditioning.

5.9 WEIGHTING AND ERRORS

It is often the case in least-squares fitting of data that the variances of the residuals are not equal. In this case a weight matrix W should be used in the calculations (Equation (4.32)). The importance of doing this has often been emphasised [4,6,7,16], but a statisically correct weighting scheme is only possible if good estimates of the elements of the variance-covariance matrix of observations are obtainable. It is usually assumed that the variances of the observations are not correlated, in which case the covariances are zero and the weight matrix is diagonal. The variances in the observations themselves are usually unknown but may be calculated from a knowledge of the errors in the experimental quantities, using error propagation rules [18]. This has been done [5,13–16,27,39,68] but weighting of this kind is only necessary when the variances in the residuals of the function are expected to change during the experimental run.

Thus one group of workers [16] fitted the stability constants to a function whose residuals were defined in terms of the mass balance equations. The sum of the squares of the residuals in the analytical hydrogen ion concentration were minimised. In this case weighting becomes very important, because an error in the measured pH corresponds to larger residuals at low pH values than at high values [13]. Generally weighting is much more critical for potentiometric than for spectrophotometric determinations, or where the residuals are defined in terms of the $\bar{n}$ function. The calculated weights are then found to vary over a very wide range [27,68,69]. Note, however, that part of the reason for this is that these authors are fitting data to functions whose dependent variable is itself a function of the experimental observations. Thus the total analytical hydrogen ion concentration is obviously an exponential function of pH. These functions do not therefore truly conform to the criteria for a least-squares analysis to be valid (Section 4.6) in that there is not an error-prone dependent variable being fitted to a function of error-free independent variables. In particular the use of residuals defined in terms of $\bar{n}$ is clearly wrong. This practice should be avoided and all potentiometric calculations done in terms of a function of the sum of the squares of the differences between the calculated and observed e.m.f.s. This has the added advantage that unless there are strong reasons for believing otherwise, unit weights can be used. An example of the use of unit weights is demonstrated by a procedure for minimising the sum of the squares of the differences in the observed and calculated volumes of titre added during a pH titration [29]. Other workers have also used the simplifying assumption of unit weights [11,15,31,51], and it has been claimed that similar values for the calculated stability constants were obtained whether or not weighting was included [70].

Certainly where the independent variable is not exact, inordinate effort in calculating weights is probably wasted [2]. In potentiometric work, confusion is clearly apparent from the variety of functional forms used to define the residual error square sum, as to which observable to treat as the dependent variable. It is the authors' belief that since concentration measurements of high accuracy should be possible on the component solutions, and in view of inherent limitations of ion-selective electrodes, the potentiometric data itself should be considered the dependent variable. This is also true of pH determinations, particularly in the presence of a high concentration of background electrolyte [71], when the measured pH data are the dependent variables. Thus the procedures for using the measured pH to calculate the free hydrogen ion concentration, which is in turn used to derive calculated volumes of titre [29], or to define residuals in terms of the mass balance equations [31,51], are not strictly rigorous. In the latter case though, there are undoubtedly mathematical advantages.

Absorbance data, traditionally, do not suffer this confusion and the residuals are always defined in terms of the difference between the observed and calculated absorbances [4,11,12,53,72–74]. Weighting is not usually necessary as the dominant errors are spectrophotometric errors rather than concentration errors [11,12], provided that certain criteria are adopted [11,75]. Also, modern spectrophotometers have a constant variance in their readings over some of their absorbance range (see Section 8.3(f)). However, when absorbance readings have been taken at more than one wavelength on the same solution, error correlation occurs and it is mathematically correct to take account of this by using a non-diagonal weight matrix which holds the covariances of the variables. Nevertheless because spectrophotometric errors dominate when the errors in the concentrations are a few tenths of 1% and the absorbance errors are a few thousandths of a unit [12], error correlation can be ignored. Even if concentration errors do dominate, neglect of error correlation has been shown to have little effect on the results [12].

5.10 SYSTEMATIC ERRORS

The importance of recognising and removing sources of systematic errors was emphasised in the previous chapter. Since it may not be always possible to do this, it is best to treat the error as an extra parameter to be determined. Sillén and co-workers pioneered this approach with success in their 'pitmapping' programs [7,21,76]. Examples have been given [76], where analytical errors in the titrant solutions, or the value of E_o for a particular potentiometric titration, are adjusted to fit the experimental data. They are referred to as 'group parameters' because they are common to a particular potentiometric titration or to a particular set of absorbance readings.

This is an important technique in chemical 'model building' because often a better fit to the data can be obtained by adjusting these group parameters, than by assuming the presence of another species. However, if these adjustments are much larger than the expected experimental error, or if they vary systematically in an implausible way, then it is likely that the model is incorrect and further species do exist [77]. We have used this technique to infer the existence of a minor species when Na_2PdCl_4 is dissolved in acetic acid [53] (see Section 13.6).

5.11 EXPERIMENTAL DESIGN

In order to obtain reliable values for the parameters of interest in an experiment, it must be well designed. Experimental design is a large and complex field of itself, particularly in non-linear situations, and the reader is referred elsewhere for detailed discussion [78–81]. However, we can say that the objective of a well designed experiment is to obtain data that 'defines' the system as unequivocally as possible. The potentiometric methods for studying equilibria in solution are described in Chapter 7, and there is little to add here. However, if it is decided to analyse the system using a curve fitting technique such as non-linear least-squares a few points are perhaps pertinent.

(a) The potentiometric titrations should be carried out at more than one total metal concentration, and preferably several.

(b) Ideally the titration ought to be followed with two or more electrodes of different types. Thus if a pH electrode and an ion-selective electrode for the metal ion could be used for each titration so much the better. The large volume of data generated is no problem with computer data handling techniques and is a positive advantage in defining the system.

(c) The residual sum of squares should be defined in terms of the observed dependent variable, that is, e.m.f. or pH, and not some function of them.

(d) The standard potential E^o of the electrodes for each titration should be carried as an adjustable parameter in the calculations and any suspect values or trends carefully investigated.

Similar considerations apply to spectrophotometrically studied systems, in that data should be gathered so as to well characterise the system. Specifically:

(a) Measurements should be made on solutions covering as wide a range of ligand to substrate ratios as possible. This is to ensure that every species is defined by its making a significant contribution to the absorbance in at least one solution. Failure to do this can result in very large stability constant errors for comparatively small errors in the concentrations [82].

(b) Generally, the more wavelengths at which absorbance readings are taken the better defined the system becomes. However, little definitive information is obtained if the wavelengths chosen are in the regions of great spectral overlap, or where the molar absorptivities of two or more species are linearly dependent. The change in absorbance with change in solution concentration then becomes rather small. This in turn produces parameter correlation problems, which constitute one of the great drawbacks of spectrophotometric determinations of stability constants [12]. It is therefore best to use wavelengths where the molar absorptivities of the species differ greatly or, failing this, to use a large number of wavelengths spaced at equal intervals [83].

(c) The residual sum of squares should be defined in terms of the observed dependent variable, that is, absorbances, and not some function of them.

(d) The absorbance blanks, the difference in the absorbance of the spectrophotometric cells when both are filled with solvent, should be carried as adjustable parameters in the calculations, and any suspect values or trends carefully investigated.

Finally it should again be pointed out that because of the particular strengths and weaknesses of potentiometric and spectrophotometric determinations in defining the model, the best procedure is undoubtedly to combine both on any given system [84] (see Section 6.3). This could easily be carried out with a computer treatment of data provided that the calculations were weighted to take account of the differing magnitudes in the variances of the two types of observable [75].

5.12 AVAILABLE NON-LINEAR LEAST-SQUARES PROGRAMS FOR THE CALCULATION OF STABILITY CONSTANTS

This section briefly describes some of the major published programs for the calculation of stability constants. It is by no means exhaustive, and many publications exist which indicate computational methods of the non-linear least-squares type have been used, but for which no details have been given.

(a) LETAGROP [7, 21]. This was the pioneering program [7] of its type and was several years ahead of its time. It employed a specially developed 'pit-mapping' technique to calculate the stability constants, as described in Sections 5.6, no doubt because the required algorithms were not available and the matrix handling capabilities of the computer employed were limited. It was developed for use with potentiometric data, and a range of functions have been minimised [34,76]. The function chosen is usually the sum of the squares of the residuals in the analytical hydrogen ion concentration. The measured pH titration data is used to derive this function. Note that careful weighting must be used in this instance [3,13] (see Section 5.9).

The program includes routines for selecting, adding, or deleting species to the chemical model and for adjustment of systematic errors [21]. The latter is particularly important in the refinement of the model and can lead to elimination [21], or the postulation [53] of a minor species.

The only criticism of this program that can be made is that the minimisation algorithm is now out of date and better ones have been developed which will converge more rapidly from poorer estimates of the parameters than is accomodated by LETAGROP.

(b) GAUSS. This program [70] was one of the first published which utilised the Gauss-Newton method of function minimisation. It was a refinement of an earlier program [16] and was used to analyse pH titrations for solutions containing one metal and one ligand [85]. The function minimised is the sum of the squares of the errors in the analytical hydrogen ion concentration. Because of this, weighting should be included in the calculations, although it has been claimed [70] that this has no effect on the final results. However, this program and its successor SCOGS, see below, have occasionally proved unreliable [35,51], because of the calculation of overshifts [2] and subsequent oscillation and non-convergence. Certainly, when several stability constants are to be estimated, the Gauss-Newton method ought never to be used without modification (see Section 5.7).

(c) SCOGS. An extension of GAUSS, this program [29] allows the calculation of stability constants from pH titration data on solutions with up to two metals and two ligands. The function minimised is the sum of the squares of the residuals in the titre values, thus facilitating the use of unit weights [29]. The minimisation algorithm is still based on the Gauss-Newton method, and although halving of large parameter shifts is incorporated in the program, the same comments apply as in (b) above.

(d) LEAST. The next development was LEAST [31], a program which incorporates the facility to use either the Gauss-Newton or the Newton-Rapheson methods of function minimisation. In the latter method, the second-order terms of the Taylor series are taken into account (see Section 5.3). The function minimised is the sum of the squares of the residuals in all three mass balance equations, total hydrogen, total metal, and total ligand. This allows exact derivatives to be obtained, whereas all the previously discussed programs have used difference approximations. The calculation treats the free metal and free ligand concentrations as parameters to be estimated at each data point on the same level as the stability constants [31]. This is different from most other programs, where these are obtained from simultaneous solution of the mass balance equations in metal and ligand, using the values of the stability constants on that iteration.

However, the procedure in LEAST can be criticised on the grounds that the distinction between the dependent and independent variables has become confused. The pH is treated as the independent, error-free, variable and is used to calculate the free hydrogen ion concentration. This in turn is used to evaluate the analytical concentrations of hydrogen ion, metal, and ligand, the dependent variables, using the mass balance equations. It would appear more correct to regard the pH as the dependent variable and the analytical concentrations as the independent error-free variables, which is the procedure essentially followed by other programs. Surprisingly the results obtained with LEAST were comparable to those obtained with other programs [31], despite the use of unit weights, an unusual approach in potentiometric work.

(e) LEASK. This program [86] has little to recommend it. It calculates the best fit stability constants by a rather primitive search technique whereby each of the parameters is shifted in turn and the effect on the error square sum examined. This error square sum is defined in terms of the mass balance equations for the total analytical concentrations, as for the previous program, LEAST. If the alterations to the parameter vector result in a larger error square sum, the magnitudes of the shifts are changed, or the sign reversed until a reduction is obtained. The procedure has converged when a lower sum of squares cannot be found in a given number of iterations. However, the methods used in conjunction with this program are good examples of the objective selection of species and model building [86].

(f) STEW. The more sophisticated Fletcher-Powell algorithm [56] is used in this program [35]. The sum of the squares of the errors is defined in terms of the analytical hydrogen ion concentration only, an experimental value for this being presumably derived from the measured pH and the concentrations of protonated species present. The concentrations of free ligand and free metal are conventionally obtained from a Newton-Rapheson iteration on the mass balance equations. This program appears to work well, even with very poor estimates of the stability constant values. This is provided that the iteration is on the stability constants themselves, rather than on their logarithms, as the latter problem is intrinsically ill-conditioned [56].

(g) MINIQUAD. After successfully demonstrating the applicability of the Fletcher-Powell method to the evaluation of stability constants, the authors of STEW described an improved version of LEAST [31], in their next paper [51]. This is basically unchanged from LEAST, but now includes the so called linear optimisation of shifts to try to ensure convergence [50,52]. This latter modification is necessary as the iterative algorithm is still the 'overshift'-prone Gauss-Newton method.

(h) SQUAD. This program [74] is a modified version of SCOGS [29] applied to the analysis of absorbance data. The sum of the squares of the errors is defined in terms of the observed and calculated absorbances and is shown to work for a comparatively simple system. The authors admit [74] that the program requires good initial estimates of the stability constants to ensure convergence, but applaud this because they believe the computer should be 'used to confirm conclusions'. However, in complex systems this is often not possible, and if several different models are to be tried, underplays the computer's rôle as an objective aid to model building.

(i) DALSFEK. The final program of this section is one developed at Southampton [36]. It uses Marquardt's method [55] to minimise a function defined in terms of the directly observed experimental variables. That is, the sum of the squares of the errors in the absorbances or in the measured e.m.f.s is minimised. The total analytical concentrations of each fundamental component are treated as the independent variables, and hence the concentrations of each species in the model are obtained by 'fitting' them to the mass balance equations involving these concentrations and the values of the stability constants on that iteration. The same algorithm is used to carry this out as in the refinement of the stability constant values. Here the analytical concentrations and the stability constants are regarded as the experimental variables, and the species concentrations as the parameters to be determined. This procedure has been found to be very well behaved, as analytical derivatives are available [36,75] for the calculations. The iteration on the stability constants has also been found to be efficient [36] owing to the incorporation of Marquardt's algorithm, and does not therefore require good initial estimates of the stability constant values. The program also includes facilities for the adjustment of systematic errors (see Section 5.10), as in the programs of Sillén [7,21,76], and an example of its use in model building has been given [53] (see Chapter 13).

A summary of all these programs is given in Table 5.1.

Table 5.1 — Summary of published non-linear least-squares programs for the calculation of stability constants.

Program	Data treated	Sum of squared residuals minimised	Iterative method used	References
LETAGROP	Potentiometric	Several ($\bar{n}$, analytical hydrogen ion concentration, e.m.f.)	Pitmapping (Newton-Rapheson)	[7, 21]
GAUSS	Potentiometric	Analytical hydrogen ion concentration	Gauss-Newton	[70]
SCOGS	Potentiometric	Volume of titrant	Gauss-Newton	[29]
LEAST	Potentiometric	Analytical concentrations	Gauss-Newton or Newton-Rapheson	[31]
LEASK	Potentiometric	Analytical concentrations	Search	[86]
STEW	Potentiometric	Analytical hydrogen ion concentration	Fletcher-Powell	[35]
MINIQUAD	Potentiometric	Analytical concentrations	Gauss-Newton	[51]
SQUAD	Spectrophoto-metric	Absorbance	Gauss-Newton	[74]
DALSFEK	Spectrophoto-metric, Potentiometric	Absorbance, e.m.f.	Marquardt	[36]

REFERENCES

[1] Rossotti, F. J. C. and Rossotti, H. S. (1961). *The Determination of Stability Constants*. N.Y.: McGraw-Hill.

[2] Rossotti, F. J. C., Rossotti, H. S., and Whewell, R. J. (1971). *J. Inorg. Nucl. Chem.*, **33**, 2051.

[3] Childs, C. W., Hallman, P. S., and Perrin, D. D. (1969). *Talanta.*, **16**, 1119.

[4] Wentworth, W. E., Hirsch, W., and Chen, E. (1967). *J. Phys. Chem.*, **71**, 218.

[5] Nagano, K. and Metzler, D. E. (1967). *J. Amer. Chem. Soc.*, **89**, 2891.

[6] Rydberg, J. (1961). *Acta. Chem. Scand.*, **15**, 1723.

[7] Sillén, L. G. (1962). *Acta. Chem. Scand.*, **16**, 159.

[8] Wentworth, W. E. (1965). *J. Chem. Ed.*, **42**, 96.

[9] Betteley, I. G., Brookes, C. J., and Loxston, S. M. (1966). *Mathematics and Statistics for Chemists*. New York: John Wiley.

[10] Draper, N. R. and Smith, H. (1966). *Applied Regression Analysis*. New York: John Wiley.

[11] Maier, T. O. and Drago, R. S. (1972). *Inorg. Chem.*, **11**, 1861.

[12] Lingane, P. J. and Hugus, Z. Z. (1970). *Inorg. Chem.*, **9**, 757.

[13] Shaeffer, W. P. (1965). *Inorg. Chem.*, **4**, 642.

[14] Varga, L. P. (1969). *Anal. Chem.*, **41**, 323.

[15] Vacca, A., Sabatini, A., and Gristina, M. A. (1972). *Coord. Chem. Rev.*, **8**, 45.

[16] Tobias, R. S., and Yasuda, M. (1963). *Inorg. Chem.*, **2**, 1307.

[17] Hamilton, W. C. (1964). *Statistics in Physical Science*. New York: Ronald Press.

[18] Ku, H. H. (1966). *J. Res. Nat. Bur. Stds.*, **70C**, 263.

[19] Behnken, D. W. (1964). *J. Polym. Sci.*, **2A**, 645.

[20] Box, G. E. P. (1960). *Annal. N.Y. Acad. Sci.*, **86**, 792.

[21] Sillén, L. G. (1964). *Acta. Chem. Scand.*, **18**, 1085.

[22] Feldberg, S., Klotz, P., and Newman, L. (1972). *Inorg. Chem.*, **11**, 2860.

[23] Draper, N. R. and Smith, H. (1966). *Applied Regression Analysis*. New York. John Wiley, Chapter 10, p. 298.

[24] Beale, E. M. L. (1960). *J. Roy. Statis. Soc.*, **228**, 41.

[25] Guttman, I. and Meeter, D. A. (1963). *Techometrics*, **7**, 623.

[26] Hartley, H. O. (1964). *Biometrika*, **51**, 347.

[27] Inman, D., Regan, I., and Girling, B. (1964). *J. Chem. Soc.*, 349.

[28] Chapoorian, J. A., Choppin, G. R., Griffith, H. C., and Chandler, R. (1961). *J. Inorg. Nucl. Chem.*, **21**, 21.

[29] Sayce, I. G. (1968). *Talanta*, **15**, 1397.

[30] Perrin, D. D. and Sayce, I. G. (1967). *Talanta*, **14**, 833.

[31] Sabatini, A. and Vacca, A. (1972). *J. Chem. Soc. (Dalton)*, 1693.

[32] Sillén, L. G. (1962). *Acta. Chem. Scand.*, **16**, 173.

[33] Sillén, L. G. (1968). *Pure and Appl. Chem.*, **17**, 55.

[34] Sillén, L. G. and Warnqvist, B. (1969). *Ark. Kemi.*, **31**, 315.

[35] Gans, P. and Vacca, A. (1974). *Talanta*, **21**, 45.

[36] Alcock, R. M., Hartley, F. R., and Rogers, D. E. (1978). *J. Chem. Soc. (Dalton)*, 115.

[37] Moore, R. H. and Zeigler, R. K. (March 1960). Los Alamos Scientific Laboratory Report, LA2367.

[38] Dyrssen, D., Ingri, N., and Sillén, L. G. (1961). *Acta. Chem. Scand.*, **15**, 694.

[39] Sullivan, J. C., Rydberg, J., and Miller, W. F. (1959). *Acta. Chem. Scand.*, **13**, 2023.

[40] Schachtschneider, J. H. Shell Technical Report No. 57-65, Project No. 31450.

[41] Long, D. A., and Gravenor, R. B. (1963). *Spectrochim. Acta*, **19**, 937.

[42] Gans, P. (1971). *J. Chem. Soc. (A)*, 2017.

[43] Roberts, S. A., Wilkinson, D. H., and Walker, L. R. (1970). *Anal. Chem.*, **42**, 886.

[44] Wynne, C. G. (1959). *Proc. Phys. Soc.*, **73**, 777.

[45] Wynne, C. G., and Wormell, P. M. J. H. (1963). *Applied Optics*, **2**, 1233.

[46] Feder, D. P. (1963). *Applied Optics*, **2**, 1209.

[47] Spencer, G. H. (1963). *Applied Optics*, **2**, 1257.

[48] Spang, H. A. (1962). *J. Soc. Ind. Appl. Maths. Rev.*, **4**, 343.

[49] Swann, W. H. (1969). *FEBS Lett.*, **2**, 539.

[50] Hartley, H. O. (1961). *Technometrics*, **3**, 269.

[51] Sabatini, A., Vacca, A., and Gans, P. (1974). *Talanta*, **21**, 53.

[52] Strand, J. G., Kohl, D. A., and Bonham, R. A. (1963). *J. Chem. Phys.*, **39**, 1307.

[53] Alcock, R. M., Hartley, F. R., Rogers, D. E., and Wagner, J. L. (1975). *J. Chem. Soc. (Dalton)*, 2189, 2194.

[54] Hartley, F. R., Searle, G. W., Alcock, R. M., and Rogers, D. E. (1977). *J. Chem. Soc. (Dalton)*, 469.

[55] Marquardt, D. W. (1963). *J. Soc. Ind. Appl. Maths.*, **11**, 431.

[56] Fletcher, R. and Powell, M. D. J. (1963). *The Comp. J.*, **6**, 163.

[57] Levenberg, K. (1944). *Quart. Appl. Maths.*, **2**, 164.

[58] Sayce, I. G. (1971). *Talanta*, **18**, 653.

[59] Sayce, I. G. (1972). *Talanta*, **19**, 831.

[60] Grey, D. S. (1963). *J. Opt. Soc. Am.*, **53**, 677.

[61] Meiron, J. (1965). *J. Opt. Soc. Am.*, **55**, 1105.

[62] Papousek, D., Toman, S., and Pliva, J. (1965). *J. Molec. Spectros.*, **15**, 502.

[63] Adams, D. M. and Churchill, R. G. (1970). *J. Chem. Soc. (A)*, 697.

[64] Box, M. J. (1966). *Computer J.*, **9**, 67.

[65] Pitha, J. and Norman Jones, R. (1966). *Can. J. Chem.*, **44**, 3031.

[66] Beckley Smith, F. Jr. and Shanno, D. F. (1971). *Technometrics*, **13**, 63.

[67] Rubin, D. I. (1963). *Chem. Eng. Prog. Symp. Ser.*, 42, **59**, 90.

[68] Tobias, R. S. and Hugus, Z. Z. (1961). *J. Phys. Chem.*, **65**, 2165.

[69] Lansbury, R. C., Price, V. E., and Smeeth, A. G. (1965). *J. Chem. Soc. (A)*, 1896.

[70] Perrin, D. D. and Sayce, I. G. (1967). *J. Chem. Soc. (A)*, 82.

[71] Bates, R. G. (1973). *The Determination of pH*, 2nd ed. New York: John Wiley.

[72] Varga, L. P. and Veatch, F. C. (1967). *Anal. Chem.*, **39**, 1101.

[73] Kankare, J. J. (1970). *Anal. Chem.*, **42**, 1322.

[74] Leggett, D. J., and McBryde, W. A. E. (1975). *Anal. Chem.*, **47**, 1065.

[75] Alcock, R. M. (1976). Ph.D. thesis, Southampton University.

[76] Braunar, P., Sillén, L. G., and Whitekar, R. (1969). *Akiv. Kemi.*, **31**, 365.

[77] Sillén, L. G. *Coordination Chemistry*, Vol. 1., A.C.S. Monograph 168, (ed. Martell, A. E.), 520.

[78] Box, G. E. P. and Hunter, W. G. (1965). *Technometrics*, 7, 23.

[79] Behnken, D. W. (1964). *J. Polym. Sci.*, **2A**, 645.

[80] Box, G. E. P. and Hunter, J. S. (1954). *Biometrica.*, **41**, 190.

[81] Box, G. E. P. and Lucas, H. L. (1959). *Biometrica.*, **46**, 77.

[82] Conrow, K., Johnson, G. D., and Bowen, R. E. (1964). *J. Amer. Chem. Soc.*, **86**, 1025.

[83] Sternberg, J. C., Stillo, H. S. and Schwendman, R. H. (1960). *Anal. Chem.*, **32**, 84.

[84] Alcock, R. M., Hartley, F. R., Rogers, D. E., and Wagner, J. L. (1975). *Coord. Chem. Rev.*, **16**, 59.

[85] Perrin, D. D. and Sayce, I. G. (1968). *J. Chem. Soc. (A)*, 53.

[86] Sarkar, B. and Kruck, T. P. A. (1973). *Can. J. Chem.*, **51**, 3541.

CHAPTER 6

Introduction to the Experimental Determination of Stability Constants

6.1 INTRODUCTION

A large number of stability constants have been determined [1], but a considerable proportion of these are of doubtful accuracy [2]. It is important, therefore, that before measuring a stability constant great care is taken to ensure that the experimental method will give a reliable result; similarly when using stability constants from the literature it is important to assess their reliability. Accordingly in Chapters 7, 8, and 9 we describe the experimental methods that can be used to determine stability constants, trying to emphasise the advantages, disadvantages and limitations of each; Chapters 7 and 8 are devoted to potentiometry and spectrophotometry respectively, which are the two most widely used methods. In Chapter 9 the other methods that have been used to determine stability constants are described.

Any property which varies with the degree of complex formation can be used in principle as the basis for determining stability constants. However, it is essential that the variation in the property is quantitatively related to the nature of the species present. This quantitative relation is reflected in what is known as an *intensive factor*, such as the molar absorptivities of species in u.v.-visible spectrophotometry or partition coefficients in gas chromatography. Experimental methods for determining stability constants fall into two broad groups:

    (a) Methods in which the observable is proportional to the number of molecules of a given type present; all spectroscopic methods fall into this group.

    (b) Methods in which the observable is proportional to the activity of the molecules of a given type; most electrochemical and distribution methods fall into this group.

Where experiments are being carried out under 'constant ionic strength conditions' (see Section 1.6) there is no distinction between the two groups, but where the activity coefficients are not being controlled and where more than one experimental technique is being used, such as potentiometry and u.v.-visible spectrophotometry, then care must be taken to ensure that the reported stability constants are a true measure of what the investigators set out to determine.

6.2 CHOICE OF METHOD

When choosing a suitable method for determining stability constants, a number of points should be considered:

(a) Is the solvent being used one in which the activity coefficients of the reacting species can be controlled by the addition of a background electrolyte? It is this extremely important factor that has led to the widespread use of water as a solvent, although some organic solvents such as alcohols, acetic acid and ethylene glycol are also capable of dissolving sufficient quantities of inert salts to enable activity coefficients to be controlled. However, when studying neutral relatively non-polar ligands such as olefins there are advantages in using non-polar solvents such as carbon tetrachloride or benzene (see Section 1.8).

(b) Are all the so-called 'constants' in the system truly constant? In a number of techniques intensive factors such as molar absorbances in spectroscopy or chemical shifts in nuclear magnetic resonance (n.m.r.) are involved. All these 'constants' must be truly constant over the entire range of experiments and must not vary with the concentration of one or more of the reacting species. This point is discussed in more detail in connection with both n.m.r. and gas chromatography (see Sections 9.2(iii) and 9.3(iv) respectively).

(c) Does the method give results in agreement with other independent methods, and what is its inherent accuracy?

(d) Is the apparatus available or obtainable? Thus potentiometry has been described [3] as "by far the most accurate and widely applicable technique currently available for the study of ionic equilibria'. However, its application to a specific system does depend on the availability of a suitable electrode that is reversible in the solvent that is to be used.

6.3 USE OF MORE THAN ONE EXPERIMENTAL METHOD

The importance of studying a given system by more than one method has been repeatedly emphasised in the literature, because this provides the best way of establishing the reliability of any particular method. Additionally the use of more than one method better defines the chemical model prior to a computer analysis of the data. This point was mentioned in Section 5.11.

The case study in Chapter 11 gives an example of two models which gave statistically indistinguishable fits to the data, as determined by hypothesis tests using a 'goodness of fit' parameter (Section 11.5). This a relatively common occurence when no previous qualitative investigation of the chemical model has been possible, as, for example, in potentiometric work. However, spectrophotometric data, as well as producing qualitative inferences as to the chemical model, also involves intensive factors. These are the molar absorptivities. The computer calculated molar absorptivities of the species in the model may be examined when a fit has been obtained to see if they are reasonable. By reasonable is meant:

(a) They should all be positive.
(b) When plotted as a function of wavelength, smooth curves should result. These are characteristic of the molecular electronic spectra, and no sharp discontinuities should be present.
(c) The prediction of any isosbestic points should be borne out by experiment.

Thus spectrophotometry provides an additional method for comparing several possible chemical models not available with potentiometry. Choice of suitable wavelengths enables each species to make a direct contribution to the measured data. However, because the u.v.-visible spectra of most complexes contain broad overlapping absorption bands, parameter correlation arises and it is not usually possible to evaluate stability constants as precisely from spectrophotometric as potentiometric data. We have therefore a dichotomy that potentiometric data may lead to a more precise analysis of the wrong model, whereas spectrophotometric data will indicate the correct model but give a less precise analysis of it [4]. Clearly, the ideal approach is to combine spectrophotometric and potentiometric data, using the former for defining the chemical model and both for evaluation of the stability constants.

6.4 STUDY OF WEAK COMPLEXES

In order to obtain the most accurate stability constants it is necessary to use solutions in which the concentration of the complex is of the same order as the free concentration of the most dilute component [5]. Although such conditions may seem intuitively obvious in that they allow both the free species and the complex to make approximately equal contributions to the observable†, they are not so straightforward to apply, since with weak complexes it is rarely possible to determine the intensive factor (molar absorptivity or n.m.r. chemical shift) of the complex independent of the stability constant. For such systems a series of experiments have to be undertaken in which solutions successively closer to the optimum concentration range are prepared.

Let us consider first a system in which only a 1:1 complex is formed. A series of solutions of constant total ligand concentration, $[L]_T$, are prepared

† It has been argued on statistical grounds that the conditions specified in Reference [5] are too rigid [6]; nevertheless for accurate results we strongly recommend following the criteria outlined here unless an alternative set of data has been carefully checked to ensure that it it is statistically sound.

and 'titrated' with varying amounts of metal. The ratio of the concentration of the complex to the total ligand concentration which we can call the saturation factor, s, is given by

$$s = \frac{[ML]}{[L]_T} \tag{6.1}$$

Since $[ML] = K[M][L]$ $\tag{6.2}$

and $[L]_T = [ML] + [L]$ $\tag{6.3}$

it follows that

$$s = \frac{K[M]}{1 + K[M]} \tag{6.4}$$

The saturation factor is formally derived from measurements of some intensive parameter proportional to the concentration of the complex. In spectrophotometry, the absorbance A per unit path is given by

$$A = \epsilon_{ML}[ML] + \epsilon_M[M] \tag{6.5}$$

at wavelengths at which the free ligand does not absorb, and the maximum absorbance A_{max} per unit path length occurs when all the free ligand has been complexed,

$$A_{max} = \epsilon_{ML}[L]_T \tag{6.6}$$

Substituting from Equations (6.5) and (6.6) into (6.1), the saturation factor is given by

$$s = \frac{[ML]}{[L]_T} = \frac{A - \epsilon_M[M]}{A_{max}} \tag{6.7}$$

If wavelengths at which ϵ_M is small are used, then the saturation factor is given approximately by,

$$s \approx A/A_{max} \tag{6.8}$$

For n.m.r., under conditions of rapid exchange the observed chemical shift (δ_{obs}) is given by

$$\delta_{obs} = \delta_{ML} \frac{[ML]}{[L]_T} + \delta_L \frac{\{[L]_T - [ML]\}}{[L]_T} \qquad (6.9)$$

where δ_L and δ_{ML} are the chemical shifts of the free and complexed ligand (see Equation (9.3)). Whence

$$\delta_{obs} = \delta_{ML} \frac{[ML]}{[L]_T} + \delta_L - \delta_L \frac{[ML]}{[L]_T} \qquad (6.10)$$

so that the saturation factor is given by,

$$s = \frac{[ML]}{[L]_T} = \frac{\delta_{obs} - \delta_L}{\delta_{ML} - \delta_L} \qquad (6.11)$$

In order to obtain the most accurate values of both K and either ϵ or δ it has been shown [7] that the saturation factor should fall in the range $0.2 \lesssim s \lesssim 0.8$. Equally importantly since the stability constants and intensive factors are linked, the accurate evaluation of both necessitates making measurements over about 75% of the saturation curve, that is from $s = 0.13$ to $s = 0.87$.

So far we have been concerned with the relatively simple case of a single ML complex being formed. How are the conclusions modified if more than one weak complex is formed? Firstly the range of the saturation curve that should be studied remains unaltered at 75% [8]; the definition of the saturation factor in this case is that it is the ratio of the concentrations of complexed and free ligand. Secondly the number of series of experiments needed to determine the optimum concentration range will increase; each series of experiments should lead us to a series of stability constants successively more accurate than the last. A similar analysis to that given above has been described specifically for spectro-photometric data [9].

It has been shown [10] that the minimum value for the stability constant due to complex formation between an electron donor and an electron acceptor that can be determined spectrophotometrically is 0.2 l.mol^{-1}. This limit arises because a change in the electronic spectrum can result from dispersion forces alone whenever an electron donor and an electron acceptor molecule are adjacent to one another in solution without the presence of an intervening solvent molecule. Thus when spectrophotometric stability constants below 0.2 l.mol^{-1} are obtained, they may arise from dispersion forces alone and may not be due to the formation of a covalent link between donor and acceptor.

6.5 STUDY OF VERY STRONG COMPLEXES

The study of very strong complexes presents a somewhat similar though perhaps more tractable problem than the study of weak complexes. All stability constant studies essentially involve competition between two ligands for a given metal ion, or competition between two metal ions (one of which may be H^+) for a given ligand. Thus if a system such as

$$Pd^{2+} + 4CN^- \xrightleftharpoons{\beta_4} [Pd(CN)_4]^{2-} \qquad (6.12)$$

is considered, in aqueous solution Pd^{2+} represents the $[Pd(H_2O)_4]^{2+}$ ion and β_4 reflects the competition between cyanide and water ligands. Since β_4 is approximately 10^{63} it is impossible to find any concentrations of free palladium or cyanide such that the saturation factor lies between 0.2 and 0.8. For all practicable concentrations the saturation factor is essentially unity.

If, however, the water ligands are replaced by ligands that coordinate much more strongly, then β_4' for a system such as,

$$[PdX_4]^{2-} + 4CN^- \xrightleftharpoons{\beta_4'} [Pd(CN)_4]^{2-} + 4X^- \qquad (6.13)$$

can be determined, where β_4' is much smaller than β_4. This technique has been used [11] to determine β_4 for Equilibrium (6.12) by determining β_4' for Equilibrium (6.13) where X = Cl. The overall stability constant for the formation of $[PdX_4]^{2-}$ from $[Pd(H_2O)_4]^{2+}$ is then determined, allowing β_4 to be evaluated. Greater accuracy still should be possible if iodide were used since the stability constants of the iodopalladium(II) complexes are much greater than of the chloropalladium(II) species.

6.6 POLYNUCLEAR COMPLEXES

Complexes which have more than one central metal ion are generally termed polynuclear. They may be further subdivided into heteropolynuclear, where more than one type of metal ion is present, and homopolynuclear where only one type of metal ion is present. Polynuclear complexes arise whenever a ligand that is capable of bonding to more than one metal ion is present. Such ligands include oxide, hydroxide, peroxide, carboxylate, sulphide, halide, cyanide, thiocyanate, and carbonyl as well as multidentate ligands that may act in either a chelating or a bridging fashion. The subject of polynuclear complexes [12,13] is an extremely difficult one, that is probably best summed up in the words of one of the foremost workers in the field, Professor Sillén, who wrote [14], "the more I work with polyions, the more I think we must be cautious with claims to have proved the existence of any particular species'.

Polynuclear complexes pose three problems which ought to be tackled consecutively:

    (a) Are polynuclear species present?
    (b) If present, what are their formulae?
    (c) What quantitative relationships (that is, stability constants) link them?

The first problem, that of deciding whether or not polynuclear species are present, is one that anyone attempting to measure any stability constant must bear in mind. In general the presence or absence of polynuclear species can be confirmed by making a series of measurements at two different metal ion concentrations. Ideally these concentrations should be as widely different as possible. Analysis of these two sets of data either using a monomeric model or by preparing plots of the average number of ligands per metal ion†, Z, against log[L] should lead in the first case to two identical sets of stability constants, and in the second case to two superimposable plots if polynuclear species are absent. If this does not occur, for example, if two distinct Z versus log[L] plots that only merge at very high and very low ligand concentrations are observed, then polynuclear species are probably present. Such tests should always be carried out, even where polynuclear complexes are not suspected, to confirm their absence. For the same reason it is recommended that when pH data is obtained, plots of pH against log(concentration) rather than the semi-logarithmic pH against concentration should be prepared, since the former show clearer inflection points when polynuclear species are present [15].

The formulae of polynuclear complexes are usually written M_mL_n and their stability constants β_{nm} defined according to the relation [1]

$$m\mathrm{M} + n\mathrm{L} \underset{\phantom{\beta_{nm}}}{\overset{\beta_{nm}}{\rightleftharpoons}} \mathrm{M}_m\mathrm{L}_n \tag{6.14}$$

whence
$$\beta_{nm} = \frac{[\mathrm{M}_m\mathrm{L}_n]}{[\mathrm{M}]^m[\mathrm{L}]^n} \tag{6.15}$$

In this way the overall formation constants for mononuclear systems ($m = 1$, that is, β_n) become special cases of the polynuclear situation. There are clearly limits for a given metal ion and ligand to the range of values of n and m that are possible. Many, though it must be emphasised not all, systems follow Sillén's 'core + links' hypothesis [16] in which cores made up of ML_a units are linked by either metal ions or ligands giving complexes with overall formulae of either $M_b(ML_a)_x$ or $(ML_a)_x L_c$. All the constants a, b, c, x, n and m are integers whose numerical values are linked by

$$c = -ab \tag{6.16}$$

$$m = an + c = a(n - b) \tag{6.17}$$

---

† Although the definition of Z is identical to that of $\bar{n}$ for mononuclear complexes, Z, unlike $\bar{n}$, is not the average coordination number of each metal ion with respect to a given ligand, and hence a different symbol is used.

(Note: a, x, n and m are always positive; b and c may be positive or negative). In Chapter 2 we have described methods for determining the total number of species present in solution, and for determining the ratio $n:m$ for as many of these as possible. These techniques used for polynuclear species are exactly the same as used for mononuclear species with the proviso that as many different physical techniques, each of as high a precision as possible, should be used.

Once a reasonable model of the system has been built up, as much high precision data as possible should be obtained over as wide a range of both total metal and total ligand concentrations as possible. This data is then analysed by the techniques described in Chapter 5 which are the same as those used for mononuclear systems.

6.7 INTERACTION OF METAL IONS WITH POLYELECTROLYTES

The bulk of this book is concerned with the interaction of metal ions with simple ligands. However, an area of growing importance is the interaction of metal ions with polymeric ligands, both man-made and natural polymers such as proteins. There are essentially two mechanisms for the binding of counter ions to polymeric ions [17,18]:

(a) Physical interaction, which is essentially electrostatic in nature and corresponds to the formation of ion-pairs in monomeric systems.

(b) Chemical interaction, which involves the formation of covalent links as in metal-ligand complex formation in monomeric systems.

There is inevitably an overlap or 'grey' region between these two. Furthermore since the conformation of the polymer often depends not only on the solvent, but also on the nature and quantity of any ions present, the overlap region is also dependent on both the nature of the solvent and any added ions, since conformation changes will influence the strength of both the physical and chemical interactions.

In addition to the problems introduced so far, further difficulties arise when attempting to interpret experimental data, since different experimental techniques appear to lead to conflicting conclusions. This arises because, although most experimental techniques measure both physical and chemical interaction, the threshold for the detection of physical interaction differs. Thus, for example, transference [19,20] and dilatometric [21] studies on the interaction of alkali metals with polyacrylates appear to point to site binding, whereas infrared studies [22] provide no confirmatory evidence. U.v.-visible spectrophotometry has been used as a technique to detect specific covalent complex formation between copper(II) and maleic acid copolymers [23], and to detect ion-pair formation between $[Co(NH_3)_6]^{3+}$ and poly(acrylic acid) [24].

Much of the quantitative data on metal-polyelectrolyte binding has been determined either calorimetrically or potentiometrically. Calorimetric measurements [25,26] are carried out by adding a metal salt solution to a polyelectrolyte solution of known degree of neutralisation. The potentiometric method [27,28] generally depends upon titrating the polyelectrolyte with acid or base in the presence and absence of metal ions to study the competition between protons and metal ions. Some of the difficulties associated with this approach are:

(a) It is essential to know the proton dissociation constants in order to evaluate the metal polyelectrolyte association constants. However, proton dissociation constants depend strongly on the ionic strength of the solution and the charge density on the polyelectrolyte chain. In the presence of metal ions the conformation of the chain may alter, so altering the charge density; in addition the binding of a dipositive ion to a given site has a different influence on the charge density felt at other local sites to the binding of a unipositive ion.
(b) For accurate stability constants it is often necessary to measure very small pH changes.
(c) It is impossible to determine the activity coefficients of the ions present in the polyelectrolyte as well as of the polyelectrolyte itself.
(d) The concept of ionic strength within a polyelectrolyte only has meaning when the product of the electronic charge and the electrostatic potential is less than the value of kT [29].

A topic related to the binding of metal ions to polyelectrolytes is the binding of metal ions to proteins. Proteins are more complex than polyelectrolytes because of the wide range of different binding sites that are available. Nevertheless the approaches used to study protein-metal binding have been somewhat similar, that is, first use as wide a range of physical measurements as possible to study the system and then carry out pH titrations in the presence and absence of metal ions [30,31].

REFERENCES

[1] Sillén, L. G. and Martell, A. E. (1964, Vol. 1; 1971, Vol. 2). *Stability Constants of Metal Ion Complexes*, Chemical Society Special Publications 17 and 25.
[2] Beck, M. T. (1972). *Reaction Mechanisms in Inorganic Chemistry*, Chapter 1, in International Review of Science, Inorganic Chemistry Series One, Vol. 9 (ed. Tobe, M. L.). London: Butterworths.
[3] Rossotti, F. J. C. and Rossotti, H. (1961). *The Determination of Stability Constants*, p. 127. New York: McGraw-Hill.
[4] Alcock, R. M., Hartley, F. R., Rogers, D. E., and Wagner, J. L. (1975). *Coord. Chem. Rev.*, **16**, 59.
[5] Person, W. B. (1965). *J. Amer. Chem. Soc.*, **87**, 167.
[6] Heric, E. L. (1969). *J. Phys. Chem.*, **73**, 3496.
[7] Deranleau, D. A. (1969). *J. Amer. Chem. Soc.*, **91**, 4044.

[8] Deranleau, D. A. (1969). *J. Amer. Chem. Soc.*, **91**, 4050.

[9] Norheim, G. (1969). *Acta. Chem. Scand.*, **23**, 2808.

[10] Prue, J. E. (1965). *J. Chem. Soc.*, 7534.

[11] Hancock, R. D. and Evers, A. (1976). *Inorg. Chem.*, **15**, 995.

[12] Sillén, L. G. (1959). *Quart. Rev.*, **13**, 146.

[13] Sillén, L. G. (1971). *Coordination Chemistry, Vol.* 1, Amer. Chem. Soc. Monograph 168, Chapter 9 (ed. Martell, A. E.). Van Nostrand Reinhold.

[14] Sillén, L. G. (1964). *Proc. Welch Foundation Conf. Chem. Res.*, 187.

[15] Murata, K. and Ikeda, S. (1976). *Anal. Chem.*, **48**, 625.

[16] Sillén, L. G. (1954). *Acta. Chem. Scand.*, **8**, 299, 318.

[17] Wall, F. T. (1957). *J. Phys. Chem.*, **61**, 1344.

[18] Mandel, M. (1967). *J. Polymer Sci.*, **C16**, 2955.

[19] Gill, S. J. and Ferry, G. V. (1962). *J. Phys. Chem.*, **66**, 995, 999.

[20] Noll, L. A. and Gill, S. J. (1963). *J. Phys. Chem.*, **67**, 498.

[21] Strauss, U. P. and Leung, Y. P. (1965). *J. Amer. Chem. Soc.*, **87**, 1475.

[22] Leyte, J. C., Zuiderwag, L. H., and Vledder, H. J. (1967). *Spectrochim. Acta.*, **23A**, 1397.

[23] Paoletti, S. and Delben, F. (1975). *European Polymer J.*, **11**, 561.

[24] Eldridge, R. J. and Treloar, F. E. (1970). *J. Phys. Chem.*, **78**, 1486.

[25] Crescenzi, V., Delben, F., Paoletti, S., and Škerjanc, J. (1974). *J. Phys. Chem.*, **78**, 607.

[26] Delben, F. and Paoletti, S. (1974). *J. Phys. Chem.*, **78**, 1486.

[27] Felber, B. J., Hodnett, E. M., and Purdie, N. (1968). *J. Phys. Chem.*, **72**, 2496.

[28] Paoletti, S., Delben, F., and Crescenzi, V. (1976). *J. Phys. Chem.*, **80**, 2564.

[29] Morawetz, H. (1975). *Macromolecules in Solution*, 2nd ed., Vol. XXI of High Polymers, p. 364. New York: Wiley-Interscience.

[30] Gurd, F. R. N. and Wilcox, P. E. (1956). *Adv. Protein Chem.*, **11**, 311.

[31] Gurd, F. R. N. (1970). In *Physical Principles and Techniques of Protein Chemistry*, Part B, Chapter 15 (ed. Leach, S. J.). New York: Academic Press.

CHAPTER 7

Experimental Methods for Studying Equilibria I. Potentiometry

7.1 INTRODUCTION

Potentiometry has been and still is the most popular method for the determination of stability constants because of its high accuracy and precision [1,2]. Indeed it is only recently that this statement has been questioned [3] and then only for very complex systems where it is not the accuracy of the experimental observation that is in question but rather the precision with which the data can be interpreted. This has been discussed in Chapter 6 Section 6.3.

The major limitation in the use of potentiometry is the essential requirement that a suitable reversible electrode exists. Electrodes develop potentials that are dependent on the activities of the species present. These potentials originate from two main types of phenomena, namely oxidation-reduction equilibria and the formation of ionic concentration gradients across membranes. In the case of an oxidation-reduction equilibrium of the type,

$$M^{m+} + z\epsilon \rightleftharpoons M^{(m-z)+} \tag{7.1}$$

the observed potential, E, is given by the Nernst equation,[†]

$$E = E^o + \frac{RT}{z\mathcal{F}} \ln \frac{\{M^{(m-z)+}\}}{\{M^{z+}\}} \tag{7.2}$$

where E^o is the standard potential at 25°C when all the species are at unit activity,

---

† In the present text we shall follow the IUPAC convention whereby a cell reaction is written with the oxidised species on the left-hand side and the reduced species on the right. For example,
$$Na^+ + \epsilon \rightarrow Na \qquad E^o = -2.71V$$

This results in couples involving powerful reducing agents, for example Na, having negative potentials and couples with powerful oxidising agents, for example MnO_4^-, having positive potentials.
$$MnO_4^- + 8H^+ + 5\epsilon \rightarrow Mn^{2+} + 4H_2O \qquad E^o = +1.51V$$

$\mathcal{F}$ = one faraday of charge (96 493 coulomb.mol^{-1}), z = number of electrons involved, and $\{X\}$ is the activity of species X. In the case of ionic potential gradients, the observed e.m.f. is given by,

$$E = E^o{}_{M^{z+}} + \frac{RT}{z\mathcal{F}} \ln\{M^{z+}\} \qquad (7.3)$$

where $E^o{}_{M^{z+}}$ is the standard potential of the M^{z+} electrode at 25°C.

It is apparent from Equations (7.2) and (7.3) that the electrode actually responds in proportion to the activities of the species present. However, we saw in Section 1.6, Equation (1.20) that activity is related to concentration by the expression

$$\{X\} = [X]\gamma_x \qquad (7.4)$$

and accordingly if the activity coefficients are maintained constant, for example by using a sufficiently high concentration of an inert background electrolyte, then we can rewrite Equations (7.2) and (7.3) in terms of concentrations, with the proviso that the standard potential E^o is replaced by the formal potential $E^{o\prime}$. Thus Equation (7.3) becomes

$$E = E^{o\prime} + \frac{RT}{z\mathcal{F}} \ln[M^{z+}] \qquad (7.5)$$

where

$$E^{o\prime} = E^o + \frac{RT}{z\mathcal{F}} \ln \gamma_M{}^{z+} \qquad (7.6)$$

It should be apparent that by combining Equation (7.2) with the relevant equations for the stability constant for Reaction (7.1) the measured potential is related not only to the free energy change but also through this to the stability constant as discussed in Section 1.10:

$$\Delta G = -z\mathcal{F}E = -RT\ln K \qquad (7.7)$$

7.2 MEASUREMENT OF POTENTIAL

Once we have an electrode that responds to some concentration change within the system, how do we measure its potential? First of all we must have some form of reference electrode present to complete the circuit. The reference electrode [4] can be either

(a) directly in contact with the solution under test, in which case it must respond to the concentration of a different component in the test solution from the sample electrode, and furthermore the concentration of this second component must be either constant or accurately known throughout; or

(b) immersed in a second solution which is in electrical contact with the sample solution.

Electrical contact is usually maintained by an electrolyte bridge which may be:

(a) A thin sliver of asbestos that is 'wet' with the solution, as used in the calomel reference electrodes of many commercial combined glass and calomel electrodes,

(b) an agar jelly containing an electrolyte and built into a glass bridge containing glass frits at each end (Figure 7.1(a)),

(c) a 'Wilhelm' salt bridge containing an electrolyte solution in which two interfaces occur, one between the sample and bridge at B and one between the bridge and the reference compartment at tap C (Figure 7.1(b)) or

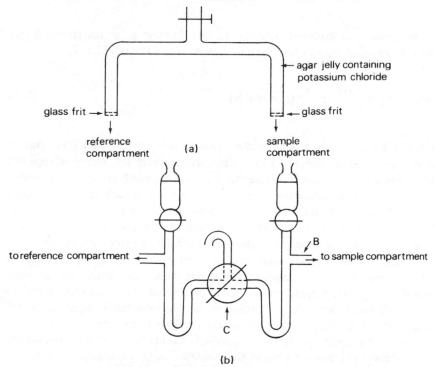

Figure 7.1 – Bridges to link reference and sample compartments: (a) agar jelly bridge, (b) 'Wilhelm' bridge.

(d) a flowing liquid junction (Figure 7.1(c)) which is rarely used because of the experimental inconvenience of the large reservoirs of electrolyte needed.

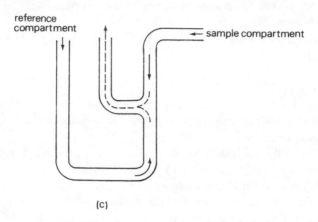

(c)

Figure 7.1(c) — Flowing liquid junction bridge for linking reference and sample compartments.

Whenever two different solutions (1 and 2) meet at an interface a liquid junction potential, E_j, which is given by Equation (7.8) occurs [1,5-7]:

$$E_j = \frac{-RT}{\mathcal{F}} \int_1^2 \sum_1^i (t_i/z_i)\,\mathrm{dln}\{i\} \qquad (7.8)$$

t_i, z_i and $\{i\}$ are the transport number, charge, and activity of ion i. Integration of this equation is complex and necessarily approximate, but it is apparent that if the electrolyte concentration in the bridge is much higher than in either the reference or sample solutions, then the potentials at each end of the bridge will be largely determined by the composition of the bridge electrolyte. If the anions and cations of the bridge electrolyte have roughly equal transport numbers the two junction potentials set up will be of approximately the same magnitude but of opposite sign, and accordingly the overall liquid junction potential will be zero. Potassium chloride and ammonium nitrate are the most suitable bridge electrolytes because their cation and anion transport numbers are almost equal, but where chloride or nitrate ions interfere, as in careful studies of metal complex formation in a perchlorate medium, a sodium perchlorate bridge electrolyte is more suitable. It has been shown both from theory and in practice [8] that any error in the evaluation of the liquid junction potential has least effect on the value determined for the first stability constant, K_1, and a successively greater effect on each succeeding stability constant, $K_2, K_3 \ldots K_n$.

So far it has been assumed that the equilibrium is being studied in aqueous solution. However, many equilibria take place in non-aqueous media and since there are a number of electrodes that are reversible in non-aqueous solvents, potentiometric measurements can be carried out in such media. Ideally, the reference electrode should either be immersed in the sample solution or, if it is in a separate compartment the solvent in the sample and reference compartments should be the same. If the two compartments contain different solvents then the liquid junction potential will be very high, and care must be taken in designing the experiment to check with the aid of calibrant solutions that it remains constant over the concentration ranges involved.

Once a complete cell has been constructed the next problem is to measure its potential accurately without disturbing it. Classically this was done with a potentiometer such as that shown in Figure 7.2. However, there are a number of disadvantages to a potentiometer:

(a) It is slow since each e.m.f. has to be 'homed in on'.

(b) Because of the inertia of the galvanometer and the potentiometer system there is an insensitive region around the null or balance point leading to uncertainty in the measured e.m.f. Although this insensitive region can be minimised the financial cost of reducing it is always greater than the cost of a millivoltmeter of comparable precision.

(c) Except at the null point a current flows from the cell under test. This leads to polarisation of the electrodes and a time lag in the cell response so that the measured voltage is always in error until the null point is reached.

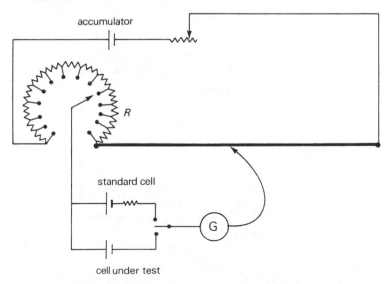

Figure 7.2 – Potentiometer circuit suitable for measuring e.m.f.

Nowadays it is more usual to use a millivoltmeter, frequently a digital millivolt-meter, to measure the cell potential. The millivoltmeter must have a high impe-dance, firstly because ideally no current should be drawn from the cell under test, and secondly because the voltage drop across the internal resistance of the cell under test should be negligible in relation to the total e.m.f. generated. Let us look at this point in a bit more detail because, although most experimentalists will use a commercial pH/millivoltmeter, it is often much cheaper to use a simple millivoltmeter, so long as one appreciates the specifications needed. In Figure 7.3, V_c is the voltage that we ideally want to measure, but because the cell has a high internal resistance (R_c, typically 10^3 ohms although this depends very much on the design of the cell and of its liquid junction) the voltage we actually measure is V_M. If a small current i flows through the circuit, then from Ohm's law,

$$V_c = iR_M + iR_c \tag{7.9}$$

where R_M is the internal resistance of the millivoltmeter. Thus V_M ($= iR_M$) will approach V_c when iR_c becomes negligible compared to iR_M. Thus the internal resistance of the millivoltmeter should always be at least 10^3 times greater than that of the cell under test. If, by chance, R_c is small, R_M must still be kept fairly large in order to ensure that the current i is kept as small as possible. If a large current is allowed to flow through the cell, dissolution at the anode and deposition at the cathode will occur in accordance with Faraday's law, and the activities of the species present in solution will change appreciably. This will alter the observed e.m.f. and the cell is then said to be polarised.

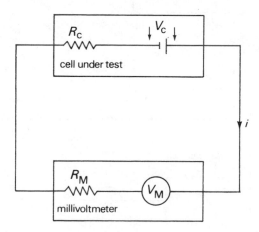

Figure 7.3 — Use of a millivoltmeter to measure e.m.f.

7.3 EXPERIMENTAL TECHNIQUE FOR DETERMINING STABILITY CONSTANTS

Two main experimental approaches may be used for determining stability constants potentiometrically. In the first a separate solution containing known total metal and total ligand concentration is prepared for each data point. This is rather slow and laborious. The alternative is to titrate one solution with another, the potential being determined after each addition of titrant. One of the possible difficulties with this latter approach for systems that form weak complexes is that the change in potential consequent to dilution of the initial solution can be large relative to the change in potential due to complex formation. If a metal ion solution is being titrated with a ligand solution, then this difficulty can be obviated by making equal volume additions of the ligand solution and a metal solution of exactly double the strength of the metal solution being titrated. This ensures that the total ion concentration remains constant (see Section 11.2).

When carrying out potentiometric studies it is extremely important to control the temperature to at least $\pm0.05°C$ and preferably to $\pm0.01°C$. This is because not only are stability constants temperature dependent (clearly this applies to any method of determination) but also the measured potential is temperature dependent (see Equation (7.2) and (7.3)). It has been shown [9] that if the error in the temperature is $\pm0.02°C$ then the error in the activities will be $0.5z\%$, where z is the number of electrons involved in Equations (7.2) and (7.3). Because of the close temperature control required it is advantageous, if temperatures far removed from room temperature are to be used, to use water-jacketted burettes.

7.4 ELECTRODES

As mentioned at the start of this chapter the use of potentiometry for determining stability constants depends on the availability of an electrode that is reversible to one of the components of the equilibrium. For convenience electrodes may be subdivided into those reversible to metal ions, those reversible to ligands, and finally those reversible to the proton.

To be suitable an electrode must fulfil the following criteria:

(a) It must be *reversible*; furthermore this reversibility should be as rapid as possible. Changes of solvent can have a profound effect on the reversibility of an electrode, and electrodes that are reversible in one solvent are not necessarily reversible in another. Reversibility should always be checked before use, by both increasing and decreasing the metal or ligand concentration to which the electrode is reversible and checking that both plots are superimposable within experimental error. The calibration solutions necessary for this are considered in Section 7.5.

(b) It must have the *widest possible dynamic range*. Ideally the electrode should exhibit a linear, preferably Nernstian, response over the widest possible concentration range. Although a non-linear, non-Nernstein response could in theory be tolerated by using suitable calibration curves, such responses are often symptomatic of non-reversibility.

(c) It must have *time stability*. All electrodes change slowly with time, but this change should be as small as possible. For many electrodes ageing in a solution similar to that to be studied is necessary in order to minimise the changes in the electrode's response with time.

(d) It must be of *low ohmic resistance*. Ideally the electrode should have as low a resistance as possible, although the availability of very high impedance millivoltmeters (see Section 7.2 above) has reduced this requirement [10,11]. Glass has a very high resistance, and so glass electrodes generally employ very thin films of glass, and this tends to lead to fragility. Modern glass technology has, however, begun to overcome this problem.

There are many different types of electrode available both commercially and for self-construction. It is outside the scope of this book to discuss them in detail; the interested reader is referred to References [1, 2, and 12–21].

7.5 CALIBRATION OF ELECTRODES

Before an electrode can be used in any potentiometric study it must be checked for reversibility (Nernstian behaviour) as well as being calibrated. Calibration is normally effected by having a series of solutions of known ionic composition and measuring the response of the elctrode to these. Whilst for the proton few people, if any, would use other than buffered solutions for calibration, there has recently been a tendency, partly encouraged by some electrode manufacturers, to ignore the need to use metal or ligand buffered solutions for the calibration of metal or ligand reversible electrodes. Instead calibration has been effected by preparing solutions by successive dilution of a concentrated stock solution, and in the same way that no serious chemist would prepare a calibration solution of pH 5 by successive dilution of $0.1 \, mol.l^{-1}$ hydrochloric acid, no serious chemist should attempt to prepare a $10^{-8} \, mol.l^{-1} \, Cu^{2+}$ solution by successive dilution of $0.1 \, mol.l^{-1} \, CuSO_4$.

In a short monograph such as the present it is inappropriate to discuss the theory of pH buffers for which the reader is referred elsewhere [1,22,23]. Since very few texts discuss metal ion buffer solutions we shall consider them here. pH buffers often involve a mixture of a weak acid and the alkali metal salt of that weak acid and function, because addition of H^+ leads to the formation of more of the weak acid and addition of OH^- leads to the formation of water and the acid anion. In a similar way pM buffers can be prepared using strong metal ion complexing agents such as citric, tartaric, and ethylediaminetetraacetic acids. If free metal ions are removed from the system then dissociation of the metal complex replenishes the concentration of the metal ion; if extra metal ions are added to the solution then the excess free ligand present complexes all but a very tiny fraction of the extra metal ions.

In order to calculate pM for a given buffer solution it is necessary to know,

(a) the total concentration of M;
(b) the total concentration of ligand L;
(c) the pK_a value(s) of L;
(d) the pH, if the ligand being used is a weak acid.

Schwarzenbach has introduced the concept of 'apparent' or 'conditional' stability constants to aid in describing equilibria in which two or more metal ions and two or more ligand species are present [24, 25]. The 'conditional' stability constant, β', for the formation of a complex ML is defined by:

$$\beta' = \frac{[ML]}{\begin{bmatrix} \text{All metal species present} \\ \text{that do not involve L} \end{bmatrix} \begin{bmatrix} \text{All ligand species present} \\ \text{that do not involve M} \end{bmatrix}} \tag{7.10}$$

Thus in a typical situation involving metal ions and a deprotonatable ligand (for example, Cu^{II} and EDTA) in aqueous solution (that is, in the presence of H^+ and OH^- ions) the species present, ignoring charges, will include $M(H_2O)_n$, $M(H_2O)_{n-1}(OH)$, $M(H_2O)_{n-2}(OH)_2$, ... L, HL, H_2L, ... H_mL together with metal ligand species ML, ML_2 ... ML_n. Now whereas the conventional stability constant K is given by

$$K = \frac{[ML]}{[M(H_2O)_n][L]} \tag{7.11}$$

β' is given by

$$\beta' = \frac{[ML]}{\{[M(H_2O)_n] + [M(H_2O)_{n-1}(OH)] + \ldots\}\{[L] + [HL] + \ldots\}} \tag{7.12}$$

and K and β' are most readily related by a 'degree of formation' function α similar to that described in Section 3.2(ii),

$$\alpha_M = \frac{[M(H_2O)_n]}{\{[M(H_2O)_n] + [M(H_2O)_{n-1}(OH)] + \ldots\}} \tag{7.13}$$

$$\alpha_L = \frac{[L]}{\{[L] + [HL] + \ldots\}} \tag{7.14}$$

Whence $\beta' = K \alpha_M \alpha_L$. $\tag{7.15}$

Although most metal ions hydrolyse to form polynuclear species (with the result that the value of α_M is dependent on the metal ion concentration), at low free metal ion concentrations (which are usually all we are interested in, and which are also all that will be present in the presence of strong complexing ligands such as EDTA), it is usually sufficient to consider the formation of mononuclear complexes only. Under these conditions,

$$1/\alpha_M = 1 + \frac{[M(H_2O)_{n-1}(OH)]}{[M(H_2O)_n]} + \frac{[M(H_2O)_{n-2}(OH)_2]}{[M(H_2O)_n]} + \ldots$$

therefore

$$1/\alpha_M = 1 + \frac{K_1^M}{[H]} + \frac{K_1^M K_2^M}{[H]^2} + \ldots \tag{7.16}$$

which can be evaluated if K_1^M, K_2^M ... etc. are known. K^M values refer to the loss of $1, 2, \ldots$ etc. protons from the hydrated metal ion.

$$K_1^M = \frac{[M(H_2O)_{n-1}(OH)][H]}{[M(H_2O)_n]} \tag{7.17}$$

$$K_2^M = \frac{[M(H_2O)_{n-2}(OH)_2][H]}{[M(H_2O)_{n-1}(OH)]} \tag{7.18}$$

Similarly

$$1/\alpha_L = 1 + \frac{[HL]}{[L]} + \frac{[H_2L]}{[L]} + \ldots$$

therefore

$$1/\alpha_L = 1 + K_1^L[H] + K_1^L K_2^L[H]^2 + \ldots \tag{7.19}$$

which can be evaluated if K_1^L, K_2^L ... etc. are known. These refer to the gain of $1, 2 \ldots$ etc. protons by the fully deprotonated ligand.

$$K_1^L = \frac{[HL]}{[H][L]} \tag{7.20}$$

$$K_2^L = \frac{[H_2L]}{[H][HL]} \tag{7.21}$$

Values of K^M and K^L can be obtained from the literature [25]. Having evaluated α_M and α_L from Equations (7.16) and (7.19), β' can be calculated using Equation (7.15) and put into Equation (7.22) which is obtained by combining Equations (7.10) and (7.13).

$$\beta' = \frac{[ML]\alpha_M}{[M(H_2O)_n] \,[\text{all ligand species not complexed to M}]} \tag{7.22}$$

If, (a) most of the total metal concentration, $[M]_T$, is present as the complex ML, that is $[ML] \approx [M]_T$,

and (b) the total concentration of ligand not complexed to metal is equal to

$$[L]_T - [ML] \; (\equiv [L]_T - [M]_T),$$

then from Equation (7.22),

$$\beta' = \frac{[M]_T\alpha_M}{[M(H_2O)_n] \,\{[L]_T - [M]_T\}} \tag{7.23}$$

whence taking logarithms,

$$pM = \log \beta' + \log \left\{ \frac{[L]_T - [M]_T}{[M]_T} \right\} - \log \alpha_M \tag{7.24}$$

Equation (7.24) thus determines the pM of the buffer solution. Careful analysis of Equation (7.24) shows:

(a) pM is independent of dilution since only the first term involves concentrations, and that is a ratio of two concentrations which will be affected identically by dilution.

(b) pM is dependent on pH because β' is pH dependent. This dependence for zinc and copper ions with EDTA is illustrated in Figure 7.4, which clearly indicates that adjustment of the pH is a convenient method for preparing solutions of a given pM.

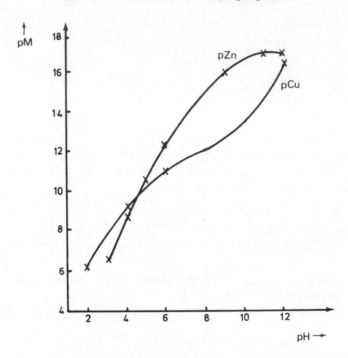

Figure 7.4 — Plots of pM v pH for solutions containing 10^{-3} mol.l^{-1} M^{2+} and 2×10^{-3} mol.l^{-1} EDTA (M^{2+} = Cu^{2+}, Zn^{2+}) (data for these plots was obtained from References [26] and [27]).

7.6 CALCULATION OF STABILITY CONSTANTS FROM POTENTIOMETRIC DATA

(i) *Free metal ion or free ligand data*

The choice of which method of calculation to use for evaluating stability constants from free metal ion or free ligand data depends to some extent on the design of the experiment. Accordingly in Table 7.1 we have indicated a number of the more commonly used methods and cross-referenced them with the rest of the text which should be consulted to check on the limitations of each method. This list is, of course, by no means comprehensive: for a more comprehensive list the reader is referred to Rossotti and Rossotti's excellent, although now somewhat dated text [13]. In the earlier literature many elaborate curve-fitting procedures were described in which curves derived from the experimental data were compared with standard curves calculated on the basis of an assumed model. These procedures have largely been replaced by computer-based non-linear least-squares fitting of the observed data to an assumed model as described in Chapter 5.

Table 7.1 – Methods for calculating stability constants from potentiometric data.

Type of data	Method of calculation	Reference
Electrode reversible to free metal ion	Leden	Sections 3.7(i) and 11.4
	Fronaeus	Section 3.7(ii)
	Method of corresponding solutions	Section 3.6
	Non-linear least-squares methods	Chapter 5 and Section 11.5
Electrode reversible to free ligand	Leden	Section 3.7(i)
	Fronaeus	Section 3.7(ii)
	Bjerrum's $\bar{n}$ function	Section 3.6 and 10.3
	Non-linear least-squares methods	Chapter 5

(ii) *pH data*

When stability constants are determined from pH data the experiment can be carried out in one of two ways. The change of pH can be measured as a function of the ligand concentration [28], which is described in Section 10.3. Alternatively the pH can be measured as a function of the concentration of acid, or alkali, added to a constant total metal and total ligand concentration [29,30]. A third approach of more limited application, which involves treating a metal-ion solution with a buffer mixture containing H_nL and its sodium salt [31], has been used for studying the weak complexes formed by carboxylate ligands.

Although pH measurement has been widely used to determine stability constants there are a number of limitations to the method:

(a) It cannot be used under conditions of extreme pH. At high pH the concentration of free ligand is insensitive to pH change. At low pH the free ligand concentration becomes negligible owing to virtually complete protonation.

(b) The method is inapplicable at very low total metal concentrations because under these conditions $[M]_T$ is close to zero so that $\bar{n}$ cannot be determined reliably from Equation (3.32).

(c) The method is inapplicable for very stable complexes such as those formed by some transition metal ions with EDTA because the protons are unable to compete effectively with such metal ions for the ligand.

Such complexes may, however, be studied by replacing the proton with another metal ion that can (i) compete effectively with the metal ion under test and (ii) be detected potentiometrically or by some other method (see Section 7.6(iii) below).

   (d) Since aqueous solutions always contain hydroxide ions and most metal ions form not only hydroxo-species but also polynuclear species, care must be taken either to work in sufficiently acidic solutions that hydroxo-complex formation is negligible or to take it into account during the analysis of the data.

(iii) Use of competing metal ions

The use of pH data as a method for studying equilibria is a specific, albeit very commonly used, example of a much more general technique in which a second metal ion is used. As mentioned at the beginning of this chapter the use of potentiometry to study metal-ligand complex equilibria depends on the availability of an electrode reversible to one of the ions. In the absence of such an electrode it is sometimes possible to add a second metal ion (M'') for which a suitable reversible electrode exists and then to determine the concentration of the uncomplexed M'' potentiometrically. If the stability constants for the M''-ligand system are known or can be measured, then by determining the free M'' concentration as a function of the total concentration of the metal ion under study, M', and the total ligand concentration it is possible to evaluate the M'-ligand stability constants. It is apparent that the use of pH data is a special case of this, and that, therefore, the limitations discussed in that connection apply also to the use of competing metal ions.

REFERENCES

[1] Bates, R. G. (1973). *Determination of pH*, 2nd ed. New York: Wiley.
[2] Rossotti, H. S. (1969). *Chemical Applications of Potentiometry*. London: D. Van Nostrand.
[3] Alcock, R. M., Hartley, F. R., Rogers, D. E., and Wagner, J. L. (1975). *Coord. Chem. Rev.*, **16**, 59.
[4] Ives, D. J. G. and Janz, S. J. (1961). *Reference Electrodes*. New York: Academic Press.
[5] Biedermann, G. and Sillén, L. G. (1952). *Ark. Kemi.*, **5**, 425.
[6] Lindeberg, E. G. B. and Østvold, T. (1974). *Acta. Chem. Scand.*, **A28**, 563.
[7] Morf, W. E. (1977). *Anal. Chem.*, **49**, 810.
[8] Olin, A. and Svanström, P. (1978). *Acta. Chem. Scand.*, **32**, 283.
[9] Vasil'ev, V. P. (1973). *Russ. J. Inorg. Chem.*, **18**, 1071.
[10] Henry, R. P., Price, J. E., Rossotti, F. J. C., and Whewell, R. J. (1971). *Chem. Commun.*, 868.

[11] Rossotti, F. J. C. and Whewell, R. J. (1977). *J. Chem. Soc. (Dalton),* 1223.

[12] Eisenman, G. (1967). *Glass Electrodes for Hydrogen and other Cations.* New York: Marcel Dekker.

[13] Rossotti, F. J. C. and Rossotti, H. (1961). *The Determination of Stability Constants.* New York: McGraw-Hill.

[14] Covington, A. K. (1969). *Chem. Brit.,* **5,** 388.

[15] Rechnitz, G. A. (1970). *Accounts Chem. Res.,* **3,** 69.

[16] Berman, H. J. and Herbert, N. C. (eds) (1974). *Ion-Selective Microelectrodes.* New York: Plenum.

[17] Koryta, J. (1975). *Ion-Selective Electrodes.* Cambridge University Press.

[18] Lakshminarayanaiah, N. (1976). *Membrane Electrodes.* New York: Academic Press.

[19] Buck, R. P. (1976). *Anal. Chem.,* **48,** 23R.

[20] Pungor, E. and Buzas, I. (1978). *Ion-Selective Electrodes.* Amsterdam: Elsevier.

[21] Mann, C. K. and Barnes, K. K. (1970). *Electrochemical Reactions in Non-Aqueous Solvents,* Chapter 1. New York: Marcel Dekker.

[22] Perrin, D. D. and Dempey, B. (1974). *Buffers for pH and Metal Ion Control.* London: Chapman and Hall.

[23] Camoes, M. F. G. F. C. and Covington, A. K. (1974). *Anal. Chem.,* **46,** 1547.

[24] Schwarzenbach, G. (1957). *Complexometric Titrations* (trans. Irving, H. M. N.). London: Methuen.

[25] Ringbom, A. (1958). *J. Chem. Ed.,* **35,** 282.

[26] Sillén, L. G. and Martell, A. E. (1964, Vol. 1; 1971, Vol. 2). *Stability Constants of Metal-Ion Complexes,* Chemical Society (London) Special Publications 17 and 25.

[27] Hansen, E. H., Lamm, C. G. and Růžička, J. (1972). *Anal. Chim. Acta.,* **59,** 403.

[28] Bjerrum, J. (1941). *Metal Ammine Formation in Aqueous Solution* (reprinted 1957). Copenhagen: P. Haase and Son.

[29] Calvin, M. and Wilson, K. W. (1945). *J. Amer. Chem. Soc.,* **67,** 2003.

[30] Irving, H. M., and Rossotti, H. S. (1954). *J. Chem. Soc.,* 2904.

[31] Fronaeus, S. (1948). *Komplexsystem hos Koppar.* Lund: Gleerupska Universitets Bokhandeln.

CHAPTER 8

Experimental Methods for Studying Equilibria II. Ultraviolet and Visible Spectrophotometry

---

8.1 INTRODUCTION

Ultraviolet and visible spectrophotometry should be regarded, in the main, as a complementary rather than an alternative technique to potentiometry. We have already described the advantages of spectrophotometery over potentiometry for defining the species present in very complex systems (see Sections 2.3 and 6.3). In addition there are occasions where potentiometry is unable to discriminate between equilibria. The potentiometric method requires a suitable electrode system, so that many reactions cannot be studied potentiometrically. The role of spectrophotometry in the determination of stability constants has been reviewed recently [1]. Some of the limitations of the spectrophotometric method have been discussed already in Sections 6.3 and 6.4.

8.2 BEER-LAMBERT-BOUGUER LAW

The Beer-Lambert-Bouguer Law, commonly called Beer's Law, is the fundamental law governing the attenuation of radiation by a specific absorber in spectrometry. Consider a parallel beam of monochromatic radiation of intensity, I_o passing normally through a solution containing an absorber in a cell of path length l cm. The emergent beam will be attenuated to an intensity I according to Equation (8.1).

$$\frac{dI_o}{dl} = -K I_o \tag{8.1}$$

This assumes that neither the solvent nor the cell containing the solution absorb or reflect an appreciable amount of the radiation.

The proportionality constant K is dependent on the wavelength of light chosen, the temperature, and the molar concentration of the absorbing species.

Integration of Equation (8.1) yields

$$I = I_o \, e^{-Kl} \tag{8.2}$$

If K is assumed to remain constant over the range of values for the number of absorbing species in solution then Equation (8.2) can be written:

$$I = I_o \, e^{-\epsilon'cl} \tag{8.3}$$

where ϵ' is the naperian molar absorptivity and c the concentration of the absorbing species in mol.l^{-1}. Rearranging Equation (8.3) yields

$$\log\left(\frac{I_o}{I}\right) = \epsilon cl \tag{8.4}$$

where ϵ is the decadic molar absorptivity, henceforth called simply the molar absorptivity. The left-hand side of the equation is called the absorbance, A, although this has sometimes been referred to as the 'optical density'. Absorbance is the preferred term. Hence,

$$A = \epsilon cl \tag{8.5}$$

which is the familiar form of Beer's Law. This may be expressed for a given wavelength λ, and n species by

$$A^\lambda_{\text{obs}} = \epsilon_1^\lambda c_1 l + \epsilon_2^\lambda c_2 l + \ldots \epsilon_n^\lambda c_n l \tag{8.6}$$

where ϵ_1^λ, ϵ_2^λ, ϵ_n^λ are the molar absorptivities of species 1, 2, and n at wavelength λ, and c_1, c_2 and c_n are their respective concentrations. Equation (8.6) is identical to Equation (2.1).

In theory, Beer's Law is obeyed always if the number and nature of absorbing species remain constant and monochromatic radiation is used. In practice, however, deviations from linearity are observed on occasions. There is good reason to suppose that Beer's Law is always obeyed and that chemical and/or instrumental factors are the proper causes of observed deviations. One of the most common chemical causes of non-linearity is the formation of other species, for example, polymers or ion pairs, as the concentration of one of the reagents is increased. This can result in either positive or negative deviations being observed. Particulate matter in solutions can cause deviations also through scattering, and the effect will vary with both the wavelength of the light used and the particle size. Instrumental factors can cause observed deviations from Beer's Law. The most important of these is stray light which produces negative deviations. As it is beyond the scope of this book to discuss these factors in detail the reader is referred to References [3-7] for a more detailed discussion.

8.3 MEASUREMENT OF ABSORBANCE

For stability constant measurement the absorbance of a solution is usually measured using either manual a single-beam spectrophotometer or a double-beam recording spectrophotometer. It must be recognised that spectrophotometers actually measure transmittance and not absorbance. The measurement is usually output as absorbance as this is a linear function of concentration. Transmittance, T, is the ratio of the intensity of the emergent beam, I, and the incident beam I_o. It is related to absorbance by Equation (8.7).

$$A = -\log T \tag{8.7}$$

Older single-beam manual instruments employing the null point principle have a scale calibrated in both transmittance and absorbance. Modern double-beam recording spectrophotometers employ logarithmic amplifiers to convert transmittance to absorbance, and the result is output on a digital display. Very recently a number of microprocessor controlled instruments have been introduced that employ software conversion for this task.

In practice, the measurement of the absorbance of a series of solutions at a variety of wavelengths against a blank or reference solution is required. Exact procedures will vary slightly according to the particular type or make of spectrophotometer used. However, a number of points regarding good spectroscopic practice hold true.

(a) Use a good pair of cells, free from abrasions or scratches, made of a material suitable for the wavelength region under examination; glass for the visible region and fused quartz for the ultraviolet [2].

(b) Ensure that they are clean and dry [3]. Very careful handling is required to avoid finger prints or electrostatic dust problems on the optical surfaces. The use of lint-free cotton gloves and an antistatic brush are advisable.

(c) Check that the spectrophotometer is working both accurately and reproducibly [4,5]. Ensure that it is photometrically linear in the wavelength region under study. Pay close attention to the wavelength resettability when doing multiwavelength studies particularly in the ultraviolet region. The spectral bandwidth of the monochromator should ideally be set of approximately $\frac{1}{8}^{th}$ of the natural bandwith of the compounds under study to ensure a 99% observation of the true band intensity [6]. However, usually, for solution work, a spectral bandwidth of 2 nm in the visible and 1 nm in the ultraviolet will be more than adequate.

(d) Place, securely, the two cleaned cells in thermostatted cell holders in the spectrophotometer and fill each, very carefully, with the blank or reference solution. Ensure that there are no liquid spills on the optical faces of the cells (or in the cell compartment!) and that there is no fibrous matter or air bubbles in the solutions themselves. Stopper the cells and allow to equilibrate. Record any difference due to cell mismatching at each of the wavelengths required. This blank correction must be taken into account as a systemic error when applying rigorous least-squares analysis (see Section 4.4).

(e) All further measurements ought to be carried out without removal of either of the cells. The transfer of solutions should be done by using a double bulb pipette with multiple rinsing. Many modern instruments have flow cells and 'sipper systems' which simplify these operations.

(f) Ensure that the absorbance range measured during the experiment is compatible with the instrument type used and lies within the optimal region of the photometric precision for the type of spectrophotometer used [7]. For single-beam instruments, this range is usually 0.2 to 0.6 absorbance units, and for double beam spectrophotometers it is 0.6 to 1.2 absorbance units.

The quality of spectrophotometric data obtained from an experiment is usually directly proportional to the care taken to obtain it. Cleanliness of instrument, cells and solutions is essential. It is strongly recommended that whenever elevated temperature studies are undertaken the solvent should be degassed by boiling to prevent bubble formation in the cells. All solutions should be carefully filtered during their preparation to remove extraneous solid material. This is particularly necessary with background electrolyte stock solutions which may be up to 5 mol.l^{-1} or even above.

8.4 CALCULATION OF STABILITY CONSTANTS FROM SPECTROPHOTOMETRIC DATA

In Chapter 2, the qualitative role of spectrophotometry in determining the number and nature of species in solution was described. Two methods, the method of continuous variations [8, 9] and the mole ratio method [10], can be extended to allow calculation of the stability constant involved if, and only if, only one complex is formed. Many other procedures for specific cases have been derived, and these have been comprehensively reviewed [1]. More recently a method for the spectrophotometric determination of stability constants by equimolar dilution has been developed [11]. Again this method, although valid for polynuclear complexes, is only applicable when metal and ligand react in one constant ratio which is not changed on dilution.

We can in principle define four possibilities that may be encountered when studying the formation of 1:1 complexes using spectrophotometry.

(a) The molar absorptivities of M, L, and ML are known or can be determined directly.

(b) The molar absorptivities of any two of M, L, and ML are known, but not the third.

(c) The molar absorptivities of only one of M, L, and ML is known.

(d) The molar absorptivities of none of the species M, L, and ML is known.

In this classification a species that does not absorb at the wavelength being used is considered to have a known molar absorptivity. Case (a) can be solved by simple algebra. Case (b) can be solved either by straight line extrapolation techniques yielding the stability constant and the unknown molar absorptivity from a combination of the slope and intercept [12], or by a method of successive approximation as described in Section 9.2(iii)(a) in connection with n.m.r. chemical shifts [13]. Two examples of the extrapolation technique are given in the third case study (Chapter 12). The third situation is usually solved iteratively [14], although it can be done arithmetically by suitable choice of the experimental conditions [12]. When the system falls into class (d), the stability constants cannot be determined spectrophotometrically.

The fundamental difficulty with spectrophotometric measurements is that they are dependent upon an intensive factor as well as concentration (see Section 6.1). One method that is ideally suited to overcome this problem is the method of corresponding solutions [15–17] (see Section 8.5). For systems with multi-complex formation, which are the most common, computational methods are usually used to determine the molar absorptivities (intensive factors). These procedures were discussed in some detail in Chapter 5.

8.5 METHOD OF CORRESPONDING SOLUTIONS

The method of corresponding solutions [15-17] can be used to overcome the problem of unknown and often unwanted molar absoptivities when using spectrophotometric data to determine stability constants. Consider an equilibrium system in which a number of species are present, M, ML, ML_2 ... ML_i ... ML_n, L. A function ϵ_{obs}^λ, can be defined such that

$$\epsilon_{obs}^\lambda = \frac{A_{obs}^\lambda - \epsilon_L^\lambda [L]_T}{[M]_T} \tag{8.8}$$

where A_{obs}^λ is the absorbance per unit path length of any solution of the equilibrium system at a wavelength λ nm. The absorbance A_{obs}^λ is given by

$$A_{obs}^\lambda = \epsilon_M^\lambda [M] + \sum_{i=1}^{i=n} (\epsilon_i^\lambda [ML_i]) + \epsilon_L^\lambda [L] \tag{8.9}$$

where ϵ_M^λ, ϵ_L^λ and ϵ_i^λ are the molar absorptivities of the metal ligand and complex ML_i at wavelength λ nm. Substituting for (8.9) in (8.8) gives,

$$\epsilon_{obs}^{\lambda} = \frac{\epsilon_M^{\lambda}[M] + \sum\limits_{i=1}^{i=n}(\epsilon_i^{\lambda}[ML_i]) - \epsilon_L^{\lambda}([L]_T - [L])}{[M]_T} \qquad (8.10)$$

and hence from Equation (3.4),

$$\epsilon_{obs}^{\lambda} = \frac{\epsilon_M^{\lambda}[M] + \sum\limits_{i=1}^{i=n}(\epsilon_i^{\lambda}[ML_i]) - \sum\limits_{i=1}^{i=n}(\epsilon_L^{\lambda}i[ML_i]^i)}{[M]_T} \qquad (8.11)$$

Expanding, using Equation (3.9) and combining terms,

$$\epsilon_{obs}^{\lambda} = \frac{\epsilon_M^{\lambda}[M] + \sum\limits_{i=1}^{i=n}(\epsilon_i^{\lambda}\beta_i[M][L]^i - \epsilon_L^{\lambda}\beta_i[M][L]^i)}{[M]_T} \qquad (8.12)$$

Dividing through by [M] gives

$$\epsilon_{obs}^{\lambda} = \frac{\epsilon_M^{\lambda} + \sum\limits_{i=1}^{i=n}(\epsilon_i^{\lambda} - i\epsilon_L^{\lambda})\beta_i[L]^i}{[M]_T/[M]} \qquad (8.13)$$

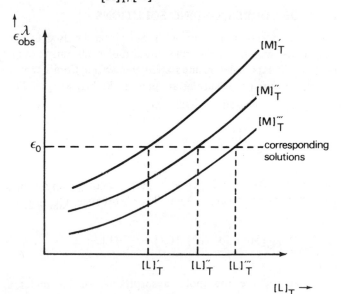

Figure 8.1 – Corresponding solutions: Plots of ϵ_{obs}^{λ} evaluated using Equation (8.8), against $[L]_T$ at various values of $[M]_T$.

and from Equations (3.3) and (3.9), ϵ_M^λ finally becomes

$$\epsilon_{obs}^\lambda = \frac{\epsilon_M^\lambda + \sum_{i=1}^{i=n} (\epsilon_i^\lambda - i\epsilon_L^\lambda)\beta_i[L]^i}{1 + \sum_{i=1}^{i=n} \beta_i[L]^i} \tag{8.14}$$

Hence ϵ_{obs}^λ is a function of [L] only, an analogous situation to $\bar{n}$ in Section 3.2(i). If ϵ_{obs}^λ is calculated from the absorbances of solutions of different $[L]_T$ and $[M]_T$ values using Equation (8.8), it follows that solutions having the same value of ϵ_{obs}^λ must have the same value for [L]. Since $\bar{n}$ is a function of [L] only, it also follows that these solutions have the same value of $\bar{n}$. Hence the origin of the term 'corresponding solutions'.

From Equation (3.5),

$$[L]_T = [L] + \bar{n}[M]_T \tag{8.15}$$

and for a constant value of [L] this is a linear equation whose slope is $\bar{n}$ and intercept [L].

In practice, A_{obs}^λ is measured for a series of solutions of constant $[M]_T$ and increasing $[L]_T$. ϵ_{obs}^λ is then calculated, using Equation (8.8). The experiment is repeated for a series of different $[M]_T$ values. A series of graphs of ϵ_{obs}^λ and $[L]_T$ are plotted as shown in Figure 8.1. Sets of values of $[M]_T$ and the corresponding $[L]_T$ can now be determined for any chosen value of ϵ_{obs}^λ. The resultant linear plots of these data (Figure 8.2) give a value of $\bar{n}$ and [L] for each ϵ_{obs}^λ chosen.

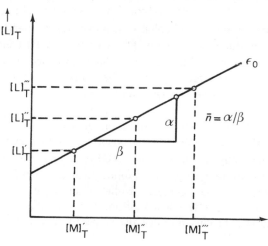

Figure 8.2 – Corresponding solutions: Plot of $[L]_T$ against $[M]_T$ for a series of solutions having the same value of ϵ_{obs}^λ (ϵ_0 data taken from Figure 8.1).

Once a series of $\bar{n}$ and [L] are obtained in this way, the stability constants can be calculated using the method of Fronaeus (Section 3.7(ii)). Equation (3.68) may be written

$$\phi = 1 + \sum_{i=1}^{i=n} \beta_i [L]^i \tag{8.16}$$

where ϕ is the degree of complex formation. From the series of $\bar{n}$ and [L] values obtained, ϕ can be calculated from Equation (3.69).

$$\phi = \exp\left(\int_0^{[L]} \frac{\bar{n}}{[L]} \, \partial[L]\right) \tag{8.17}$$

either by graphical or preferably numerical integration. The weighting function for Equation (8.16) has been derived from error propagation theory and shown [18,19] to be $1/\phi^2[L]$. Polynomials of a rearranged form of (8.16)

$$1 - \frac{1}{\phi} = \sum_{i=1}^{i=n} \frac{\beta_i [L]^i}{\phi} \tag{8.18}$$

are fitted to the computed values of ϕ using the method of weighted least-squares, and hence a best fit solution for β_i values is obtained. In this way, the β_i values are determined without the necessity of knowing any of the ϵ_i^{λ} values.

The use of the method of corresponding solutions is not confined to equilibrium systems whose positions are directly determinable. For example, competition studies can be done using a highly coloured very stable complex such as tris(1,10-phenanthroline)-iron(II) [20]. This blood-red complex has a strong absorption band at about 510 nm. On the other hand neither 1,10-phenanthroline nor its complexes of cobalt(II), nickel(II), copper(II), and zinc(II) absorb strongly in the visible region. For a given iron(II) concentration, the addition of 1,10-phenanthroline increases the absorbance of the solution at 510 nm until a constant value A_{max} is reached (Figure 8.3). Because the value of β_3 for $[Fe(phen)_3]^{2+}$ is very large, a very sharp breakpoint is observed. If the value of the 1,10-phenanthroline concentration, [phen], at this breakpoint is taken and divided by the total concentration of iron in solution the result is almost exactly 3, thereby establishing the stoichiometry (see Section 2.5(i), mole ratio method). Increasing amounts of cobalt(II) are added to a series of solutions containing slightly more 1,10-phenanthroline than that needed to form completely $[Fe(phen)_3]^{2+}$. The decrease in the observed absorbance at 510 nm increases with the cobalt(II) concentration. Further additions of 1,10-phenanthroline to these solutions produce the series of curves illustrated in Figure 8.3.

Observe a line, in Figure 8.3, drawn parallel to the x-axis from a point $A_{obs}^{510} = 0.75$. This intersects the iron(II)–1,10-phenanthroline curve at a and four

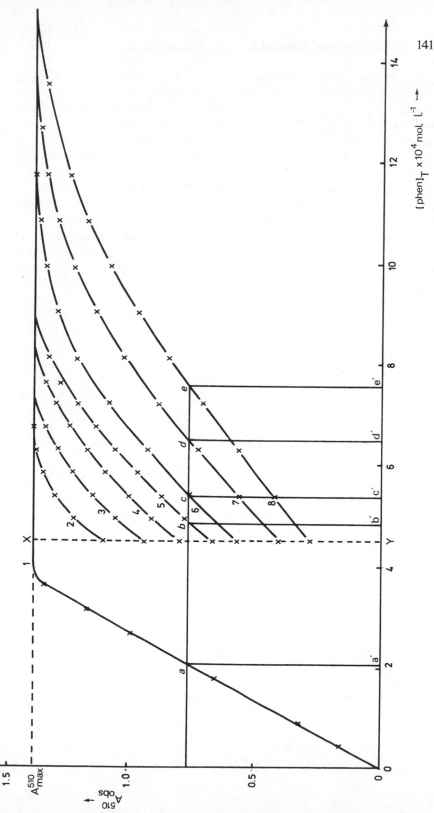

Figure 8.3 — Method of corresponding solutions for competing metal ions: the iron(II)–1,10-phenanthroline–cobalt(II) system at 25.0°C and μ = 0.10 mol.l⁻¹; cobalt(II) concentrations: (1) 0 mol.l⁻¹, (2) 1.205 × 10⁻⁴, (3) 1.807 × 10⁻⁴, (4) 2.410 × 10⁻⁴, (5) 3.012 × 10⁻⁴, (6) 3.614 × 10⁻⁴, (7) 4.819 × 10⁻⁴ and (8) 6.024 × 10⁻⁴ mol.l⁻¹.

of the curves for solutions containing cobalt(II) at b, c, d and e. The reduction in the values of A_{obs}^{510} at constant $[phen]_T$, that is line X–Y, is due to the lower concentration of 1,10-phenanthroline available to complex with iron(II) as complexes of the type $[Co(phen)]^{2+}$, $[Co(phen)_2]^{2+}$ and $[Co(phen)_3]^{2+}$ are formed in competition. Mixtures having the same absorbance, that is a, b, c, d and e are corresponding solutions since $[Fe]_T$ is the same for each, and hence identical concentrations of Fe^{2+}, $[Fe(phen)]^{2+}$, $[Fe(phen)_2]^{2+}$ and $[Fe(phen)_3]^{2+}$ must be present. Therefore the whole of the 1,10-phenanthroline represented by the concentration difference $b'-a'$ must have complexed with the cobalt(II) present in solution 5. Similarly the whole of the 1,10-phenanthroline represented by the concentration difference $c'-b'$ must have complexed with an amount of cobalt(II) equal to the difference in the cobalt(II) concentrations of solutions 5 and 6. In this way a series of plots of $[Co]_T$ corresponding to $[phen]$ can be prepared for a series of A_{obs}^{510} values (Figure 8.4). Since the absorbance at 510 nm

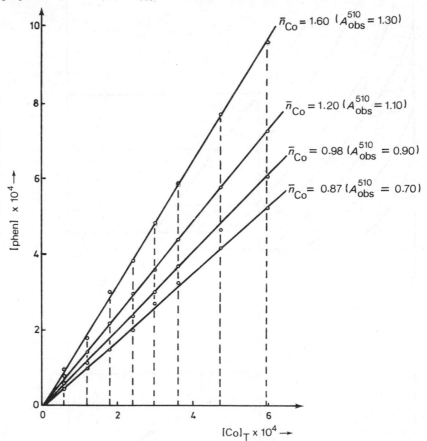

Figure 8.4 — Plot of $[Co]_T$ versus corresponding values of $[phen]$ for the iron(II)–1,10-phenanthroline–cobalt(II) system.

is due solely to $[Fe(phen)_3]^{2+}$ then,

$$A_{obs}^{510} = \frac{\epsilon_{obs}^{510} l}{[Fe(phen)_3]} \tag{8.19}$$

and

$$A_{max}^{510} = \frac{\epsilon_{obs}^{510} l}{[Fe]_T} \tag{8.20}$$

hence

$$\frac{A_{obs}^{510}}{A_{max}^{510}} = \frac{[Fe(phen)_3]}{[Fe]_T} \tag{8.21}$$

From Equations (3.3) and (3.9) this becomes

$$\frac{A_{obs}^{510}}{A_{max}^{510}} = \frac{\beta_3 [phen]^3}{(1 + \beta_1 [phen] + \beta_2 [phen]^2 + \beta_3 [phen]^3)} \tag{8.22}$$

As the values for $\log \beta_1$, $\log \beta_2$ and $\log \beta_3$ are known at $25.0°C$ and 0.1 mol.l^{-1} ionic strength from other studies [20] to be 5.85, 11.15 and 21.15 respectively, $A_{obs}^{510}/A_{max}^{510}$ values corresponding to [phen] concentrations of 1×10^{-8} to 3×10^{-7} mol.l^{-1} are calculated. The result is shown in the first curve on Figure 8.5. Hence from the ratios found from Figure 8.4, the corresponding [phen] value for each $\bar{n}$ value can be obtained. The formation curve for cobalt(II)-1,10-phenanthroline is plotted as the second curve in Figure 8.5. Data previously obtained [20] is plotted for comparison purposes.

Although this method neatly avoids the usual difficulties associated with spectrophotometric studies, the limitations of competition reactions of this type are clearly indicated in Figure 8.5. Firstly, the reliable working range over which accurate values of the ratio $A_{obs}^{510}/A_{max}^{510}$ can be obtained is 0.1 to 0.9. This in turn governs the range of [phen] values accessible and hence the $\bar{n}$ spread for the cobalt(II)-1,10-phenanthroline equilibrium which is about 0.6 to 1.5. This in itself is clearly insufficient to define the stepwise equilibrium processes for $N = 3$. As may be expected, the range of applicability is governed by the β values and the chromophoric properties of the system chosen for the competition reaction. However, this method has great potential in being able to study systems that could not readily be studied by other methods. Although discussion has been limited to metal ion competition studies in relation to corresponding solutions, ligand-ligand competition reactions can be treated in a similar manner. In practice, however, it is much more difficult to find a suitable pair of ligands for such a study.

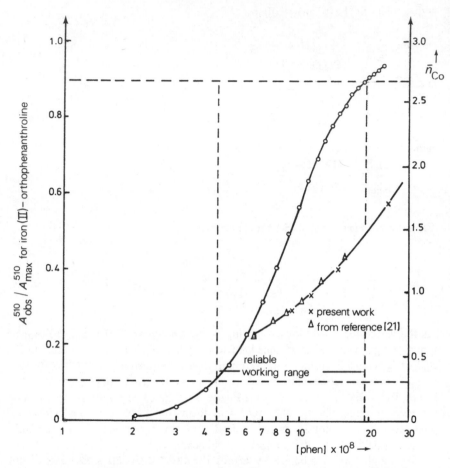

Figure 8.5 – Fraction of $[Fe(phen)_3]^{2+}$ present as a function of [phen] and the formation curve of cobalt(II)–1,10-phenanthroline.

REFERENCES

[1]   McBryde, W. A. E. (1974). *Talanta.*, **21**, 979.
[2]   British Standard 3875 (1965).
[3]   Goddard, D. A. (Dec. 1976). *U.V. Spectrometry Group Bulletin*, No. 4, 19.
[4]   Edisbury, J. R. (3rd impression 1969). *Practical Hints on Absorption Spectrometry*, Chapter 9. London: Adam Hilger Ltd.
[5]   Burgess, C. (Dec. 1977). *U.V. Spectrometry Group Bulletin*, No. 5, 77.
[6]   Everett, A. J. (Oct. 1977). *U.V. Spectrometry Group Bulletin*, No. 5, 23.
[7]   Bauman, R. P. (1962). *Absorbance Spectroscopy*. New York: Wiley.
[8]   Likussar, W. and Boltz, D. F. (1971). *Anal. Chem.*, **43**, 1265.
[9]   Budesinsky, B. W. (1969). *J. Inorg. Nucl. Chem.*, **31**, 1345.

[10] Betts, R. H. and Michels, R. K. (1949). *J. Chem. Soc.*, 286.

[11] Budesinsky, B. W. (1975). *Anal. Chem.*, **47**, 560.

[12] Ingman, F. (1973). *Talanta.*, **20**, 993.

[13] Denning, R. G., and Hartley, F. R., and Venanzi, L. M. (1967). *J. Chem. Soc. (A)*, 324.

[14] Ramette, R. W. (1967). *J. Chem. Educ.*, **44**, 647.

[15] Bjerrum, J. (1944). *Kgl. Denske Videnskab. Selskab. Matt-fys. Medd.*, **21**, No. 4.

[16] Fronaeus, S. (1951). *Acta. Chem. Scand.*, **5**, 139.

[17] Grabaric, B., Piljac, I., and Filipovic, I. (1963). *Anal. Chem.*, **45**, 1932.

[18] Momoki, K., Sato, H., and Ogawa, H. (1967). *Bull. Fac. Eng. Yokohama Nat. Univ.*, **16**, 127.

[19] Momoki, K., Sato, H., and Ogawa, H. (1967). *Anal. Chem.*, **39**, 1072.

[20] Irving, H., and Mellor, D. H. (1955). *J. Chem. Soc.*, 3457.

CHAPTER 9

Experimental Methods for Studying Equilibria III. Further Methods

---

9.1 INTRODUCTION

Potentiometry and spectrophotometry are by far the most important methods for the determination of stability constants; accordingly we have devoted a separate chapter to each method, Chapters 7 and 8 respectively. In the present chapter we describe some of the most important of the other methods that have been used, emphasising the strengths and potential weaknesses of each. The general factors that influence the choice of which method to use have been discussed in Section 6.1. For convenience the methods described in the present chapter have been grouped as follows:

Spectroscopic methods
Distribution methods
Electrochemical methods
Calorimetric methods
Miscellaneous methods

9.2 SPECTROSCOPIC METHODS

Spectroscopic methods for the determination of stability constants are so dominated by u.v.-visible spectrophotometry that a separate chapter (Chapter 8) is devoted to this technique.

(i) *Infrared*

The widespread availability of infrared spectrometers might suggest that this should be an important technique for the determination of stability constants. That it is not, is due to a number of fundamental problems:

(a) The molar absorptivities in the infrared region are relatively low, so that fairly concentrated solutions must be used. High concentrations are not only inconvenient but they are also detrimental to the accuracy of the determination, as discussed in Section 1.6.

(b) Even when 'windows' exist in the spectra of the solvents, the residual absorption by the solvent is usually such as to necessitate the use of concentrated solutions to minimise solvent absorption.

(c) Special cell windows must be used if aqueous solutions are to be studied.

(d) A feature of the design of infrared spectrometers is that polychromatic light is passed through the sample. This inevitably limits the accuracy of the resulting absorbance values.

(e) Thermostatically controlled infrared cells are not widely available.

A number of stability constants have been determined using infrared spectroscopy with systems involving cyanide [1-4], nitrosyl [5], ethylene [6], triphenylstibine [7], dimethylsulphoxide [8], and pyridine [8] ligands. Even when only a single metal-ligand complex is formed an accuracy of only about 10% is obtainable, although in a study of the hydrogen bonded complexes formed between HF and a number of organic compounds very much higher accuracies have been claimed [9]. The techniques used to extract stability constants from infrared data are essentially the same as those described in Chapter 8 for u.v.-visible spectroscopy.

(ii) *Raman*
There has been a resurgence of interest in Raman spectroscopy following the commercial manufacture of instruments using lasers as the source of exciting radiation [10], but this has not led to the widespread use of Raman spectroscopy for determining stability constants in spite of the fact that, in principle, the method should be of more widespread use than infrared because glass cells and aqueous solutions can be used. The disadvantages of Raman spectroscopy are:

(a) Raman spectra are weak, necessitating the use of concentrated solutions, which should normally be avoided (see Section 1.6).

(b) Because of the need to use very concentrated solutions, together with the Raman spectra of the ions themselves, it is rarely possible to control activity coefficients using a constant ionic medium.

(c) Effective thermostatting is essential to prevent heating of the sample by the intense radiation source.

(d) The background intensity due to the solvent and any components except those under investigation must be determined and subtracted from the intensity measurements before these are correlated with concentration.

(e) The practical difficulty of setting up the instrument in an identical manner for every solution to be studied can be obviated [11] by comparing the relative intensities of two bands, one arising from the free ligand and the other from the complex. The ratio of the integrated intensities can then be used to evaluate the stability constant.

In spite of these disadvantages Raman spectroscopy has been used to study a number of metal-ligand systems [12–15] as well as the interaction of platinum(II) complexes with the bases cytidine and uridine [16]. The problem of very weak Raman spectra may be alleviated by using Resonance Raman Spectroscopy in which the Raman excitation frequency coincides with an electronic absorption band of the ligand or complex. An initial study of the application of this technique to the interaction of tetracyanoethylene with organic electron donors indicated that whilst the precision of the stability constants was low the results were in good agreement with the results obtained by other methods [17]. A solvent band was used as an internal standard to compensate for the loss in overall intensity resulting from the absorption of the excitation light by the complex formed.

(iii) *Nuclear magnetic resonance*

Nuclear magnetic resonance yields three parameters that may be used in the evaluation of stability constants: chemical shifts, coupling constants, and relaxation times in the presence of paramagnetic ions, of which the first two have been used the most extensively.

(a) *Chemical shifts*

In the absence of exchange effects n.m.r. is potentially a very attractive method for determining the position of an equilibrium since the spectrum yields two signals, one for free and the other for coordinated ligand. The keto-enol tautomerism of acetylacetone has been studied in this way [19]. Similarly ^{13}C n.m.r. has been used to determine the position of Equilibrium (9.1) by determining the integrated intensities of the methyl ^{13}C resonances of the free and coordinated acetate [20].

$$[Ni(H_2O)_6]^{2+} + CH_3COO^- \rightleftharpoons [Ni(CH_3COO)(H_2O)_5]^+ \qquad (9.1)$$

An essential part of the experiment involves getting good signal-to-noise ratios. Although this is normally improved, where necessary, by signal averaging it has recently been shown that cross-correlation provides a more powerful quantitative technique, particularly when low concentrations are involved [21]. The relative signal areas may be determined by triangulation, machine integration, or cutting and weighing, of which cutting and weighing is usually the favoured method [22]. Ideally there should be no overlapping of bands; if there is any overlapping then Gaussian [22] or Lorentzian [20] deconvolution can be used to resolve the bands, although this will severely limit the accuracy of the resulting stability constants. One of the difficulties of applying n.m.r. spectroscopy to the determination of stability constants is that the magnitude of the chemical shifts is often dependent on the nature and the concentrations of the inert ions present [23,24] and therefore, by implication, on the concentrations of the metal ligand species. However, for many systems a further and more serious problem can arise in the form of rapid exchange between free and coordinated ligand.

One of the complications of n.m.r. arises from the fact that the frequency of the radiation is relatively low, typically in the range $(\sim 2 - \sim 100) \times 10^6$ Hz. This should be compared with infrared $(\sim 10^{12} - \sim 10^{15})$ Hz and u.v.-visible $(\sim 10^{15} - \sim 10^{18})$ Hz spectroscopy. As a result whilst infrared and u.v.-visible spectroscopy give a largely static picture of chemical equilibria, it is possible for some systems to change significantly during the time taken to make an n.m.r. observation. Consequently when free and complexed ligands exchange more rapidly than the n.m.r. frequency, only a single time-averaged chemical shift is observed. To use this, it is essential to determine, directly or indirectly, the chemical shift expected for the coordinated ligand. On occasions this has been determined by the addition of more metal salt until no further change in the chemical shift was observed when it was assumed that all the ligand had been complexed [25]. Such a technique is open to many objections; in particular it is liable to underestimate the change in chemical shift on coordination and hence overestimate the stability constant.

It is possible, for systems in which only a single metal-ligand complex ML is formed, to determine the chemical shift of the complexed ligand indirectly. Thus for the system

$$M + L \xrightleftharpoons{K_1} ML \tag{9.2}$$

the observed chemical shift (δ_{obs}) is given by

$$\delta_{obs} = \delta_L \frac{\{[L]_T - [ML]\}}{[L]_T} + \delta_{ML} \frac{[ML]}{[L]_T} \tag{9.3}$$

where δ_L and δ_{ML} are the chemical shifts of the free and complexed ligand. Rearrangement of Equation (9.3) gives

$$[ML] = \frac{[L]_T \{\delta_{obs} - \delta_L\}}{\{\delta_{ML} - \delta_L\}} \tag{9.4}$$

Since $\quad K_1 = \dfrac{[ML]}{[M][L]} = \dfrac{[ML]}{\{[M]_T - [ML]\}\{[L]_T - [ML]\}} \tag{9.5}$

it follows that,

$$K_1 = \frac{[L]_T \{\delta_{obs} - \delta_L\}\{\delta_{ML} - \delta_L\}}{([M]_T \{\delta_{ML} - \delta_L\} - [L]_T \{\delta_{obs} - \delta_L\}) [L]_T \{\delta_{ML} - \delta_{obs}\}} \tag{9.6}$$

The stability constants for a series of solutions of different metal and ligand concentrations are calculated using a 'guessed' value for the chemical shift of the complex (δ_{ML}). If the calculated stability constant K_1 is plotted against either total ligand or total metal concentration, plots of the type shown in Figure 9.1 will be obtained. Since the true stability constant must be independent of the metal and ligand concentrations it is possible to determine the least-squares deviations of each of the plots in Figure 9.1 and hence to plot the

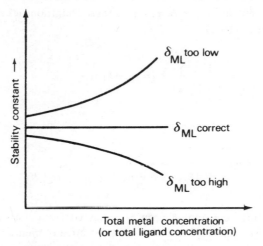

Figure 9.1 – Stability constants calculated using Equation (9.6) for guessed values of δ_{ML}.

guessed value of δ_{ML} against the resulting standard deviation in K_1 and to determine the true value of δ_{ML} from the point of minimum standard deviation, Figure 9.2. Substituting this true δ_{ML} back into Equation (9.6) enables the

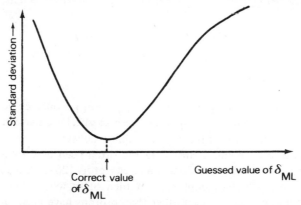

Figure 9.2 – Plot of standard deviation of stability constants in Figure 9.1 as a function of the guessed value of δ_{ML}.

stability constant to be calculated. It must be emphasised that this procedure is totally dependent on the initial assumption that only one complex ML is formed. This assumption is often a problem with the n.m.r. method because, whilst the n.m.r. experiment itself can distinguish between free and coordinated ligand, it can rarely distinguish between complexes containing different numbers of ligands due to their having indistinguishable chemical shifts.

An alternative calculation procedure that can be extended to include the case when both ML and ML_2 are formed uses a different procedure in which the ligand L is kept in large excess. Under these conditions it can be shown [26] that for Equilibrium (9.2).

$$\delta_{obs} - \delta_L = \frac{[L]_T K_1}{1 + [L]_T K_1} \{\delta_{ML} - \delta_L\} \tag{9.7}$$

Equation (9.7) is best rearranged to

$$\frac{\{\delta_{obs} - \delta_L\}}{[L]_T} = -\{\delta_{obs} - \delta_L\} K_1 + \{\delta_{ML} - \delta_L\} K_1 \tag{9.8}$$

so that the stability constant K_1 can be obtained from the slope of a plot of $\{\delta_{obs} - \delta_L\}/[L]_T$ against $\{\delta_{obs} - \delta_L\}$ [27]. As already mentioned a frequently encountered problem with the n.m.r. method is the occurence of higher complexes because the ligand chemical shifts in ML and ML_2 are often indistinguishable. However, if ML_2 were formed in the present example, then it would be detected because Equation (9.8) would become [28]

$$\frac{\{\delta_{obs} - \delta_L\}}{[L]_T} =$$
$$-\{\delta_{obs} - \delta_L\} K_1 (1 + [L]_T K_2) +$$
$$K_1(\{\delta_{ML} - \delta_L\} + \{\delta_{ML_2} - \delta_L\}[L]_T K_2 \tag{9.9}$$

and a plot of $\{\delta_{obs} - \delta_L\}/[L]_T$ against $\{\delta_{obs} - \delta_L\}$ would curve so that the formation of higher complexes would not be missed. This curve can be analysed by a computer program to get the best fit stability constants.

Although n.m.r. chemical shift data has often been used to study the 1:1 complexes formed by electron donors and acceptors [26-29], it has less often been used to study metal-complexes and then often with other independent methods in support. Many nuclei other than protons have been used including ^7Li [30], ^{23}Na [30,31], ^{87}Rb [30], ^{133}Cs [30], ^{67}Zn [32] and ^{199}Hg [33].

(b) *Coupling constants*

The variation of n.m.r. coupling constants with complex formation can be used to determine stability constants for systems such as:

$$[(CH_3)_3SnCl] + L \rightleftharpoons [(CH_3)_3SnClL] \tag{9.10}$$

The attraction of coupling constants over chemical shifts is that coupling constants are relatively unaffected by non-specific solvent or inert ion effects [8]. In the case of rapid exchange the observed coupling constant ($^3J_{119_{Sn}-1_H}$) is described by

$$J_{obs} = J_M \frac{\{[L]_T - [ML]\}}{[L]_T} + J_{ML} \frac{[ML]}{[L]_T} \tag{9.11}$$

where J_{obs}, J_M and J_{ML} are the observed constant and the coupling constants in the free metal (that is, $(CH_3)_3SnCl$) and the complexed metal (that is, $(CH_3)_3SnClL$) respectively. This is analogous to Equation (9.3) and can be solved by an analogous approach.

(iv) *Electron spin resonance*

Electron spin resonance yields four parameters that can be used in the determination of stability constants, (a) coupling constants, (b) line widths (relaxation times), (c) line intensities (spin concentrations), and (d) g-values. All four parameters have been used.

(a) *Coupling constants*

For equilibrium (9.2)

$$M + L \xrightleftharpoons{K_1} ML \tag{9.2}$$

it is possible to relate the observed coupling constant (A_{obs}) to that of the free ligand (A_L), and the complex (A_{ML}) by an equation analogous to Equations (9.3) and (9.11):

$$A_{obs} = A_L \frac{\{[L]_T - [ML]\}}{[L]_T} + A_{ML} \frac{[ML]}{[M]_T} \tag{9.12}$$

In Equation (9.12) we have assumed that the observed coupling constant arises within the ligand species, but an analogous equation can be set up if it arises within the metal species. When Equation (9.12) is combined with the expression for the stability constant ((Equation (9.5)), an equation analogous to (9.6) is obtained. If accurate estimates of A_L and A_{ML} are available, then the stability constant can be determined directly as has been reported in the literature for the equilibria formed between organic radical ions and alkali metal ions [34,35] and also for nitrobenzene association with hydrogen bond donors [36]. However as with n.m.r. it is very difficult to obtain an accurate value of A_{ML} directly, and indirect methods have been used, analogous to those described above for n.m.r. Such methods have been used to study the association of iodide ions with organic anion radicals [37] and between sodium naphthenide and tetraglyme [38].

(b) Line widths

The use of line-width analysis to determine stability constants depends on the influence of complex formation on the line width of the signal of either the free metal ion or the free ligand. As with e.s.r. coupling constants, equations analogous to either (9.3) or (9.7) may be set up and solved in the same manner as described previously:

$$W_{obs} = W_M \frac{\{[M]_T - [ML]\}}{[M]_T} + W_{ML} \frac{[ML]}{[M]_T} \tag{9.13}$$

$$W_{obs} - W_M = \frac{[M]K_1}{1 + [M]K_1}\{W_{ML} - W_M\} \tag{9.14}$$

where W represents line width. This approach has been used to study the inner and outer sphere complexes of manganese(II) with halides [39], sulphate [40], dithionite [41], nitrate and perchlorate [42]. However, a word of warning concerning the use of line-width analysis has recently been sounded by the observation that studies of the ion pair dissociation constants of potassium ions with the cyclooctatetraene dianion by this method yield results that are significantly different from those obtained by other techniques. This is attributed to the fact that the observed rate constants are sensitive to changes in the viscosity of the solution that are brought about by the addition of salt [43].

(c) Line intensities

Line intensities of e.s.r. signals where both the free ligand and the complex give rise to separate signals have been used to determine stability constants in essentially the same manner as in n.m.r. in the case where no exchange occurs [44–46]. Exchange between free and complexed ligand is less common in e.s.r. than in n.m.r. because of the higher frequency of radiation used in an e.s.r. spectrometer, typically in the range $(\sim3 - \sim140) \times 10^9$ Hz. Since the signal intensity is proportional to the number of spins present, it is essential before evaluating the stability constant to take account of the number of spins present in each species.

(d) g-values

When a paramagnetic species, such as a metal ion, reacts with a ligand, the g-values may vary. If association and dissociation are rapid on an e.s.r. timescale then a time-averaged g-value will be observed, given by Equation (9.15), which is analogous to other time-averaged equations such as (9.3), (9.7), and (9.14).

$$g_{obs} - g_M = \frac{(g_{ML} - g_M)[ML]}{[M]_T} \tag{9.15}$$

This can be solved in a manner exactly analogous to Equation (9.7), an approach that has been used to determine the stability constant of the iodide/2,6-di-tert-butyl-benzoquinone ion pair [47].

(v) *Mössbauer*

The Mössbauer effect involves the recoilless absorption of γ-radiation followed by its subsequent re-emission [48-50]. The fact that the absorption must necessarily be recoilless limits the technique to solid examples where the absorbing atom is firmly bound in a lattice. As a result the technique is of limited application to the study of inorganic solution equilibria. However, it has been used to study the interaction of tin tetrahalides with donor ligands in frozen benzene or carbon tetrachloride solution, by making the assumption that the information obtained for a solution prepared at 20°C and rapidly cooled to liquid nitrogen temperature actually referred to 20°C and that all equilibria were effectively frozen [51, 52]. Apart from this serious disadvantage the experimenter must take care either to use a very thin sample or to take suitable account of sample thickness [50].

(vi) *Refractometry*

Refractometry has recently been demonstrated to be a potential method for the determination of stability constants that is quick, applicable to the determination of low stability constants that are difficult by other methods and simple if the following requirements are fulfilled: (a) The nature of the interactions between solvent and solute must not change in the concentration range studied. (b) The structure of the solvent must not be influenced, thus solutions must be kept dilute. (c) There must be no change in the degree of association of the solute. (d) The density of the solution should vary linearly with concentration.

The main limitation of the method arises when the apparent molar refractive coefficient of the complex is nearly the sum of those of the reactants, in which case no interaction can be observed.

The relation between refractive index and concentration is

$$\eta = \eta_o + kc \tag{9.16}$$

where η = measured refractive index, η_o = refractive index of solvent, c = concentration of solute, and k = refractive coefficient. In general, refractive coefficients are constant up to about $0.5\,mol.l^{-1}$ and sometimes higher. The use of refractometry has been demonstrated for the evaluation of K_3 and K_4 for the chloro-mercury(II) system [53]

$$HgCl_2 \underset{-Cl^-}{\overset{+Cl^-,K_3}{\rightleftharpoons}} HgCl_3^- \underset{-Cl^-}{\overset{+Cl^-,K_4}{\rightleftharpoons}} HgCl_4^{2-} \qquad (9.17)$$

as well as for hydrogen-bridged complexes [54, 55].

(viii) *Spectropolarimetry*

Werner [56] observed that when a dissymetric species interacts with any other species in solution the molecular rotation of the dissymetric species is changed. Three approaches to the study of molecular rotation have been developed:

(a) Polarimetry, in which the angle of rotation of a monochromatic beam of plane polarised light is measured [57].

(b) Optical Rotary Dispersion (o.r.d.), in which the angle of rotation of plane polarised light as a function of wavelength is measured [58].

(c) Circular Dichroism (c.d.), in which the difference in the molar absorptivities ($\epsilon_1 - \epsilon_r$) between left (ϵ_1) and right (ϵ_r) circularly polarised light are determined [58].

These three spectropolarimetric techniques have been used to study three types of system:

(a) The interaction of an optically active ligand with an optically inactive metal complex which results in a change of the activity of the ligand that may be used to measure the extent of complex formation. This approach has been used in studying the interaction of tartrate ions with boric acid [59] and aluminium(III) [60] (using polarimetry), mandelate ions with cobalt(II), nickel(II) and zinc(II) [61] (using polarimetry), and the interaction of d(-)mannitol with arsenious acid [62] (using o.r.d.).

(b) The outer-sphere interaction of an optically active complex with optically active ligands. This approach has been used to study the interaction of tris(ethylenediamine)cobalt(III) cations with a range of anions [63] and polyanions [64] using c.d.

(c) A change in the nature of the ligands present in a dissymetric complex results in a change in the molecular rotation. This phenomenon has been exploited [65] in using c.d. to determine the pK_a values for the successive deprotonation of the two aquo ligands in the optically active complex cis-$[Rh(en)_2(H_2O)_2]^{3+}(ClO_4^-)_3$, where en = ethylenediamine.

In this approach the c.d. spectra were recorded as a function of pH and the results analysed in the same way as for any spectroscopic technique.

(viii) *Light scattering*

Light scattering can be used to determine weight-average molecular weights which are valuable in determining the nature of the high molecular weight species formed on hydrolysis of metal ions [66-68]. The technique is too imprecise to give rise to stability constants.

(ix) *Ultrasonic absorption*

The use of ultrasonic absorption to study complex formation depends on the fact that complex formation is pressure dependent. It has been shown [69,70] that if the excess sound absorption is due only to the formation of a complex ML,

$$M + L \underset{k_{-1}}{\overset{k_1}{\rightleftharpoons}} ML \tag{9.2}$$

then the frequency of maximum excess absorption (ν) is given by

$$\nu = k_{-1} \left[1 - \left\{ \frac{[M]_T - [M]}{[M]} \right\} \left(\frac{[L]_T - [M]_T - 2[M]}{[L]_T - [M]_T + [M]} - F[M] \right) \right] \tag{9.18}$$

$$F = \left(\frac{1}{f_{\pm}^2} \right) \frac{df_{\pm}^2}{d[M]} \tag{9.19}$$

where F is a function of the mean activity coefficient $f_{\pm}$ (Equation (9.19)) and k_{-1} is the rate of dissociation of the complex ML. k_{-1} is determined by plotting ν against $[M]_T$ and extrapolating to zero concentration. Substituting k_{-1} back into Equation (9.18) enables a series of values of $[M]_T$, $[L]_T$ and $[M]$ to be determined, from which the stability constant can be evaluated. The method has only been used at low concentrations because only under such conditions can the mean activity coefficient necessary to calculate F (Equation (9.19)) be determined with reasonable precision. The technique has been used to measure K_1 for magnesium(II) and manganese(II) sulphate systems [71] as well as for monitoring ion association and complex formation in kinetic studies of rapidly reacting metal ions.

9.3 DISTRIBUTION METHODS

Distribution methods comprise a group of techniques that have been used fairly extensively for stability constant measurement. Whilst not yielding results of the highest accuracy they are convenient. However, the successful use of the distribution methods does depend upon their very careful use. It is probably fair to say that a greater proportion of the results obtained by distribution methods are questionable than of the results obtained by any other group of methods.

(i) *Liquid-liquid partition (solvent extraction)*

The distribution of a ligand between two immiscible liquid phases, one of which contains the ligand under examination, has been very extensively used [72–74] especially for organic ligands such as olefins. The results, however, are not always consistent with those obtained by other methods, for a number of reasons:

(a) It is essential to choose an organic solvent that is only very sparingly soluble in the aqueous phase. Further, the degree of miscibility of the two solvents must remain constant over the whole range of metal and ligand concentrations used; this condition may limit the range of these concentrations that can be studied.

(b) Although the activity coefficients in the aqueous phase can be controlled by the use of an inert background electrolyte, this is impossible in the organic phase since ionic salts are not generally soluble in solvents that are immiscible with water. In a system such as

$$[MA_n] + L \rightleftharpoons [MA_{n-1}L] + A \qquad (9.20)$$

it is possible to determine the range of concentration over which the activity coefficients in the organic solvent remain constant. This is achieved by determining the concentration range over which the ratio of the total metal concentration in each phase is a function of the concentration of the auxiliary ligand, A, in the aqueous phase. Ligand A must be an ionic ligand that is insoluble in the organic phase and is independent of the total concentrations of metal and ligand under examination. Such a result cannot be obtained unless the activity coefficients in both phases remained constant [75]. Although most workers have either neglected the activity coefficients in the organic phase, or assumed that they are unity, a recent study of the zinc chloride system has involved determination of the activity coefficient of the extractant in the organic phase [76].

(c) In the case of weak complexes large changes in the free ligand concentration must be made. Care must be taken to ensure that, if the ligand is appreciably soluble in the aqueous phase, these large changes in concentration do not lead to changes in the composition of the solvents and hence to gross changes in the activity coefficients. Furthermore, even when the ligand L is insoluble in water, changes in its concentration are liable to lead to variations in its activity coefficient in the organic phase.

(d) The possibility of the formation of polynuclear species must be considered, since even if these are not formed in aqueous solution they may still be formed in the organic phase.

(e) Although it is generally assumed that only neutral species cross the phase boundary, this is not always true. For example, there is evidence that neutral ion-pairs such as $H^+FeCl_4^-$ may exist in organic solvents [77].

Although liquid-liquid partition is not as accurate as potentiometry it can in suitable cases be as good as u.v.-visible spectrophotometry. If a very sensitive technique is used to determine the concentrations of the species in the two solvents, then low concentrations of metal and ligand may be used. This overcomes many of the difficulties noted above. If only one species ML_c partitions between the two solvents, rigorous description of the system only requires one parameter, the partition coefficient of ML_c, in addition to the stability constants. Thus data obtained in this way may be more reliable than data obtained, for example, by conductance or spectrophotometry where a number of species contribute to the property measured.

An important aspect of stability constants obtained by liquid-liquid partition that must be borne in mind when studying the literature is that some authors record their stability constants as $[ML]_{H_2O}/[M]_{H_2O}[L]_{organic\ solvent}$, where the subscripts refer to the phase in which the concentration is determined. Such constants are not strictly stability constants at all, although they may give indications of trends with a group of ligands if the distribution coefficients of the ligands between the two immiscible solvents are virtually independent of the ligand L.

(ii) *Solubility*

The use of sparingly soluble systems is one of the oldest methods available for the determination of stability constants. The solubilities of metal salts in ligand solutions [78] and of ligands in metal salt solutions [79] have both been used. For accurate results four criteria must be met:

(a) Care must be taken to ensure that the system has come to equilibrium; since two different phases are involved equilibrium times tend to be lengthy.

(b) A constant ionic medium should be used to ensure that the activity coefficients remain constant.

(c) Since the solubility product is fixed so that the concentrations of the metal and ligand cannot be varied independently, it is impossible to obtain sufficient data to ascertain whether or not polynuclear species are present. Accordingly, the method cannot be used where polynuclear species are suspected.

(d) It is essential to ensure that the composition of the solid phase and hence its solubility product remains constant over the concentration ranges of metal and ligand being investigated.

Unless the ligand is a gas, the use of solubility methods [80] depends upon the accurate analysis of the saturated solution. A wide range of analytical techniques is available [81]; high concentrations are often determined gravimetrically or volumetrically and low concentrations can be determined by atomic absorption, atomic fluorescence, radiometry [82], spectrophotometry, polarography and g.l.c. as well as other standard analytical techniques. The principles for determining stability constants from solubility data have been established over the years [83–87] so that it is possible to use solubility measurements to determine the stability constants for the formation of successive complexes. The method has been applied to the bismuth(III)-chloride [88] and -bromide [89], tin(II)-iodide [90] and copper(II)-chloride [91] systems, as well as to the outer-sphere complex formation between $[Co(en)_3]^{3+}$, and iodide ions [92].

(iii) *Ion-exchange*

Ion-exchange is a widely used separation technique that depends on the differing affinities of species for the resin [93,94]. As such it can, in theory, be used to determine the amounts of different species present in a mixture. However, whilst it is an excellent qualitative technique, ion-exchange is neither very convenient nor accurate for the quantitative determination of stability constants. Ion-exchange resins come in two major classes, cation exchange resins in which negatively charged groups such as carboxylate or sulphonate built into the resin bind cations (9.21) and anion exchange resins in which positively charge quaternary ammonium groups are built into the resin (9.22).

$$z(\circledR - O^-H^+) + ML_n^{z+} \; \underset{}{\overset{K_n^R}{\rightleftharpoons}} \; (\circledR - O^-)_z ML_n^{z+} + zH^+ \qquad (9.21)$$

$$z(\circledR - N^+Cl^-) + ML_n^{z-} \; \underset{}{\overset{K_n^R}{\rightleftharpoons}} \; (\circledR - N^+)_z ML_n^{z-} + zCl^- \qquad (9.22)$$

The resin which, of course, must be neutral overall is initially provided with suitable counter ions such as protons or chloride ions, and these are displaced by the charged metal complex ions as shown in (9.21) and (9.22). The experimental procedure involves:

(a) Washing the resin thoroughly until all the fine particles have been removed.

(b) Treatment of the resin to ensure that all the counter ions are of the correct type, that is H^+, Na^+, or Cl^-, followed by thorough washing with water to ensure that any surplus counter ions have been removed.

(c) Air-drying to reduce the water content to a constant reproducible amount, usually about 20%. This is probably the most difficult and potentially inaccurate part of the experiment since the water content must not be reduced too far or the resin becomes very hygroscopic as well as erratic in its exchange behaviour [95].

(d) The dry-weight of the resin is determined by heating at 105–110°C to constant weight.

(e) Equilibration of a known weight of air-dried resin (m) with a known volume of solution (v) of known total metal and ligand concentration at constant temperature. The ratio v/m should be varied to ensure that the exchange is reversible [96]. With cation exchange resins an inert background electrolyte can be present, but with anion exchange resins this is not possible because the background electrolyte anion will be absorbed on to the resin, and thus not be 'inert'.

(f) After equilibration the supernatant liquid is removed and an aliquot analysed for total metal or ligand. Analysis requires a sensitive technique, such as radiometry [82], since the load on the resin should be low. The concentration of metal in the resin, $[M]_R$ is given by:

$$[M]_R = \frac{v}{m}([M]_T - \delta[M])$$ (9.23)

where δ is the swelling factor of the resin. δ is determined by equilibrating a volume v of a standard solution of a strong acid containing the resin counter ion with an amount m of resin and measuring the final concentration of the counter ion in the aqueous phase [96].

(g) A distribution coefficient Φ is defined as

$$\Phi = \frac{\text{total M/g of air-dried resin}}{\text{total M/ml of solution}}$$ (9.24)

Φ depends on:

1. The stability constants of the complexes present.
2. The distribution coefficients of the individual complexes (ϕ_n) between resin (subscript R) and solution are given by

$$\phi_n = \frac{[ML_n]_R}{[ML_n]}$$ (9.25)

Combining (9.25) with the stability constant for the exchange reaction (9.21), yields

$$\phi_n = \beta_n K_n^R \left(\frac{[M]_R}{[M]}\right)^z$$ (9.26)

and the overall distribution Φ is given by

$$\Phi = \frac{\displaystyle\sum_{n=0}^{n=N} \phi_n[L]^n}{\displaystyle\sum_{n=0}^{n=N} \beta_n[L]^n} \tag{9.27}$$

Normally systems are chosen in which only the free metal ion partitions between resin and solution, so that the numerator reduces to ϕ_1 which is obtained either by measuring the distribution ratio in the absence of ligand L, or by extrapolating the determined values of Φ to zero ligand concentration. The partition coefficient of a species depends on its concentration, so that only relatively narrow concentration ranges may be used. Because of this the method is inapplicable when polynuclear species are present. Further, chemisorption effects are superimposed on the true ion-exchange effects, which necessitate the use of some arbitrary assumptions which decrease the reliability of the stability constants obtained. It has been suggested that a way of overcoming many of these problems, which essentially result from the non-linearity of the distribution equation in the distribution coefficients, is to repeat the experiment with a series of cation exchangers differing in the degree of their cross-linking. Then by division or subtraction of the distribution equations for the individual exchangers, it is possible to get equations from which accurate distribution coefficients can be obtained. This approach has been used to study the complexes formed by bismuth(III) with halide ions [97,98]. Other examples of stability constants determined by ion-exchange include copper(II) and cadmium(II) sulphate and acetate complexes [99,100] and alkali metal perchlorate ion association [101,102].

(iv) *Gas chromatography*
Gas chromatography is potentially a very fast elegant method for determining the stability constants of complexes involving volatile ligands such as olefins. A sample of the ligand is introduced on to the column of a gas chromatograph and eluted with an inert carrier gas [103]. The columns are generally packed with a suitable solid support coated with the stationary liquid phase which is a solution of the metal salt in either water [104] or a solvent such as ethyleneglycol [105] in which the activity coefficients can be controlled by the addition of an inert background electrolyte. The partition coefficient, H, for the distribution of ligand between the stationary liquid and vapour phases is given by [105]

$$H = \frac{3Ft_r\{(P_i/P_o)^2 - 1\}}{2V_1\{P_i/P_o)^3 - 1\}} \tag{9.28}$$

where P_i is the inlet pressure, P_o = outlet pressure, F = carrier gas flow rate, t_r = retention time, and V_1 = volume of the liquid phase at the temperature of the column. Thus by measuring retention time and knowing the values of the other factors, the partition coefficient can be evaluated. By measuring the distribution coefficient of the ligand in the presence, H_M, and absence, H_0, of the metal, the stability constant can be evaluated since

$$K = \frac{[ML]}{[M][L]} = \frac{H_M - H_0}{H_0 [M]} \tag{9.29}$$

whence

$$H_M = H_0 + H_0 K [M] \tag{9.30}$$

Thus a plot of the distribution coefficient against the concentration of the metal should be a straight line of slope $H_0 K$ and intercept H_0. Unfortunately this simple situation does not always arise [106], and plots of H_M against the metal concentration are not always linear owing to a salting-out effect at high metal concentrations. This salting-out effect can, however, be overcome sometimes by using very high concentrations (for example 4 mol.l^{-1}) of an inert electrolyte in the liquid phase. Salting-out is a particular problem where very weak metal-ligand interactions are involved [107].

There are a number of major disadvantages connected with the use of gas chromatography:

(a) It is impossible to account for higher complexes, and thus the method is restricted to situations where only a single complex ML is formed.

(b) For weak complexes, such as silver(I)-olefin complexes, it has been necessary to use high concentrations of metal ion (up to 4 mol.l^{-1}) in order to get accurately measurable differences between the partition coefficients in the presence and absence of the metal. High metal concentrations are undesirable. The control of activity coefficients over a wide concentration range is impossible. In addition the approximation normally made that the solvent can be neglected in evaluating the stability constant is far less valid than with the much lower metal concentrations used in other techniques.

(c) The value of the calculated stability constant is dependent on the flow rate of the inert carrier gas, increasing slightly with increasing flow rate [108]. This is a major problem, firstly because it has generally been neglected in the literature and secondly because it is very difficult to take account of. Although, in theory, a series of flow rates could be used and extrapolated to zero flow rate, in practice this is not possible, firstly because the number of runs necessary would lead to deterioration of the column and hence the incorporation of further errors, and secondly because as the flow rate is lowered the peak broadens and so the accuracy of the measurement of the retention time drops.

(d) The value of the calculated stability constant is dependent on the sample size, decreasing with increasing sample size. Again, ideally an extrapolation to zero sample size would be made, but this involves an undesirable number of runs which would lead to the same problems as encountered in (c).

Notwithstanding these disadvantages gas chromatography is a very quick convenient method for measuring stability constants. However, because of the importance of both sample size and carrier gas flow rate, a given set of stability constants for a series of ligands obtained by a single group of workers should be internally consistent, but any agreement with stability constants obtained by other methods is likely to be fortuitous rather than an indication of the reliability of the stability constants obtained by gas chromatography.

(v) *Liquid chromatography*

In liquid chromatography a metal-ligand system is applied to a column, and for stability constant determination is eluted with a solution containing either excess metal [109] or excess ligand [110]. When the sample is eluted with a mobile phase containing the metal, two peaks corresponding to free and complexed metal are obtained, from which the stability constant of the complex can be determined [109]. To date, the method has only been applied to systems where a single complex is formed. When the sample is eluted with a mobile phase containing excess ligand, only a single metal-containing peak is observed with a retention time t_{obs} that is intermediate between the retention time of the free metal t_M and the complex t_{ML}. t_{obs} is related to t_M and t_{ML} by Equation (9.31), which is analogous to Equation (9.3).

$$t_{obs} = \frac{t_M [M] + t_{ML} [ML]}{[M]_T} \tag{9.31}$$

If the concentration of ligand in the eluent $[L]_E$ is large relative to the amount of metal present, then it follows that

$$t_{obs} = \frac{t_M + K[L]_E t_{ML}}{1 + K[L]_E} \tag{9.32}$$

where K is the stability constant for the formation of ML. The stability constant for the magnesium tetrametaphosphate complex was determined in this way by measuring t_{obs} as a function of the tetrametaphosphate ion concentration and then rearranging (9.32) to

$$t_{obs} = t_{ML} + \frac{1}{K} \left\{ \frac{t_M - t_{obs}}{[L]_E} \right\} \tag{9.33}$$

and plotting t_{obs} against $(t_M - t_{obs})/[L]_E$ to obtain a straight line of slope $1/K$ [110].

(vi) *Thin layer and paper chromatography*

Two approaches have been adopted to develop thin layer and paper chromatography for the determination of stability constants. In one, used with the thin layer technique, a metal-impregnated support was used to study the migration of the ligand; in the other, used with paper chromatography, a spot of metal-containing solution was placed on the paper and eluted with the ligand solution. The former approach has been used to study silver(I)-olefin complexes [111] and the latter the pK_B's of alkaloids [112]. Whilst both techniques are of value in determining relative stability constants for a series of related ligands with a given metal ion their accuracies are limited for quantitative work.

9.4 ELECTROCHEMICAL METHODS

By far the most important electrochemical method used for the determination of stability constants is potentiometry. This forms the subject of Chapter 7. In the present section we consider other electrochemical methods, of which the most widely used is polarography.

(i) *Polarography*

When polarography is used to determine stability constants, the effect of the ligand on the reduction potential of a metal ion at a dropping mercury electrode, or less commonly a rotating platinum electrode, is determined [113]. The method is difficult to use successfully and also rather inaccurate, but it does have two important advantages: the equipment is relatively simple, and the technique can identify and determine the properties of a number of species simultaneously.

If the electrode process is reversible[†], the potential (E) of the dropping mercury electrode is given by the Heyrovský-Ilkovič equation [114] with an accuracy of about ±2%.

$$E = (E_{\frac{1}{2}})_M - \left(\frac{RT}{z\mathcal{F}}\right)\ln\left(\frac{i}{i_d - i}\right) \tag{9.34}$$

$(E_{\frac{1}{2}})_M$ = half-wave potential of the free metal ion in the solvent, z = number of electrons involved in the electrode reaction, i_d = limiting diffusion current, and i = current corresponding to the potential E. On adding a ligand the half-wave potential of the system is shifted by an amount ΔE proportional to the

[†] To determine whether a reduction is reversible, a plot of E against $\ln(i/(i_d - i))$ should be prepared. A reversible system will give rise to a straight line of slope $RT/z\mathcal{F}$ mV whereas an irreversible system will give rise to a line of greater slope.

stability constant of the complex [115,116]. If the activity coefficients of all the species present are constant and if the diffusion coefficients of the metal ion and its complexes are equal, then,

$$\Delta E = (E_{\frac{1}{2}})_M - (E_{\frac{1}{2}})_{ML_n} = \left(\frac{RT}{z\mathcal{F}}\right)\left\{\ln\beta_n + n\ln[L]\right\} \tag{9.35}$$

where $(E_{\frac{1}{2}})_{ML_n}$ is the half-wave potential of the ML_n complex and β_n is the formation constant of ML_n. A plot of ΔE against $\ln[L]$ should be a straight line from which n can be obtained from the slope and β_n from the intercept. Experimentally, a large excess of ligand is typically used so that the approximation that the free ligand concentration equals the total ligand concentration is usually made. When several complexes are formed, then if their stabilities are widely different the plot of ΔE against $\ln[L]$ will consist of several segments, from each of which the appropriate values of n and β_n may be evaluated. Examples where this has been found include the zinc-ammonia [117] and copper-pyrazole [118] systems. If the stabilities are more closely related then it can be shown [119] that

$$\exp\left\{\frac{z\mathcal{F}}{RT}(\Delta E) + \ln\frac{D_{\text{free}}}{D_{\text{complexed}}}\right\} = \sum_{i=0}^{i=N} \beta_i[L]^i \tag{9.36}$$

D_{free} and $D_{\text{complexed}}$ are the diffusion coefficients of the free and complexed metal ions. This equation can be solved either manually by Leden's method (see Section 3.7(i)) or with the aid of a computer [120,121]. The method has been applied to many systems including the zinc and cadmium thiocyanate complexes [120,122], the cadmium-azide system [123], and the copper(I)-substituted thiourea systems [121].

So far we have considered systems where the metal ions are reduced reversibly on the electrode. Unfortunately such systems are rare. Where the reduction is irreversible then a competitive system may be used in which a second reversibly reduced metal ion is added that also complexes with the ligand under examination [124]. In addition it has been assumed that the diffusion coefficients of the free metal ion and its complexes are the same. This may not necessarily be valid. If the diffusion coefficients are the same then the limiting diffusion current will be independent of ligand concentration. Thus if the limiting diffusion current does depend on ligand concentration it is possible to show that [125] the mean diffusion coefficient $\bar{D}$ is given by

$$\bar{D} = \frac{D_M + D_{ML_n}\beta_n[L]^n}{1 + \beta_n[L]^n} \tag{9.37}$$

where D_M and D_{ML_n} are the diffusion coefficients of the free and complexed metal respectively.

Although there are only a few methods that are potentially as powerful for determining stability constants as polarography, because of its ability to allow the identification and study of several metal complexes at once, the method has not lived up to its promise for several reasons. Firstly, since many half-wave potentials are very small, it is difficult to determine them accurately so that the resulting stability constants are of low precision (a typical reproducibility that can be achieved is ±0.2 mV). Secondly, electrical double layers pose many problems. Thirdly, temperature control must be very precise since not only does the temperature influence the position of the equilibrium, both the diffusion current and the half-wave potential are temperature dependent.

(ii) *Anodic stripping voltammetry*

In systems where there is a very low metal concentration the polarographic current will be small, and thus the half-wave potential will be very difficult to determine. However, if the metal ion deposited in reduced form on the electrode can be reoxidised by reversing the polarity, then the current corresponding to the rapid reoxidation of all the deposited metal will be greater than in conventional polarography. This is the principle of anodic stripping voltammetry [126] which can be used to detect metal ion concentrations as low as 10^{-8} mol.l^{-1}. For reversible systems the peak potential, E_p, for anodic stripping voltammetry lies close to the polarographic half-wave potential. Like the half-wave potential, E_p is shifted to more negative values as a consequence of complex formation giving rise to a relationship for the shift of E_p, ΔE_p, as a function of ligand concentration analogous to Equation (9.35) above.

$$\Delta E_p = \frac{RT}{z\mathscr{F}}\{\ln\beta_n + n\ln[L]\} \tag{9.38}$$

A plot of ΔE_p against $\ln[L]$ has a slope of $\dfrac{nRT}{z\mathscr{F}}$ and intercept $\dfrac{RT}{z\mathscr{F}}\ln\beta_n$. If more than one complex is formed a segmented plot will be obtained and can be analysed as described for polarography. Although suffering from the disadvantages discussed in relation to polarography, anodic stripping voltammetry is useful at very low metal ion concentrations where other methods are impossible, and it has been used to study the interaction of lead, copper, cadmium, and zinc with hydroxide and carbonate ions where owing to solubility restrictions metal ion concentrations are limited to the range 10^{-5} to 10^{-7} molar [127].

(iii) *Conductivity*

When a charged metal ion forms a complex with a charged ligand there is a decrease in the number of charged species in solution, and hence in the conductivity, that can potentially be used to determine stability constants [128].

Conductivity studies, either at low or high field strengths, are rarely used to determine stability constants, for several reasons:

(a) It is not possible to use an inert background electrolyte to maintain a constant ionic strength since if such an electrolyte were present the change in conductivity due to the actual complex formation would be insignificant.

(b) Ionic mobilities are very sensitive to ionic interactions; thus the mobility of each species present is very dependent on the nature and quantity of the other species present.

(c) Quantitative stability constants can only be determined when a single complex ML^{n+} is formed, and even in this situation the interpretation is complex [129]; however, conductivity has proved useful for determining the stoichiometry of species formed in solution [130,131], and for determining the stability constants for the fomation of the 1:1 complexes of crown ethers with alkali metal ions in a range of organic solvents [132].

(iv) *Dielectric constant*

Dielectric constant measurements have been used to determine stability constants for both non-electrolytes and ionic systems [133]. For non-electrolytes in very dilute solution,

$$\Delta\epsilon_d = x_L[L] + \sum_{n=0}^{n=N} x_{ML_n}[ML_n] \tag{9.39}$$

where $\Delta\epsilon_d$ is the difference between the dielectric constant of the solution and that of the pure solvent, and x_L and x_{ML_n} are empirical constants. Such an approach has been used to measure the position of equilibrium between tribenzylamine, picric acid and tribenzylammonium picrate in benzene [134], and also to study the dimerisation of lithium and silver perchlorates in solvents of low dielectric constant [135]. The method is only strictly applicable in dilute solution because in more concentrated solution the intensive factors, x, become concentration dependent. In aqueous solution the method is even more complex because the electric field around an ion causes dielectric saturation in water molecules that approach within about 4 Å, so that the measured dielectric constant decreases with increasing concentration.

9.5 CALORIMETRIC METHODS

The enthalpy of complex formation is more accurately determined by direct calorimetry than by measuring the temperature dependence of the stability constants (see Section 1.10(ii)). However, calorimetry can only be used in situations where equilibria are established relatively rapidly, that is within an hour or so. There are two broad approaches to calorimetric studies. In the first, all the metal and all the ligand solutions are mixed at once and the resulting heat change measured. This is described below in Section 9.5(i) as 'direct calorimetry'. If instead of adding all the ligand at once, the ligand solution is added in aliquots, a 'thermometric titration' is carried out, and, as described below in Section 9.5(ii), under certain conditions it is possible to evaluate not only the enthalpy of complex formation but also the stability constant. Since these two pieces of data can be combined to yield the entropy, such titrations are sometimes known as 'entropy titrations'.

(i) Direct calorimetry [136]

When a metal ion and ligand react the heat liberated or absorbed, Q, is given by

$$Q = V\{[ML]\Delta H_{ML} + [ML_2]\Delta H_{ML_2} + \ldots\} + \Delta H_{dil} \tag{9.40}$$

where V is the volume, ΔH_{dil} is the enthalpy of dilution, and ΔH_{ML_n} is the molar enthalpy of formation of ML_n. Equation (9.40) is very similar to Equation (8.6), where $(Q - \Delta H_{dil})$ is equivalent to absorbance, used in spectrophotometry. As a result all the calculation techniques developed for the analysis of spectrophotometric data are applicable to calorimetric data. Since every chemical reaction involves the evolution or absorption of heat, calorimetry can be used to study any reaction. A number of authors have described suitable apparatus, the more recent of which use thermistors to enable very small temperature changes to be measured accurately [137-140]. Examples of the application of calorimetry to the study of equilibria include the mercury(II)-halide system [141], the interaction of $(CH_3)_3SnCl$ with organic Lewis bases [142], the interaction of $2,2',2''$-terpyridine with cobalt(II), nickel(II) and copper(II) [143], and ion-pair formation between nitrate and chlorate ions with divalent first transition series metal ions [144].

(ii) Thermometric titration calorimetry

If instead of mixing all the metal and ligand together at once, as in direct calorimetry, the ligand is added slowly and the temperature recorded as the addition proceeds, a thermometric titration is carried out [145-147]. An idealised plot in which stirring effects, heat losses and heats of dilution are assumed to be zero is shown in Figure 9.3a. A typical observed thermogram based on that found when a perchloric acid solution of mercury(II) perchlorate is titrated with sodium cyanide [148] is shown in Figure 9.3b. This shows a sharp discontinuity at (e) corresponding to the formation of $Hg(CN)_2$, a rounded second end-point at (f) corresponding to the reaction of the original excess H^+ with CN^- to form HCN, followed by a slow temperature rise in the region (f-g) as $[Hg(CN)_3]^-$ and $[Hg(CN)_4]^{2-}$ are formed.

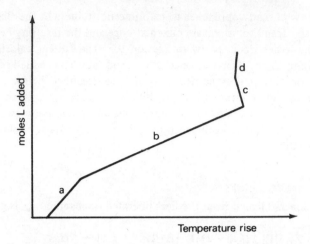

Figure 9.3a – Idealised thermogram for a system in which both ML and ML_2 are formed:

    (a) Formation of ML.
    (b) Formation of ML_2.
    (c) Slight temperature drop due to cooling effect of excess L.
    (d) No further L added.

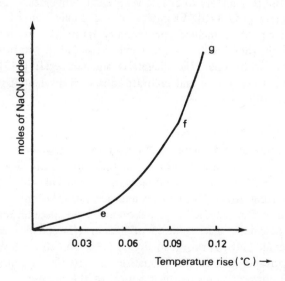

Figure 9.3b – Typical observed thermogram (see text).

The advantages of titration over direct calorimetry are:

(a) Titration calorimetry can be used to study a number of simultaneous equilibria.
(b) More data can be determined in a given time.
(c) Provided that (i) the stability constants and reaction conditions are such that the amount of reaction occurring is measurable, but (ii) the stability constants are not so large that the reaction is virtually quantitative, and (iii) enthalpy values for the reactions are far from zero, then it is possible to obtain free energy and entropy as well as enthalpy data.

Consider the system

$$M + L \underset{}{\overset{K_1}{\rightleftharpoons}} ML \qquad (9.2)$$

then from Equation (9.40) the heat produced $(Q - \Delta H_{dil})$ is given by

$$(Q - \Delta H_{dil}) = V[ML]\Delta H_{ML} \qquad (9.41)$$

from which, using the mass balance equations

$$[M]_T = [M] + [ML] \qquad (9.42)$$

$$[L]_T = [L] + [ML] \qquad (9.43)$$

it follows

$$\frac{\Delta H_{ML}}{K_1} = \frac{V[M]_T[L]_T(\Delta H_{ML})^2}{(Q - \Delta H_{dil})} - \{[M]_T + [L]_T\}\Delta H_{ML} + \frac{Q - \Delta H_{dil}}{V} \qquad (9.44)$$

in which there are two unknowns ΔH_{ML} and K_1. By carrying out at least two calorimetric measurements of $(Q - \Delta H_{dil})$ at different total metal and ligand concentrations, two equations of the form (9.44) are obtained which can be solved for ΔH_{ML} and K_1 [149]. An analogous treatment can be applied when higher complexes (ML_n) are formed; the equation corresponding to (9.44) will now contain $2n$ unknowns [150]. In such cases approximate methods of solution are used in which initial guessed stability constants $K_1 \ldots K_n$ are refined by an iterative process until the error square sum S given by (9.45) has been minimised [151,152] as described in Chapter 5.

$$S = \sum \left\{ (Q - \Delta H_{dil}) - V \sum_{n=1}^{n=N} [ML_n]\Delta H_{ML_n} \right\}^2 \qquad (9.45)$$

Some examples of systems that have been studied by thermometric titration calorimetry include copper(I)-cyanide [153], copper(I)- [154] and silver(I)-pyridine [154,155], mercury(II)-bromide [155,156], silver(I), thallium(I), mercury(II) and lead(II) with sulphur derivatives of crown ethers [157] rhodium(I)-imidazole [158] and poly(1-pyrazolyl)borates with divalent first transition series metals in both water and acetonitrile [159].

9.6 MISCELLANEOUS METHODS

A wide range of techniques not so far referred to have been used on occasion to determine stability constants. An incomplete list includes colligative properties [160–162], viscometry [163], coagulation [164], magnetic susceptibility [165], and reaction kinetics. The use of reaction kinetics is based on Guldberg and Waage's relationship (Section 1.1, Equation (1.5)) and depends upon measuring the rate of both the forward and reverse reactions. The method is necessarily limited to cases in which reaction occurs in a single step, but has been successfully applied to the aquation of platinum(II)- and palladium(II)-halide complexes [166–169] and to determining the stability constant for the formation of the $[FeCrO_4]^+$ ion [170].

Where complexes are sufficiently inert to allow the separation of each of the components without re-establishment of the equilibrium it is possible to use relatively slow separation techniques in order to separate and hence identify individually each of the species present. Chromatographic techniques including the recently developed high-performance liquid chromatography provide powerful separation tools. Undoubtedly one of the most elegant investigations of an inert system is Bjerrum's study of the chromium(III) thiocyanate equilibria where all the species $[Cr(H_2O)_{6-n}(SCN)_n]^{(3-n)+}$ ($n = 0$ to 6) were separated by a combination of selective precipitation and solvent extraction [171].

REFERENCES

[1] Penneman, R. A. and Jones, L. H. (1956). *J. Phys. Chem.*, **24**, 293.

[2] Penneman, R. A. and Jones, L. H. (1961). *J. Inorg. Nucl. Chem.*, **20**, 19.

[3] Coleman, J. S., Petersen, H., and Penneman, R. A. (1965). *Inorg. Chem.*, **4**, 135.

[4] Cooney, R. P. L. and Hall, J. R. (1966). *J. Inorg. Nucl. Chem.*, **28**, 1675.

[5] Ghedini, M., Denti, G., and Dolcetti, G. (1978). *Inorg. Chem.*, **17**, 2157.

[6] Cramer, R. (1967). *J. Amer. Chem. Soc.*, **89**, 4621.

[7] Cardaci, G. and Sorriso, S. (1976). *Inorg. Chem.*, **15**, 1242.

[8] Bolles, T. F. and Drago, R. S. (1966). *J. Amer. Chem. Soc.*, **88**, 3921.

[9] Tsuda, M. Touhara, H., Nakanishi, K., and Watanabe, N. (1976). *J. Phys. Chem.*, **80**, 362.

[10] Gilson, T. R. and Hendra, P. J. (1970). *Laser Raman Spectroscopy.* New York: Wiley.

[11] Hood, G. C., Jones, A. C., and Reilly, C. A. (1959). *J. Phys. Chem.*, **63**, 101.

[12] Delwaulle, M. L. (1965). *Bull. Soc. Chim. France.*, 1294 and references therein.

[13] Spiro, T. G. (1965). *Inorg. Chem.*, **4**, 731.

[14] Nixon, J., and Plane, R. A. (1962). *J. Amer. Chem. Soc.*, **84**, 4445.

[15] Yellin, N. and Marcus, Y. (1974). *J. Inorg. Nucl. Chem.*, **36**, 1331.

[16] Chu, G. Y. H., Duncan, R. E., and Tobias, R. S. (1977). *Inorg. Chem.*, **16**, 2625.

[17] Michaellan, K. H., Rieckhoff, K. E., and Voight, E. M. (1977). *J. Phys. Chem.*, **81**, 1489.

[18] Hinton, J. F. and Amis, E. S. (1967). *Chem. Rev.*, **67**, 367.

[19] Bhar, B. N. (1956). *Ark. Kemi.*, **10**, 223.

[20] Fuentes, R., Morgan, L. O., and Matwiyoff, N. A. (1975). *Inorg. Chem.*, **14**, 1837.

[21] Beech, G. (1976). *Anal. Chim. Acta.*, **83**, 133.

[22] Redfield, D. A. and Nelson, J. H. (1973). *Inorg. Chem.*, **12**, 15.

[23] Axtmann, R. C., Shuler, W. E., and Murray, B. B. (1960). *J. Phys. Chem.*, **64**, 57.

[24] Connick, R. E. and Poulson, R. E. (1958). *J. Phys. Chem.*, **62**, 1002.

[25] Solodar, J. and Petrovich, J. P. (1971). *Inorg. Chem.*, **10**, 395.

[26] Hanna, M. W. and Ashbaugh, A. L. (1964). *J. Phys. Chem.*, **68**, 811.

[27] Foster, R., and Fyfe, C. A. (1965). *Trans. Faraday Soc.*, **61**, 1626.

[28] Dodson, B., Foster, R., Bright, A. A. S., Foreman, M. I., and Gorton, J. (1971). *J. Chem. Soc. (B).*, 1283.

[29] Meille, J. P. and Merlin, J. C. (1977). *Anal. Chim. Acta.*, **90**, 289.

[30] Popov, A. I. (1976). *Solute-Solvent Interactions*, (eds. Coetzee, J. F. and Ritchie, C. D.) Vol. 2, 271. New York: M. Dekker.

[31] Laszlo, P. (1978). *Angew. Chem. Int. Ed.*, **17**, 254.

[32] Maciel, G. E., Simeral, L., and Ackerman, J. J. H. (1977). *J. Phys. Chem.*, **81**, 263.

[33] Lucchini, V. and Wells, P. R. (1975). *J. Organomental. Chem.*, **92**, 283.

[34] Hirota, N. (1967). *J. Phys. Chem.*, **71**, 127.

[35] Hermann, R. M., Rembaum, A., and Carper, W. R. (1967). *J. Phys. Chem.*, **71**, 2661.

[36] Stevenson, G. R. and Hidalgo, H. (1973). *J. Phys. Chem.*, **77**, 1027.

[37] Alegria, A. E., Concepción, R., and Stevenson, G. R. (1975). *J. Phys. Chem.*, **79**, 361.

[38] Hoefelmann, K., Jagur-Grodzinski, J., and Szwarc, M. (1969). *J. Amer. Chem. Soc.*, **91**, 4645.

[39] McCain, D. C. and Myers, R. J. (1968). *J. Phys. Chem.*, **72**, 4115.

[40] Burlemacchi, L. and Tiezzi, E. (1969). *J. Phys. Chem.*, **73**, 1588.

[41] Burlemacchi, L. and Tiezzi, E. (1968). *J. Mol. Struct.*, **2**, 261.

[42] Burlemacchi, L., Martini, G., and Tiezzi, E. (1970). *J. Phys. Chem.*, **74**, 3980.

[43] Stevenson, G. R., Concepción, R., and Ocasio, I. (1976). *J. Phys. Chem.*, **80**, 861.

[44] Aylendoefer, R. D. and Papez, R. J. (1972). *J. Phys. Chem.*, **76**, 1012.

[45] Stevenson, G. R. and Echegoyen, L. (1973). *J. Phys. Chem.*, **77**, 2339.

[46] Stevenson, G. R. and Alegria, A. E. (1973). *J. Phys. Chem.*, **77**, 3100.

[47] Stevenson, G. R. and Alegria, A. E. (1975). *J. Phys. Chem.*, **79**, 1043.

[48] Greenwood, N. N. (1967). *Chem. Britain*, **3**, 56.

[49] Danon, J. (1968). In *Physical Methods in Advanced Inorganic Chemistry* (eds. Hill, H. A. O. and Day, P.) Chapter 8. London: Interscience.

[50] Goldanskii, V. I. and Herber, R. H. (1968). *Chemical Applications of Mössbauer Spectroscopy*. New York: Academic Press.

[51] Vértes, A., Nagy, S., Czakó-Nagy, I., and Csákváry, E. (1975). *J. Phys. Chem.*, **79**, 149.

[52] Vértes, A., Czakó-Nagy, I., and Burger, K. (1976). *J. Phys. Chem.*, **80**, 1314.

[53] Barcza, L. (1976). *J. Phys. Chem.*, **80**, 821.

[54] Yoshida, Z. and Osawa, E. (1965). *Bull. Chem. Soc. Japan*, **38**, 140.

[55] Giles, G. H., Gallangher, J., McIntosh, A., and Nakhwa, S. N. (1972). *J. Soc. Dyers Colourists*, **88**, 360.

[56] Werner, A. (1912). *Ber.*, **45**, 121.

[57] Ewing, G. W. (1969). *Intrumental Methods of Analysis*, 3rd ed. New York: McGraw-Hill.

[58] Ciardelli, F. and Salvadori, P. (eds.) (1973). *Fundamental Aspects and Recent Developments in Optical Rotatory Dispersion and Circular Dichroism*. London: Heyden and Sons.

[59] Frei, V. and Solcova, A. (1965). *Coll. Czech. Chem. Comm.*, **30**, 961.

[60] Frei, V. and Solcova, A. (1967). *Coll. Czech. Chem. Comm.*, **32**, 1815.

[61] Folkesson, R. and Larsson, R. (1968). *Acta. Chem. Scand.*, **22**, 1953.

[62] Antikainen, P. J. and Tevanen, K. (1970). *J. Inorg. Nucl. Chem.*, **32**, 1915.

[63] Larsson, R., Mason, S. F., and Norman, B. J. (1966). *J. Chem. Soc. (A).*, 301.

[64] Crescenzi, V., Quadrifoglio, F., and Pispisa, B. (1968). *J. Chem. Soc. (A).*, 2175.

[65] Pedrosa de Jesus, J. D. and Gillard, R. D. (1977). Results reported in J. D. Pedrosa de Jesus, Ph.D. thesis, University of Cardiff.

[66] Nelson, W. H. and Tobias, R. S. (1964). *Inorg. Chem.*, **3**, 653.

[67] Nelson, W. H. and Tobias, R. S. (1964). *Can. J. Chem.*, **42**, 731.

[68] Hentz, F. C. and Tyree, S. Y. (1965). *Inorg. Chem.*, **4**, 873.

[69] Maues, M. (1953). *J. Chem. Phys.*, **21**, 1791.

[70] Bies, D. A. (1955). *J. Chem. Phys.*, **23**, 428.

[71] Kor, S. K. (1959). *Z. Physik. Chem. Leipzig.*, **210**, 288.

[72] Dyrssen, D., Liljenzin, J. O., and Rydberg, J. (1967). *Solvent Extraction Chemistry.* Amsterdam: North-Holland.

[73] Kertes, A. S. and Marcus, Y. (1969). *Solvent Extraction Research.* New York: Wiley-Interscience.

[74] Marcus, Y. and Kertes, A. S. (1970). *Ion-Exchange and Solvent Extraction of Metal Complexes.* New York: Wiley-Interscience.

[75] Rossotti, F. J. C. and Rossotti, H. (1961). *The Determination of Stability Constants*, p. 206-207. New York: McGraw-Hill.

[76] Sato, T. and Murakami, S. (1976). *Anal. Chim. Acta.*, **82**, 217.

[77] Laurene, A. H., Campbell, D. E., Wilberley, S. E., and Clark, H. M. (1956). *J. Phys. Chem.*, **60**, 901.

[78] Keefer, R. M., Andrews, L. J., and Kepner, R. E. (1949). *J. Amer. Chem. Soc.*, **71**, 3906.

[79] Brandt, P. (1959). *Acta. Chem. Scand.*, **13**, 1639.

[80] Johansson, L. (1968). *Coord. Chem. Rev.*, **3**, 293.

[81] Zimmerman, H. K. (1952). *Chem. Rev.*, **51**, 25.

[82] Hubert, S., Hussonnois, M., and Guillaumont, R. (1978). *Structure and Bonding*, **34**, 1.

[83] Berne, I., and Leden, I. (1953). *Svensk. Kem. Tidskr.*, **65**, 88.

[84] Ahrland, S. and Grenthe, I. (1957). *Acta. Chem. Scand.*, **11**, 111.

[85] Lieser, K. H. (1957). *Z. Anorg. Allgem. Chem.*, **292**, 97.

[86] Haight, G. P. (1962). *Acta. Chem. Scand.*, **16**, 209.

[87] Johansson, L. (1970). *Acta. Chem. Scand.*, **24**, 1578.

[88] Haight, G. P., Springer, C. H., and Heilmann, O. J. (1964). *Inorg. Chem.*, **3**, 195.

[89] Preer, J. R. and Haight, G. P. (1966). *Inorg. Chem.*, **5**, 656.

[90] Haight, G. P. and Johansson, L. (1968). *Acta. Chem. Scand.*, **22**, 961.

[91] Ahrland, S. and Rawthorne, J. (1970). *Acta. Chem. Scand.*, **24**, 1578.

[92] Johansson, L. (1971). *Acta. Chem. Scand.*, **25**, 3752.

[93] Inczédy, J. (1966). *Analytical Applications of Ion Exchangers.* Oxford: Pergamon.

[94] Marcus, Y. (1967). *Ion Exchange* (ed. Marinsky, J. A.) p. 101. New York: M. Dekker.

[95] Carleson, B. G. F. and Irving, H. (1954). *J. Chem. Soc.*, 4390.

[96] Schubert, J. (1956). *Methods of Biochemical Analysis*, Vol. 3 (ed. Glick, D.). New York: Interscience.

[97] Loman, H. and van Dalen, E. (1966). *J. Inorg. Nucl. Chem.*, **28**, 2037.

[98] Loman, H. and van Dalen, E. (1967). *J. Inorg. Nucl. Chem.*, **29**, 699.

[99] Fronaeus, S. (1951). *Acta. Chem. Scand.*, **5**, 859.

[100] Fronaeus, S. (1954). *Acta Chem. Scand.*, **8**, 1174.

[101] Rodriguez, A. R. and Poitrenaud, C. (1976). *Anal. Chim. Acta.*, **87**, 125.

[102] Rodriguez, A. R. and Poitrenaud, C. (1976). *Anal. Chim. Acta.*, **87**, 141.

[103] Schupp, O. E. (1968). Gas Chromatography, Vol. XIII of *Technique of Organic Chemistry*, (eds. Perry, E. S. and Weissberger, A.). New York: Interscience.

[104] Wasik, S. P. and Tsang, W. (1970). *J. Phys. Chem.*, **74**, 2970.

[105] Muhs, M. A., and Weiss, F. T. (1962). *J. Amer. Chem. Soc.*, **84**, 4697.

[106] Schneko, H. (1968). *Anal. Chem.*, **40**, 1391.

[107] Kraitr, M., Komers, R., and Čuta, F. (1973). *J. Chromatogr.*, **86**, 1.

[108] Fueno, T., Kajimoto, O., Okuyama, T., and Furukawa, J. (1968). *Bull. Chem. Soc. Japan*, **41**, 785.

[109] Yoza, N., Kouchiyama, K., Miyajima, T., and Ohashi, S. (1975). *Anal. Lett.*, **8**, 641.

[110] Miyajima, T., Yoza, N., and Ohashi, S. (1977). *Anal. Lett.*, **10**, 709.

[111] Kieboom, A. P. G., De Kruyf, N., and van Bekkum, H. (1974). *J. Chromatogr.*, **95**, 175.

[112] Debska, W. (1958). *Nature*, **182**, 666.

[113] Crow, D. R. and Westwood, J. V. (1965). *Quart. Rev.*, **19**, 57.

[114] Heyrovský, J. and Ilkovič, D. (1935). *Coll. Czech. Chem. Comm.*, **7**, 198.

[115] Lingane, J. J. (1941). *Chem. Rev.*, **29**, 1.

[116] Kolthoff, I. M. and Lingane, J. J. (1952). *Polarography*, p. 214. New York: Interscience.

[117] Cernatescu, R., Popescu, I., Cracium, A., Bostan, M., and Iorga, N. (1958). *Studii si Cercetari Sti. Chim. (Fil. Iasi)*, **9**, 1.

[118] Andrews, A. C. and Romary, J. K. (1963). *Inorg. Chem.*, **2**, 1060.

[119] DeFord, D. D. and Hume, D. N. (1951). *J. Amer. Chem. Soc.*, **73**, 5321.

[120] Momoki, K., Sato, H., and Ogewa, H. (1967). *Anal. Chem.*, **39**, 1072.

[121] Frost, J. G., Lawson, M. B., and McPherson, W. G. (1976). *Inorg. Chem.*, **15**, 940.

[122] Hume, D. N., DeFord, D. D., and Cave, G. C. B. (1951). *J. Amer. Chem. Soc.*, **73**, 5323.

[123] Senise, P. and de Almeida Neves, E. F. (1961). *J. Amer. Chem. Soc.*, **83**, 4146.

[124] Ringbom, A. and Erikson, L. (1963). *Acta. Chem. Scand.*, **87**, 1105.

[125] Koryta, J. (1962). *Progress in Polarography*, (ed. P. Zuman), Vol. 1, p. 291. New York: Interscience.

[126] Meites, L. (1965). *Polarographic Techniques*, 2nd ed., p. 538. New York: Interscience.

[127] Bilinski, H., Huston, R., and Stumm, W. (1976). *Anal. Chim. Acta.*, **84**, 157.

[128] Davies, C. W. (1962). *Ion Association*. London: Butterworths.

[129] Beronius, P. (1975). *Acta. Chem. Scand.*, **A29**, 289.

[130] Hara, R. and West, P. (1954). *Anal. Chim. Acta.*, **11**, 264.

[131] Ryabchikov, D. I. and Zarinsky, V. A. (1967). *Talanta.*, **14**, 133.

[132] Matsuura, N., Umemoto, K., Takeda, T., and Sasaki, A. (1976). *Bull. Chem. Soc. Japan*, **49**, 1246.

[133] Smith, J. W. (1955). *Electric Dipole Moments*. London: Butterworths.

[134] Maryott, A. A. (1948). *J. Res. N.B.S.*, **41**, 7.

[135] Ménard, D. and Chabanel, M. (1975). *J. Phys. Chem.*, **79**, 1081.

[136] Rossini, F. D. (ed. Vol. 1) (1956) and Skinner, H. A. (ed. Vol. 2) (1962). *Experimental Thermochemistry*. New York: Interscience.

[137] Schlyter, K. and Sillén, L. G. (1959). *Acta. Chem. Scand.*, **13**, 385.

[138] Johansson, S. (1965). *Arkiv. Kemi.*, **24**, 189.

[139] Christensen, J. J., Izatt, R. M., and Hansen, L. D. (1965). *Rev. Sci. Instr.*, **36**, 779.

[140] Arnett, E. M., Bentrude, W. G., Burke, J. J., and Duggleby, P. M. (1965). *J. Amer. Chem. Soc.*, **87**, 1541.

[141] Arnek, R. (1965). *Arkiv. Kemi.*, **24**, 531.

[142] Bolles, T. F. and Drago, R. S. (1966). *J. Amer. Chem. Soc.*, **88**, 3921.

[143] Kim, K.-Y. and Nancollas, G. H. (1977). *J. Phys. Chem.*, **81**, 948.

[144] Aruga, R. (1975). *J. Chem. Soc. (Dalton)*, 2534.

[145] Christensen, J. J. and Izatt, R. M. (1968). *Physical Methods in Advanced Inorganic Chemistry* (eds. Hill, H. A. O. and Day, P.) p. 538. London. Interscience.

[146] Vaughan, G. A. (1973). *Thermometric and Enthalpimetric Titrimetry*. London: Van Nostrand Reinhold.

[147] Barthel, J. (1975). *Thermometric Titrations*, Vol. 45, in *Chemical Analysis* (eds. Elving, P. J., Winefordner, J. D., and Kolthoff, I. M.) New York: Wiley-Interscience.

[148] Christensen, J. J., Izatt, R. M., and Eatough, D. (1965). *Inorg. Chem.*, **4**, 1278.

[149] Hansen, L. D., Christensen, J. J., and Izatt, R. M. (1965). *Chem. Comm.* 36.

[150] Christensen, J. J., Izatt, R. M., Hansen, L. D. and Partridge, J. A. (1966). *J. Phys. Chem.*, **70**, 2003.

[151] Eatough, D. (1968). Ph.D. dissertation, Brigham Young University, 1967. *Diss. Abs.*, **B28**, 2788.

[152] Sillén, L. G. (1964). *Acta. Chem. Scand.*, **18**, 1085 and references therein.

[153] Brenner, A. (1965). *J. Electrochem. Soc.*, **112**, 611.

[154] Izatt, R. M., Eatough, D., Snow, R. L., and Christensen, J. J. (1968). *J. Phys. Chem.*, **72**, 1205.

[155] Becker, F., Barthel, J., Schmahl, N. G., and Lüschow, H. M. (1963). *Z. Phys. Chem. (Frankfurt)*, **37**, 52.

[156] Björkman, B. and Sillén, L. G. (1963). *Trans. Roy. Inst. Technol. Stockholm*, 199, *Chem. Abs.*, **58**, 9682.

[157] Izatt, R. M., Terry, R. E., Hansen, L. D., Avondet, A. G., Bradshaw, J. S., Dalley, N. K., Jensen, T. E., and Christensen, J. J. (1978). *Inorg. Chim. Acta.*, **30**, 1.

[158] Das, K. and Bear, J. L. (1976). *Inorg. Chem.*, **15**, 2093.

[159] Jezorek, J. R. and McCurdy, W. H. (1975). *Inorg. Chem.*, **14**, 1939.

[160] Rossotti, F. J. C. and Rossotti, H. (1954). *J. Phys. Chem.*, **63**, 1041.

[161] Tobias, S. R. (1961). *J. Inorg. Nucl. Chem.*, **19**, 348.

[162] Ogston, A. G. and Winzor, D. J. (1975). *J. Phys. Chem.*, **79**, 2496.

[163] Irving, H. M. N. H. and Smith, J. S. (1969). *J. Inorg. Nucl. Chem.*, **31**, 159, 3163.

[164] Stryker, L. J. and Matijevic, E. (1969). *J. Phys. Chem.*, **73**, 1484.

[165] Coryell, C. D., Stitt, F., and Pauling, L. (1937). *J. Amer. Chem. Soc.*, **59**, 633.

[166] Elding, L. I. (1966). *Acta. Chem. Scand.*, **20**, 2559.

[167] Drougge, L., Elding, L. I., and Gustafson, L. (1967). *Acta. Chem. Scand.*, **21**, 1647.

[168] Elding, L. I. (1973). *Inorg. Chim. Acta.*, **7**, 581.

[169] Elding, L. I. (1975). *Inorg. Chim. Acta.*, **15**, L9.

[170] Espenson, J. H. and Helzer, S. R. (1969). *Inorg. Chem.*, **8**, 1051.

[171] Bjerrum, N. (1921). *Z. Anorg. Allgem. Chem.*, **119**, 179.

CHAPTER 10

First Case Study:
Linear (ñ) Treatment of pH Data;
the Nickel(II)-Ethylenediamine System

10.1 INTRODUCTION

The nickel(II)-ethylenediamine system is illustrative of the classical potentiometric approach to the determination of stability constants. The essential experimental details will be described and three ways of treating the data to obtain reliable estimates of the stability constants given. In Section 2.5(ii) the number of absorbing species in an aqueous solution containing nickel(II) and ethylenediamine was shown to be four. This was consistent with a three-equilibrium system,

$$\text{Ni}^{2+} + \text{en} \xrightleftharpoons{K_1} [\text{Ni(en)}]^{2+} \tag{10.1}$$

$$[\text{Ni(en)}]^{2+} + \text{en} \xrightleftharpoons{K_2} [\text{Ni(en)}_2]^{2+} \tag{10.2}$$

$$[\text{Ni(en)}_2]^{2+} + \text{en} \xrightleftharpoons{K_3} [\text{Ni(en)}_3]^{2+} \tag{10.3}$$

In attempting to quantify the values for K_1, K_2 and K_3, the acid-base equilibria of ethylenediamine itself must be taken into account.

$$\text{en} + \text{H}^+ \xrightleftharpoons{K_4} [\text{enH}]^+ \tag{10.4}$$

$$[\text{enH}]^+ + \text{H}^+ \xrightleftharpoons{K_5} [\text{enH}]^{2+} \tag{10.5}$$

Indeed, it is by monitoring the free hydrogen ion concentration of the equilibrium mixture that the values of the formation function, $\bar{n}$, and the free ligand concentration, [en], may be obtained. Three methods of proceeding from these parameters to the K_n values are described in Section 10.4.

10.2 EXPERIMENTAL

The apparatus described is essentially that of Bjerrum [1]. A titration vessel of approximately 125 ml capacity and equipped with a suitable stirrer is thermo-statted in a water bath to better than $\pm 0.05°C$. The solution is protected from atmospheric carbon dioxide via a nitrogen blanket. A suitable combined pH electrode and a 10 ml burette capable of being read to ± 0.005 ml are fitted to the titration vessel. The vessel contains 100 ml of an aqueous solution of known nickel and hydrogen ion concentration which is $1 \, mol.l^{-1}$ with respect to potassium nitrate. The latter is to hold the activity coefficients constant. The titration is carried out at $30.0 \pm 0.05°C$. The titrant is a concentrated ($\approx 10 \, mol.l^{-1}$) aqueous solution of ethylenediamine and is protected from carbon dioxide. This solution has been previously standardised potentiometrically. The nickel and hydrogen ion concentrations have been adjusted such that the experiment can be conducted for a titration of between one and five ml of the ethylenediamine solution. As the titrant is very viscous, the addition must be done slowly and with great care to prevent inaccurate burette readings. Values for the pH at each ethylenediamine concentration are obtained after allowing sufficient time for the system to equilibrate.

10.3 CALCULATION OF THE FORMATION FUNCTION, $\bar{n}$, AND FREE LIGAND CONCENTRATION, [en]

(i) Theory

At any point in the titration, four parameters are known, the total nickel concentration, $[Ni]_T$, the total ethylenediamine concentration, $[en]_T$, the total hydrogen ion concentration, $[H]_T$, and the free hydrogen ion concentration $[H]$. These are obtained from the initial concentration, the volume of ethylenediamine added, and the pH. Thus two mass balance equations can be drawn up

$$[en]_T = [en]_u + \bar{n}[Ni]_T \tag{10.6}$$

$$[H]_T = [H] + [H]_{en} \tag{10.7}$$

where $[en]_u$ represents the uncomplexed ethylenediamine, that is the total concentration of the two protonated forms of ethylenediamine and the free ethylenediamine:

$$[en]_u = [en] + [enH^+] + [enH_2^{2+}] \tag{10.8}$$

and $[H]_{en}$ is the concentration of protons bound to ethylenediamine:

$$[H]_{en} = [enH^+] + 2[enH_2^{2+}] \tag{10.9}$$

It is vital to note from Equations (10.4) and (10.5) that it is solely the free hydrogen ion concentration [H] that determines the [en] concentration. The formation function, $\bar{n}$, is the average number of ethylenediamine molecules coordinated to each nickel ion. As K_4 and K_5 are known, it is possible, by using Equations (10.4) and (10.9), to calculate both $\bar{n}$ and [en].

Let us define a function, α_{en}, as the fraction of free ethylenediamine present in solution. That is to say

$$\alpha_{en} = \frac{[en]}{[en]_u} \tag{10.10}$$

From Equation (10.8) this becomes

$$\alpha_{en} = \frac{[en]}{[en] + [enH^+] + [enH_2^{2+}]} \tag{10.11}$$

Equations (10.4) and (10.5) can be rewritten

$$[enH^+] = K_4 [en] [H] \tag{10.12}$$

and

$$[enH_2^{2+}] = K_4 K_5 [en] [H]^2 \tag{10.13}$$

Substituting these in (10.11) we get

$$\alpha_{en} = \frac{[en]}{[en] + K_4 [en] [H] + K_4 K_5 [en] [H]^2} \tag{10.14}$$

and dividing through by [en]

$$\alpha_{en} = \frac{1}{1 + K_4 [H] + K_4 K_5 [H]^2} \tag{10.15}$$

Similarly a function, $\bar{n}_{en}$, the average number of protons per ethylenediamine molecule, can be defined:

$$\bar{n}_{en} = \frac{[H]_{en}}{[en]_u} \tag{10.16}$$

and hence from Equations (10.8) and (10.9):

$$\bar{n}_{en} = \frac{[enH^+] + 2[enH_2^{2+}]}{[en] + [enH^+] + [enH_2^{2+}]} \tag{10.17}$$

On substituting from (10.12) and (10.13) and dividing through by [en] as before we obtain:

$$\bar{n}_{en} = \frac{K_4[H] + 2K_4 K_5 [H]^2}{1 + K_4 [H] + K_4 K_5 [H]^2} \tag{10.18}$$

Rearranging (10.6) and substituting for $[en]_u$ from (10.16),

$$\bar{n} = \frac{[en]_T - \dfrac{[H]_{en}}{\bar{n}_{en}}}{[Ni]_T} \tag{10.19}$$

and equating $[en]_u$ via (10.10) and (10.16):

$$\frac{[H]_{en}}{\bar{n}_{en}} = \frac{[en]}{\alpha_{en}} \tag{10.20}$$

Rearranging, taking logarithms and expressing $-\log[en]$ as $p[en]$:

$$p[en] = \log\left(\frac{\bar{n}_{en}}{\alpha_{en}}\right) - \log[H]_{en} \tag{10.21}$$

It is interesting to note that if K_4 and K_5 are not known then they may be readily obtained by repeating the experiment, omitting the nickel ion. In that case the system is described by (10.4) and (10.5) alone, and $\bar{n}_{en}$ of (10.16) reduces to the ratio of the total hydrogen ion concentration to the total ethylenediamine concentration because $[H]_T \gg [H]$. In this example the difference between the values of K_4 and K_5 is such that for values of $0.8 > \bar{n}_{en} > 1.2$ an approximation makes their determination simple.

At $\bar{n}_{en}$ values below 0.8, only Reaction (10.4) need to be considered to be taking place and therefore,

$$\bar{n}_{en} = \frac{[enH^+]}{[en] + [enH^+]} \tag{10.22}$$

and substituting for (10.4) we obtain,

$$\bar{n}_{en} = \frac{K_4 [en][H]}{[en] + K_4 [en][H]} \tag{10.23}$$

Dividing through by [en] and rearranging we obtain,

$$\frac{\bar{n}_{en}}{1-\bar{n}_{en}} = K_4\,[H] \qquad\qquad (10.24)$$

and taking logarithms,

$$\log K_4 = \log\left\{\frac{\bar{n}_{en}}{1-\bar{n}_{en}}\right\} + pH \qquad\qquad (10.25)$$

and similarly assuming that for $\bar{n}_{en} > 1.2$ only Equation (10.5) is involved we obtain:

$$\log K_5 = \log\left\{\frac{\bar{n}_{en}-1}{2-\bar{n}_{en}}\right\} + pH \qquad\qquad (10.26)$$

(ii) *Results*

(a) *Determination of the protonation constants of ethylenediamine, K_4 and K_5*

A known volume (100.0 ml) of a solution containing hydrochloric acid (0.2010 mol.l^{-1}), potassium chloride (1.00 mol.l^{-1}) and barium chloride (0.10 mol.l^{-1}) is titrated with varying known amounts of 9.74 mol.l^{-1} ethylenediamine solution. The equilibrium pH value is measured at 30°C after each addition of ethylene-diamine solution. The barium and postassium chloride solutions are present to hold the ionic strength approximately constant. Barium does not form complexes with ethylenediamine under these conditions.

The average number of protons per ethylenediamine molecule, $\bar{n}_{en}$, in the absence of other ions capable of complex formation is given by

$$\bar{n}_{en} = \frac{[H]_T}{[en]_T} \qquad\qquad (10.27)$$

A formation function defined in this way is effectively treating the proton as a ligand and ethylenediamine as a metal ion. A worked set of data is given in Table 10.1. The total ethylenediamine and hydrogen ion concentrations $[en]_T$ and $[H]_T$ are calculated from the initial concentrations corrected for dilution. $\bar{n}_{en}$ is calculated by using Equation (10.27) and using the pH values measured. $\log K_4$ and $\log K_4$ can be calculated by using Equations (10.25) and (10.26). Final values for K_4 and K_5 are 1.122×10^{10} and 2.042×10^7 respectively.

Table 10.1 — The determination of the protonation constants of ethylenediamine (K_4 and K_5 as defined by Equations (10.4) and (10.5)).

ml 'en' added	$[en]_T$	$[H]_T$	$\bar{n}_{en}$	pH	$\log\left(\dfrac{\bar{n}_{en}-1}{2-\bar{n}_{en}}\right)$	$\log\left(\dfrac{\bar{n}_{en}}{1-\bar{n}_{en}}\right)$	$\log K_4$	$\log K_5$
1.397	0.1342	0.1982	1.477	7.353	−0.040	—	—	7.313
1.497	0.1437	0.1980	1.378	7.531	−0.216	—	—	7.315
1.645	0.1575	0.1977	1.254	7.782	−0.468	—	—	7.314
1.757	0.1682	0.1975	1.174	7.982	−0.676	—	—	7.306
3.182	0.3004	0.1948	0.649	9.788	—	0.267	10.055	—
3.270	0.3084	0.1946	0.631	9.806	—	0.233	10.039	—
4.497	0.4191	0.1923	0.459	10.125	—	−0.071	10.054	—
4.815	0.4474	0.1918	0.429	10.168	—	−0.124	10.044	—
6.550	0.5988	0.1886	0.315	10.388	—	−0.337	10.051	—
7.975	0.7194	0.1861	0.259	10.513	—	−0.457	10.056	—
9.990	0.8846	0.1827	0.207	10.648	—	−0.583	10.065	—
						Mean	10.05	7.31

(b) *Determination of the formation function, $\bar{n}$, and* p[en] *for the nickel(II)-ethylenediamine system*

The initial conditions are the same as for the protonation of ethylenediamine experiment with the exception that the barium chloride solution is replaced by $0.1006 \text{ mol.l}^{-1}$ nickel chloride solution. The titration is then carried out in an identical manner.

The formation function, $\bar{n}$, can be calculated as follows:

1. Calculate the total analytical concentration of ethylenediamine, hydrogen ions and nickel ions at each titration point, allowing for dilution effects ($[en]_T$, $[H]_T$ and $[Ni]_T$). Note that as the free hydrogen ion concentration [H] is very much less than the total, $[H]_T$, Equation (10.7) reduces to $[H]_{en}$ being equal to $[H]_T$.
2. Using the values of K_4 and K_5 determined in the previous section and the pH values obtained, calculate α_{en} and $\bar{n}_{en}$ using Equations (10.15) and (10.18).
3. $\bar{n}$ and p[en] are now readily calculated using Equations (10.19) and (10.21).

A worked set of results is given in Table 10.2.

10.4 DETERMINATION OF THE STABILITY CONSTANTS FROM $\bar{n}$/p[en] DATA

(i) *Determination of approximate values using the half $\bar{n}$ method*

As was shown in Section 3.6, when the ratios of the successive stability constants are sufficiently large, Equation (3.35) leads directly to a value for the stability constant K_n.

$$K_n = \left(\frac{1}{[L]}\right)_{\text{at } \bar{n}=n-\frac{1}{2}} \tag{10.28}$$

If the $\bar{n}$/p[en] data is plotted for our nickel(II)-ethylenediamine system then the approximate values of K_1, K_2 and K_3 can be read off directly at $\bar{n} = 0.5$, 1.5 and 2.5 respectively. This is shown in Figure 10.1; it is achievable because taking logarithms of (10.28) leads to:

$$\log K_n = \log \left(\frac{1}{[L]}\right)_{\text{at } \bar{n}=n-\frac{1}{2}} = -\log([L])_{\text{at } \bar{n}=n-\frac{1}{2}} \tag{10.29}$$

Values of $\log K_1$, $\log K_2$ and $\log K_3$ are found to be 7.72, 6.34, and 4.54 respectively.

Table 10.2 – Determination of the formation function, $\bar{n}$, and p[en] for the nickel(II)-ethylenediamine system.

ml 'en' added	$[en]_T$	$[H]_{en}$	$[Ni]_T$	pH	$K_4[H]$	$K_4K_5[H]^2$	α_{en}	$\bar{n}_{en}$	$\log\left(\dfrac{\bar{n}_{en}}{\alpha_{en}}\right)$	$-\log[H]_{en}$	p[en]	$\dfrac{[H]_{en}}{\bar{n}_{en}}$	$\bar{n}$
1.365	0.1310	0.1983	0.09924	5.180	7.413×10^4	1.000×10^7	9.930×10^{-8}	1.993	7.303	0.7027	8.006	0.0995	0.318
1.600	0.1534	0.1978	0.09902	5.359	4.909×10^4	4.385×10^6	2.255×10^{-7}	1.989	6.946	0.7037	7.650	0.0995	0.544
2.000	0.1910	0.1971	0.09863	5.622	2.679×10^4	1.306×10^6	7.502×10^{-7}	1.980	6.422	0.7054	7.127	0.0995	0.928
2.500	0.2376	0.1961	0.09815	5.948	1.264×10^4	2.910×10^5	3.294×10^{-6}	1.959	5.774	0.7076	6.482	0.1001	1.403
2.504	0.2379	0.1961	0.09815	5.940	1.288×10^4	3.019×10^5	3.177×10^{-6}	1.959	5.790	0.7076	6.498	0.1001	1.404
3.000	0.2837	0.1951	0.09767	6.330	5.248×10^3	5.011×10^4	1.806×10^{-5}	1.905	5.023	0.7097	5.733	0.1024	1.856
3.495	0.3289	0.1942	0.09720	6.747	2.010×10^3	7.349×10^3	1.068×10^{-4}	1.785	4.223	0.7118	4.935	0.1088	2.264
4.005	0.3751	0.1933	0.09672	7.096	8.995×10^2	1.473×10^3	4.212×10^{-4}	1.620	3.585	0.7138	4.299	0.1193	2.645
4.486	0.4182	0.1922	0.09628	7.464	3.855×10^2	2.705×10^2	1.522×10^{-3}	1.410	2.967	0.7159	3.683	0.1365	2.926

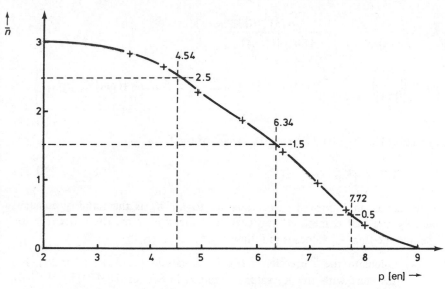

Figure 10.1 – Plot of $\bar{n}$ against p[en] for the nickel(II)-ethylenediamine system.

(ii) *Refinement of approximate K_n values using Bjerrum's convergence method*
According to Bjerrum [1], the equation for the formation function, Equation (3.13), can be rewritten in the form

$$\sum_{i=0}^{i=n} (\bar{n} - n)[L]^i K_1 \ldots K_i = 0 \tag{10.30}$$

This equation is the concise form of Equation (3.50). As was shown in Chapter 3, this leads to the convergence formula:

$$K_n = \left\{ \left(\frac{1}{[L]}\right)_{\text{at } \bar{n}=n-\frac{1}{2}} \right\} \left\{ \frac{1 + \displaystyle\sum_{i=1}^{i=n-1} \left[\dfrac{1 + 2i}{\{([L]^i)_{\text{at } \bar{n}=n-\frac{1}{2}}\} K_{n-1} \ldots K_{n-i}} \right]}{1 + \displaystyle\sum_{i=1}^{i=N-n} [(1 + 2i)\{([L]^i)_{\text{at } \bar{n}=n-\frac{1}{2}}\} K_{n+1} \ldots K_{n+i}]} \right\} \tag{10.31}$$

In our example where n has a maximum value, N, of 3 this simplifies to:

$$K_1 = \left\{ \left(\frac{1}{[en]}\right)_{\text{at } \bar{n}=0.5} \right\} \left\{ \frac{1}{1 + 3K_2\{([en])_{\text{at } \bar{n}=0.5}\} + 5K_2 K_3\{([en]^2)_{\text{at } \bar{n}=0.5}\}} \right\} \tag{10.32}$$

$$K_2 = \left\{ \left(\frac{1}{[en]} \right)_{at\ \bar{n}=1.5} \right\} \left\{ \frac{1 + 3/K_1 \{([en])_{at\ \bar{n}=1.5}\}}{1 + 3K_3 \{([en])_{at\ \bar{n}=1.5}\}} \right\} \tag{10.33}$$

$$K_3 = \left\{ \left(\frac{1}{[en]} \right)_{at\ \bar{n}=2.5} \right\} \left\{ 1 + 3/K_2 \cdot [([en])_{at\ \bar{n}=2.5}] + 5/K_1 K_2 \{([en]^2)_{at\ \bar{n}=2.5}\} \right\}$$

$$\tag{10.34}$$

Equations (10.32), (10.33) and (10.34) are of the form:

$$K_n{}^* = \{K_n\}\{C\} \tag{10.35}$$

where $K_n{}^*$ is an improved approximation to K_n, K_n is the stability constant found by the half $\bar{n}$ method, and C is the correction term. The procedure for obtaining the final K_n values is as follows:

    (a) Calculate the correction terms in Equations (10.32) to (10.34). For this start with the K_n values, obtained in Section 10.4(i), by the half $\bar{n}$ method and the experimentally determined 1/[en] values at the appropriate $\bar{n} = n - \frac{1}{2}$ values.

    (b) Calculate new values for K_n. These are called $K_n{}^*$.

    (c) Repeat steps (a) and (b) using the refined K_n values to recalculate the correction factors. Repeat until the correction factors reach a constant value.

The results for the nickel(II)-ethylenediamine system using this procedure are summarised in Table 10.3. It is apparent that after the third insertion into the convergence formula little significant difference results and the refined values of the stability constants are effectively unchanged through further cycles.

(iii) Block and McIntyre's method

K_1, K_2 and K_3 for the nickel(II)-ethylenediamine system can be evaluated by Block and McIntyre's method [2] described in Section 3.6(ii). For this the half $\bar{n}$ values and their equivalent free ligand concentrations are taken from Figure 10.1. The values are as follows:

$$\bar{n}_1 = 0.500, \quad [en]_1 = 1.91 \times 10^{-8} \text{ mol.l}^{-1}$$
$$\bar{n}_2 = 1.500, \quad [en]_2 = 4.57 \times 10^{-7} \text{ mol.l}^{-1}$$
$$\bar{n}_3 = 2.500, \quad [en]_3 = 2.88 \times 10^{-5} \text{ mol.l}^{-1}$$

These are then used to calculate the functions J_n, L_n and M_{np} defined in Table 3.2. The results are shown in Table 10.4. These functions are then used to calculate the K_n values using the equations listed in Table 3.3. The results are shown in Table 10.5. In theory, all the equations should, for a given set of data,

Table 10.3 – Results for the refinement of the nickel(II)-ethylenediamine stability constants using Bjerrum's convergence method.

Approximation	[en]			Correction factor for			K_n		
	$\bar{n}=0.5$	$\bar{n}=1.5$	$\bar{n}=2.5$	Equation (10.32)	Equation (10.33)	Equation (10.34)	K_1	K_2	K_3
Initial values	1.91×10^{-8}	4.57×10^{-7}	2.88×10^{-5}	—	—	—	5.240×10^{7}	2.190×10^{6}	3.470×10^{4}
1st	1.91×10^{-8}	4.57×10^{-7}	2.88×10^{-5}	0.8884	1.0742	1.0476	4.651×10^{7}	2.350×10^{6}	3.638×10^{4}
2nd	1.91×10^{-8}	4.57×10^{-7}	2.88×10^{-5}	0.8812	1.0869	1.0444	4.614×10^{7}	2.378×10^{6}	3.626×10^{4}
3rd	1.91×10^{-8}	4.57×10^{-7}	2.88×10^{-5}	0.8799	1.0882	1.0439	4.607×10^{7}	2.381×10^{6}	3.624×10^{4}
4th	1.91×10^{-8}	4.57×10^{-7}	2.88×10^{-5}	0.8798	1.0884	1.0438	4.606×10^{7}	2.382×10^{6}	3.624×10^{4}
5th	1.91×10^{-8}	4.57×10^{-7}	2.88×10^{-5}	0.8798	1.0884	1.0438	4.606×10^{7}	2.382×10^{6}	3.624×10^{4}

Table 10.4 – Numerical values for the Block and McIntyre functions defined in Table 3.2 obtained using the nickel(II)-ethylenediamine data.

$$
\begin{aligned}
J_1 &= 9.5500 \times 10^{-9} & L_1'' &= -2.1624 \times 10^{-5} \\
J_2 &= 5.4722 \times 10^{-16} & L_2'' &= -2.0736 \times 10^{-10} \\
J_3 &= 1.7420 \times 10^{-7} & L_3'' &= 5.9720 \times 10^{-15} \\
J_1' &= -2.2850 \times 10^{-7} & L_1''' &= -6.4229 \times 10^{-5} \\
J_2' &= 1.0442 \times 10^{-13} & L_2''' &= -6.2230 \times 10^{-10} \\
J_3' &= 1.4317 \times 10^{-19} & L_3''' &= 1.7916 \times 10^{-14} \\
J_1'' &= 4.3200 \times 10^{-5} & M_{13}' &= 1.3712 \times 10^{-27} \\
J_2'' &= -4.1472 \times 10^{-10} & M_{23}' &= 7.6524 \times 10^{-35} \\
J_3'' &= 1.1944 \times 10^{-14} & M_{13}'' &= 1.1407 \times 10^{-22} \\
L_1' &= -1.2858 \times 10^{-7} & M_{23}'' &= 6.5431 \times 10^{-30} \\
L_2' &= 5.1391 \times 10^{-14} & M_{13}''' &= -2.7230 \times 10^{-21} \\
L_3' &= 7.1557 \times 10^{-20} & M_{23}''' &= 1.3066 \times 10^{-27}
\end{aligned}
$$

Table 10.5 – Stability constants evaluated by substituting the values of the functions in Table 10.4 into the equations in Table 3.3.

Number of equation in Table 3.3	Stability constant
4	$K_1 = 4.606 \times 10^7$
5	$K_1 = 5.167 \times 10^7$
6	$K_1 = 4.606 \times 10^7$
7	$K_2 = 2.382 \times 10^6$
8	$K_2 = 2.382 \times 10^6$
9	$K_2 = 2.382 \times 10^6$
10	$K_2 = 2.382 \times 10^6$
11	$K_2 = 2.116 \times 10^6$
12	$K_3 = 3.624 \times 10^4$
13	$K_3 = 3.624 \times 10^4$
14	$K_3 = 3.624 \times 10^4$

Table 10.6 — Application of Block and McIntyre's procedure to determine the stability constants for the nickel(II)-ethylene-diamine system.

Dataset	$\bar{n}_1$	$\bar{n}_2$	$\bar{n}_3$	[en]$_1$	[en]$_2$	[en]$_3$	K_1	K_2	K_3
1	0.318	1.403	2.264	9.863×10^{-9}	3.296×10^{-7}	1.161×10^{-5}	4.461×10^{7}	2.455×10^{6}	3.610×10^{4}
2	0.544	1.404	2.645	2.239×10^{-8}	3.177×10^{-7}	5.023×10^{-5}	4.500×10^{7}	2.572×10^{6}	3.689×10^{4}
3	0.318	1.404	2.645	9.863×10^{-9}	3.177×10^{-7}	5.023×10^{-5}	4.449×10^{7}	2.577×10^{6}	3.689×10^{4}
4	0.544	1.403	2.264	2.239×10^{-8}	3.296×10^{-7}	1.161×10^{-5}	4.534×10^{7}	2.447×10^{6}	3.612×10^{4}
5	0.318	1.404	2.264	9.863×10^{-9}	3.177×10^{-7}	1.161×10^{-5}	4.448×10^{7}	2.580×10^{6}	3.585×10^{4}
6	0.544	1.403	2.645	2.239×10^{-8}	3.296×10^{-7}	5.023×10^{-5}	4.534×10^{7}	2.446×10^{6}	3.692×10^{4}
Mean							4.488×10^{7}	2.513×10^{6}	3.646×10^{4}
Standard Deviation (%)							0.9	2.8	1.3
log K_n							7.65	6.40	4.56

yield identical answers. However, on some occasions, especially where small differences between certain values of the J_n, L_n and M_{np} functions listed in Table 3.2 exist, differences can occur in the final answer owing to loss of significant figures on subtraction. With the present data it is apparent from Table 10.5 that Equations 5 and 11 provide instances of this.

If we apply this method of calculation directly to the six possible combinations of suitable† data given in Table 10.2 we can obtain a better estimate of the values for K_1, K_2 and K_3. This is summarised in Table 10.6. The half $\bar{n}$ data considered in Tables 10.4 and 10.5 are not included in Table 10.6 because they are interpolated and not experimentally determined.

10.5 SUMMARY

In Section 10.4 we have evaluated stability constants for Equilibria (10.1) to (10.3). Using the half $\bar{n}$ method the values of the stability constants were as follows:

$$\log K_1 = 7.72; \ K_1 = 5.2 \times 10^7$$
$$\log K_2 = 6.34; \ K_2 = 2.2 \times 10^6$$
$$\log K_3 = 4.54; \ K_3 = 3.5 \times 10^4$$

Using Bjerrum's convergence method the stability constants obtained were:

$$K_1 = 4.61 \times 10^7; \ K_2 = 2.38 \times 10^6; \ K_3 = 3.62 \times 10^4$$

Using Block and McIntyre's approach the stability constants obtained were:

$$K_1 = 4.49 \times 10^7; \ K_2 = 2.51 \times 10^6; \ K_3 = 3.65 \times 10^4$$

There is a steady increase in reliability in these results, with those obtained by Block and McIntyre's method having standard deviations of less than 3% (see Table 10.6).

REFERENCES

[1] Bjerrum, J. (1941). *Metal Ammine Formation in Aqueous Solution*, (reprinted 1957). Copenhagen: P. Haase and Son.
[2] Block, B. P. and McIntyre, G. H. (1953; 1955). *J. Amer. Chem. Soc.*, **75**, 5667; **77**, 6723.

† To be suitable the data should involve $\bar{n}$ values that fall in the ranges, $0.2 < \bar{n}_1 < 0.8$, $1.2 < \bar{n}_2 < 1.8$, and $2.2 < \bar{n}_3 < 2.8$ as described in Section 3.6 (ii).

CHAPTER 11

Second Case Study:
Leden and Non-Linear Treatment
of Potentiometric Data;
the Silver(I)-allylalcohol System

11.1 INTRODUCTION

In this second case study we shall determine the species formed when silver ions interact with an olefin (allyl alcohol, $CH_2=CH-CH_2OH$) in aqueous solution at $25°C$ and an ionic strength of $1 \, mol.l^{-1}$ obtained using chloride-free sodium perchlorate [1,2]. The equilibria will be studied potentiometrically using silver-silver chloride electrodes. Since the apparatus necessary for this experiment can be made quite cheaply, this case study differs from the others in that the apparatus used is described at the outset. After reporting the experimental readings, we examine how the data may be analysed in four ways, each of increasing sophistication.

11.2 APPARATUS

The apparatus used is shown in Figure 11.1. Silver-silver chloride electrodes may be bought from commercial suppliers, or prepared, following Brown's procedure [3], by electroplating silver on to platinum and then chloridising the outer silver layer. They should be aged for at least a week, whilst shorted together and then checked to ensure (a) that their e.m.f.s in a given solution differ by no more than $0.02 \, mV$ and (b) that they are reversible (see Section 7.4(a)). Chloride-free perchlorate may be obtained commercially or prepared from perchloric acid and sodium carbonate [4], and for the purest material we strongly recommend the latter.

Because silver-silver chloride electrodes do on occasions fail, the apparatus is designed to take three reference and three sample electrodes. Since the potentiometric errors are greater than the titration errors this has the further advantage that, in the absence of electrode failure, one titration yields three sets of data. Oxygen-free nitrogen, presaturated with water, is bubbled through the sample solution between readings to prevent polarisation of the electrodes, and the reference compartment solution is deaerated before the experiment is commenced. The e.m.f. can be measured using an Advance DPM 3000 digital millivoltmeter which has an impedance of >100 megohms (see Section 7.2). As the complexes formed are of low stability, the total silver concentration in the titration cell should be kept constant to eliminate e.m.f. change due to dilution (see Section 7.3). This can be achieved by adding equal volumes of allyl alcohol solution and a silver solution of exactly double the strength of the silver solution being titrated. The reference compartment solution contains the same silver perchlorate/sodium perchlorate solution as that initially present in the sample compartment. In order to check whether polynuclear species are present the titration should be repeated for at least two silver concentrations (see Section 6.6).

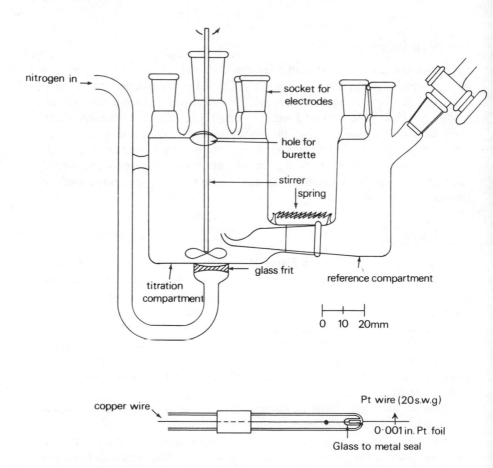

Figure 11.1 – Apparatus used to study the equilibria between silver(I) and allyl alcohol.

11.3 READINGS

The titration was performed at 0.009820 mol.l^{-1} and 0.004910 mol.l^{-1} silver perchlorate concentrations. Table 11.1 records the mean e.m.f. readings at the higher silver concentration. In order to determine how much the liquid junction potential varies during the titration, the titration can be repreated using n-propyl alcohol, which is unable to form an olefin complex, instead of allyl alcohol. The observed e.m.f.'s remain essentially constant during this titration, indicating that the liquid junction potential is effectively zero throughout the titration. Thus in the present work no correction to the observed e.m.f. values is necessary.

11.4 CALCULATIONS

The data reported in Table 11.1 may either be analysed by a linear method such as that of Leden (see Section 3.7(i)) or by the use of a major computer program

Table 11.1 – E.m.f. readings for the titration of 0.009820 mol.l^{-1} silver(I) perchlorate with allyl alcohol in water at 25°C.

Concentration of allyl alcohol solution = 0.3062 mol.l^{-1}.
Total ionic strength = 1.00 mol.l^{-1} (made up using sodium perchlorate).
Initial volume of solution in sample compartment = 50.0 ml.

Volume of allyl alcohol solution added (ml)	e.m.f. (mV)	Volume of allyl alcohol solution added (ml)	e.m.f. (mV)
0.0	0.00†	11.0	14.78
1.0	2.23	12.0	15.49
2.0	4.19	13.0	16.16
3.0	5.91	14.0	16.80
4.0	7.42	15.0	17.40
5.0	8.80	16.0	17.94
6.0	10.06	17.0	18.44
7.0	11.19	18.0	18.94
8.0	12.20	19.0	19.39
9.0	13.12	20.0	19.80
10.0	14.02		

† The e.m.f.s were obtained by backing off to zero the e.m.f. between the sample and reference electrodes for this solution.

using a non-linear treatment of the data such as DALSFEK [6] or LETAGROP VRID [7] (see Chapter 5 and Appendix III). We look at both approaches here, starting with Leden's method. The approach adopted is to illustrate each of the methods in turn and comment on their applicability:

Linear treatment of the data

Simple Leden method (Section 11.4(i))
The least-squares straight line (Section 11.4(ii))
Weighting of the data points (Section 11.4(iii))

Non-linear treatment of the data

Use of a major computer program (Section 11.5)

(i) *Simple Leden method*

In Leden's method we assume that only two equilibria, represented by K_1 and K_2, are present:

$$Ag^+ + al \xrightleftharpoons{K_1} [Ag(al)]^+ \tag{11.1}$$

$$[Ag(al)]^+ + al \xrightleftharpoons{K_2} [Ag(al)_2]^+ \tag{11.2}$$

where al = allyl alcohol. Equation (3.60) may be written in the form,

$$F(al) = \beta_1 + \beta_2 [al] \tag{11.3}$$

where

$$F(al) = \frac{[Ag]_T - [Ag]}{[Ag][al]} \tag{11.4}$$

Thus from Equation (11.4) a plot of $F(al)$ against [al] will give a straight line of slope β_2 and intercept β_1. If Equations (11.1) and (11.2) do not include all the species present then one of two possibilities will occur:

(a) If higher species, such as $[Ag(al)_3]^+$, are present then the plot of $F(al)$ against [al] will start to curve away from the [al] axis at higher values of [al]. We shall then have to use an alternative method of calculation (see Section 3.6(ii) or Chapter 5).

(b) If polynuclear species, such as $[Ag_2(al)]^{2+}$, are present then the values of β_1 and β_2 will depend on the total silver concentration. If this happens more experiments at more silver ion concentrations (see Section 6.6) together with a more sophisticated method of calculation, probably computer based, will be necessary to evaluate all the stability constants.

The problem at this stage of the calculation is to determine [al], the free allyl alcohol concentration, which we do with the aid of the $\bar{v}$ function defined in Chapter 3, Equation (3.62). In the present case,

$$\bar{v} = \frac{[al]_T - [al]}{[Ag]_T - [Ag]} \tag{11.5}$$

whence

$$[al] = [al]_T - \bar{v}\{[Ag]_T - [Ag]\} \tag{11.6}$$

If only the first complex, $[Ag(al)]^+$ is formed, $\bar{v}$ is unity. If two complexes are formed, $\bar{v}$ will increase from 1 to 2 as the free ligand concentration increases. Accordingly a cyclic procedure can be used to evaluate [al]. In the first run [al] determined from Equation (11.6) assuming $\bar{v}$ to be unity, is used obtain β_1 and β_2 from Equation (11.3). These β_1 and β_2 values are used to update $\bar{v}$, using Equation (11.9), which is obtained as follows:

$$\begin{aligned} [Ag]_T &= [Ag] + [Ag(al)] + [Ag(al)_2] \\ &= [Ag]\{1 + \beta_1[al] + \beta_2[al]^2\} \end{aligned} \tag{11.7}$$

$$\begin{aligned} [al]_T &= [al] + [Ag(al)] + 2[Ag(al)_2] \\ &= [al]\{1 + \beta_1[Ag] + 2\beta_2[Ag][al]\} \end{aligned} \tag{11.8}$$

Combining Equations (11.7) and (11.8) with (11.5) yields:

$$\bar{v} = \frac{\beta_1 + 2\beta_2[al]}{\beta_1 + \beta_2[al]} \tag{11.9}$$

which is used to calculate $\bar{v}$ values for each titration point. These values are in turn used to update the [al] values until further recycling leads to no further change in the [al] values.

The application of this approach is illustrated in Table 11.2a for the data in Table 11.1. As a result of the first cycle Figure 11.2 is prepared. The best least-squares straight line (see Section 11.4(ii) has slope (β_2) 11.23 and intercept (β_1) 17.79. These values are used to recalculate $\bar{v}$ (Table 11.2b) for a second iteration. It is apparent that all the $\bar{v}$ values in Table 11.2b are close to unity, so that the new plot (Figure 11.3), not surprisingly, has a similar slope and intercept to the original, 11.84 and 17.81 respectively. Further iteration yields essentially no change, so that the simple Leden approach yields a value for K_1 of 17.81 l.mol^{-1} and for K_2 of 0.66 l.mol^{-1}. It must be emphasised that this method of treatment was developed to handle the data graphically in the early days of stability constant work. Straight line plots are simple and convenient to use and deviations can often be seen. The absence of any pronounced curvature towards the free allyl alcohol axis in Figures 11.2 and 11.3 supports the assumption that higher species such as $[Ag(al)_3]^+$ are not present to any significant extent.

Table 11.2a – First iteration ($\bar{v} = 1$) of simple Leden approach to the data in Table 11.1.[†]

Vol of allyl alcohol added (ml) (a)	Total volume (ml) (50 + 2a)	e.m.f. (ΔE)	$[al]_T (mol.l^{-1})$ $\left(\equiv \dfrac{0.3062 \times n}{\text{total volume}}\right)$	$\log_{10}[Ag]_T/[Ag]$ $(\equiv \Delta E/59.21^{‡})$	$\dfrac{[Ag]_T}{[Ag]}$	$[Ag]$ $(mol.l^{-1})$	$[Ag]_T − [Ag]$ $(mol.l^{-1})$	$[al] (mol.l^{-1})$ $\left(\equiv [al]_T − [Ag]_T − [Ag]\right)$	$[Ag][al]$ $(mol^2.l^{-2})$	$F(al)$ $(l.mol^{-1})$ $\left(\equiv \dfrac{[Ag]_T − [Ag]}{[Ag][al]}\right)$
1.0	52	2.23	0.00589	0.0377	1.0906	0.009004	0.000816	0.005072	0.00004567	17.86
2.0	54	4.19	0.01134	0.0708	1.1770	0.008344	0.001476	0.009865	0.00008234	17.93
3.0	56	5.91	0.01640	0.0998	1.2584	0.007804	0.002016	0.014388	0.00011228	17.95
4.0	58	7.44	0.02112	0.1256	1.3355	0.007353	0.002467	0.018653	0.00013716	17.99
5.0	60	8.80	0.02552	0.1486	1.4080	0.006974	0.002846	0.022674	0.00015813	18.00
6.0	62	10.06	0.02963	0.1699	1.4788	0.006640	0.003180	0.026450	0.00017563	18.11
7.0	64	11.19	0.03349	0.1890	1.5452	0.006355	0.003465	0.030025	0.00019081	18.16
8.0	66	12.20	0.03711	0.2060	1.6071	0.006110	0.003710	0.033400	0.00020407	18.18
9.0	68	13.12	0.04053	0.2216	1.6657	0.005895	0.003925	0.036605	0.00021579	18.19
10.0	70	14.02	0.04374	0.2368	1.7250	0.005693	0.004127	0.039610	0.00022552	18.30
11.0	72	14.78	0.04678	0.2496	1.7766	0.005527	0.004293	0.042487	0.00023483	18.29
12.0	74	15.49	0.04965	0.2616	1.8265	0.005376	0.004444	0.045206	0.00024303	18.20
13.0	76	16.16	0.05238	0.2729	1.8747	0.005238	0.004582	0.047798	0.00025037	18.30
14.0	78	16.80	0.05496	0.2837	1.9219	0.005109	0.004711	0.050249	0.00025672	18.35
15.0	80	17.40	0.05741	0.2939	1.9673	0.004992	0.004828	0.052582	0.00026249	18.39
16.0	82	17.94	0.05975	0.3030	2.0090	0.004888	0.004932	0.054818	0.00026795	18.41
17.0	84	18.44	0.06197	0.3114	2.0485	0.004794	0.005026	0.056944	0.00027299	18.41
18.0	86	18.94	0.06409	0.3199	2.0887	0.004701	0.005119	0.058971	0.00027722	18.46
19.0	88	19.39	0.06611	0.3275	2.1256	0.004620	0.005200	0.060910	0.00028140	18.48
20.0	90	19.80	0.06804	0.3344	2.1597	0.004547	0.005273	0.062767	0.00028540	18.48

† Note, to illustrate the calculation more figures have been carried than are experimentally meaningful in order to avoid introducing rounding errors.
‡ The slope of the Nernst plot for the electrodes was 59.21 mV.

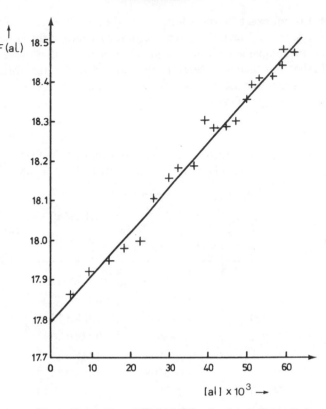

Figure 11.2 – Plot of F(al) v[al] for the data in Table 11.2a.

The absence of polynuclear species, such as $[Ag_2(al)]^{2+}$ cannot be demonstrated from the present calculation; however, when K_1 and K_2 are calculated from potentiometric data obtained at a different silver ion concentration it is found that K_1 and K_2 are independent of silver ion concentration within experimental error. Thus species such as $[Ag_2(al)]^{2+}$ are not present to any significant extent.

(ii) Least-squares straight line

The subjective method of drawing a straight line through a set of points having experimental errors can be made more objective by fitting a straight line using the principle of least-squares (see Chapter 4). This procedure was in fact used to draw the lines shown in Figures 11.2 and 11.3. However, it should be clearly noted that to use least-squares techniques on an equation such as (11.3) is strictly incorrect (see Section 4.6). The errors in both the dependent and the independent variables will be highly correlated as they are both functions calculated from the e.m.f. values. In addition, the independent variable (x-coordinate) is not exact. Nevertheless, this method has been used in the past and is described here for illustrative purposes. It appears, when the values calculated in this way are compared with those from other methods, that the results are not too dissimilar. Fortunately, therefore, it may be that some fortuitous error cancellation is taking place and that the method performs better than might be expected for this type of system.

Table 11.2b – Second iteration ($\bar{v}$ determined from Equation (11.9) taking $\beta_1 = 17.79$ and $\beta_2 = 11.23$ from Figure 11.2) of the data in Table 11.2a.[†]

Volume of allyl alcohol added (ml) (n)	$\bar{v}$ $\left(\equiv \dfrac{\beta_1 + 2\beta_2\,[al]}{\beta_1 + \beta_2\,[al]}\right)$	[al] (mol.l^{-1}) $(\equiv [al]_T - \bar{v}([Ag]_T-[Ag]))$	[Ag][al] (mol^2.l^{-2})	F(al) (l.mol^{-1}) $\left(\equiv \dfrac{[Ag]_T-[Ag]}{[Ag][al]}\right)$
1.0	1.00319	0.005070	0.00004565	17.87
2.0	1.00619	0.009856	0.00008224	17.95
3.0	1.00900	0.014370	0.00011214	17.98
4.0	1.01162	0.018624	0.00013694	18.01
5.0	1.01411	0.022634	0.00015785	18.03
6.0	1.01642	0.026398	0.00017528	18.14
7.0	1.01860	0.029961	0.00019040	18.20
8.0	1.02065	0.033323	0.00020360	18.22
9.0	1.02258	0.036516	0.00021526	18.23
10.0	1.02439	0.039512	0.00022494	18.35
11.0	1.02612	0.042375	0.00023421	18.33
12.0	1.02774	0.045083	0.00024237	18.34
13.0	1.02929	0.047664	0.00024966	18.35
14.0	1.03074	0.050104	0.00025598	18.40
15.0	1.03213	0.052427	0.00026172	18.45
16.0	1.03345	0.054653	0.00026714	18.46
17.0	1.03470	0.056770	0.00027233	18.46
18.0	1.03589	0.058787	0.00027636	18.52
19.0	1.03703	0.060717	0.00028051	18.54
20.0	1.04067	0.062552	0.00028442	18.54

† Note, to illustrate the calulation more figures have been carried than are experimentally meaningful in order to avoid introducing rounding errors.

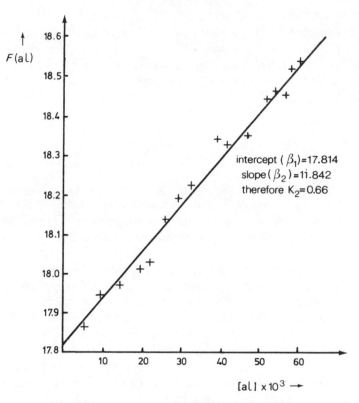

Figure 11.3 – Plot of F(al) v [al] for the data in Table 11.2b.

Following the theory given in Chapter 4, the best straight line will be given by minimising the sum of the squares of the residuals, S, given by:

$$S = \sum_{i=1}^{i=n} r_i^2 \tag{11.10}$$

and by analogy with Equation (4.16),

$$r_i = F(\text{al}_i) - \beta_1 - \beta_2(\text{al}_i) \tag{11.11}$$

whence,

$$S = \sum_{i=1}^{i=n} [F(\text{al}_i) - \beta_1 - \beta_2(\text{al}_i)]^2 \tag{11.12}$$

This type of analysis is usually performed using standard programs on a small programmable calculator.

(iii) *Weighting of the data points*

In an experimental run, the variance, or error, in the dependent variable is often not constant throughout the run. This may be manifest in a straight line plot, for example, by a greater experimental scatter over one part of the plot than another. Accordingly, a weighting factor may be incorporated into Equation (11.10) to give:

$$S = \sum_{i=1}^{i=n} w_i r_i^2 \tag{11.13}$$

where w_i is equal to $1/\sigma_{r_i}^2$, $\sigma_{r_i}^2$ being the variance of the residual r_i. This is dependent on the variances of the experimental quantities, in this case the total allyl alcohol and silver concentrations and the e.m.f. measurements. We shall consider the variances in these experimental quantities to be equal to the squares of their estimated errors.

Before deriving the weighting function it should be pointed out again that Equation (11.13) is not a good example of a situation where this procedure should be applied, because neither the dependent nor the independent variables are directly observed values. They are each a function of the data and will have correlated variances. The procedure below, however, whilst it should be regarded with caution, does calculate the errors propagated into these variables by the experimental errors, and thereby provides a sounder basis for data analysis by Equation (11.13). A similar method has been described using the $\bar{n}$ function [5].

Beginning by substituting Equation (11.4) into (11.2) and combining this with (11.3) gives.

$$S = \sum_{i=1}^{i=n} w_i r_i^2 = \sum_{i=1}^{i=n} \frac{r_i^2}{\sigma_{r_i}^2} = \left\{ \frac{\frac{1}{[al_i]}\left\{\frac{[Ag]_T}{[Ag_i]} - 1\right\} - \beta_1 - \beta_2 [al_i]}{\sigma_{r_i}^2} \right\}^2 \tag{11.14}$$

It now remains to calculate the variance of the residual, $\sigma_{r_i}^2$. If it is assumed that there is no correlation between the experimental errors in $[Ag]_T$, $[al]_T$ and e.m.f. (E), then,

$$\sigma_{r_i}^2 = \left(\frac{\partial r}{\partial E}\right)^2 \sigma_{E_i}^2 + \left(\frac{\partial r}{\partial [Ag]_T}\right)^2 \sigma_{[Ag]_T}^2 + \left(\frac{\partial r}{\partial [al]_T}\right)^2 \sigma_{[Al]_T}^2 \tag{11.15}$$

where σ_X^2 is the variance of X. From Equation (11.11)

$$\partial r = \partial F(al) - \beta_2 \partial [al] \tag{11.16}$$

Rearranging Equation (11.4) gives

$$F(\text{al}) = \frac{1}{[\text{al}]}\left\{\frac{[\text{Ag}]_T}{[\text{Ag}]} - 1\right\} \tag{11.17}$$

which on partial differentiation yields

$$\partial F(\text{al}) = \frac{1}{[\text{al}]^2}\left\{\frac{[\text{Ag}]_T}{[\text{Ag}]} - 1\right\}\partial[\text{al}] - \frac{[\text{Ag}]_T}{[\text{al}][\text{Ag}]^2}\partial[\text{Ag}] + \frac{1}{[\text{al}][\text{Ag}]}\partial[\text{Ag}]_T \tag{11.18}$$

Substituting (11.18) into (11.16) gives

$$\partial r =$$
$$-\left[\frac{1}{[\text{al}]^2}\left\{\frac{[\text{Ag}]_T}{[\text{Ag}]} - 1\right\} + \beta_2\right]\partial[\text{al}] - \frac{[\text{Ag}]_T}{[\text{al}][\text{Ag}]^2}\partial[\text{Ag}] + \frac{1}{[\text{al}][\text{Ag}]}\partial[\text{Ag}]_T \tag{11.19}$$

It now remains to replace $\partial[\text{Ag}]$ and $\partial[\text{al}]$ by partial differentials involving the total silver and total olefin concentrations and the e.m.f.

Let us take $\partial[\text{Ag}]$ first. The measured e.m.f. is the difference between that developed by the sample and reference electrodes, both of which are dipping into solutions of the same *total* silver ion concentration. The measured e.m.f. (E) is given by (see Equation (7.5)):

$$E = E_{\text{sample}} - E_{\text{reference}} = \frac{RT}{\mathscr{F}}\ln\frac{[\text{Ag}]}{[\text{Ag}]_T} \tag{11.20}$$

whence
$$[\text{Ag}] = [\text{Ag}]_T\, e^{-RTE/\mathscr{F}} \tag{11.21}$$
and
$$\partial[\text{Ag}] = e^{-RTE/\mathscr{F}}\,\partial[\text{Ag}]_T - (RT/\mathscr{F})[\text{Ag}]_T\, e^{-RTE/\mathscr{F}}\,\partial E \tag{11.22}$$

$\partial[\text{al}]$ may be eliminated from Equation (11.19) by partial differentiation of Equation (11.8) to obtain

$$\partial[\text{al}]_T = (1 + \beta_1[\text{Ag}] + 2\beta_2[\text{Ag}][\text{al}])\,\partial[\text{al}]$$
$$+ (\beta_1[\text{al}] + \beta_2[\text{al}]^2)\,\partial[\text{Ag}] \tag{11.23}$$

and then substituting for $\partial[\text{Ag}]$ from Equation (11.22).

Collecting all the terms together and substituting them into Equation (11.19) gives an equation of the form

$$\partial r = X\partial[\text{Ag}]_T + Y\partial[\text{al}]_T + Z\partial E \tag{11.24}$$

where

$$X = \frac{1}{[Ag][al]} - \frac{[Ag]_T\, e^{-RTE/\mathscr{F}}}{[Ag]^2 [al]}$$

$$+ \frac{\left\{\dfrac{1}{[al]^2}\left(\dfrac{[Ag]_T}{[Ag]} - 1\right) + \beta_2\right\}(\beta_1[al] + \beta_2[al]^2)\, e^{-RTE/\mathscr{F}}}{1 + \beta_1[Ag] + 2\beta_2[Ag][al]}$$

$$\text{(11.25)}$$

$$Y = \frac{\dfrac{-1}{[al]^2}\left(\dfrac{[Ag]_T}{[Ag]} - 1\right) + \beta_2}{1 + \beta_1[Ag] + 2\beta_2[Ag][al]} \tag{11.26}$$

$$Z = \left\{\frac{(RT/\mathscr{F})[Ag]_T^2\, e^{-RTE/\mathscr{F}}}{[Ag]^2[al]}\right\} -$$

$$\left\{\frac{\left[\dfrac{1}{[al]^2}\left(\dfrac{[Ag]_T}{[Ag]} - 1\right) + \beta_2\right]\left[\beta_1[al] + \beta_2[al]^2\right](RT/\mathscr{F})[Ag]_T\, e^{-RTE/\mathscr{F}}}{1 + \beta_1[Ag] + 2\beta_2[Ag][al]}\right\}$$

$$\text{(11.27)}$$

Substituting from Equation (11.24) into (11.15) gives

$$\sigma_{r_i}^2 = X^2\sigma_{[Ag]_T}^2 + Y^2\sigma_{[al]_T}^2 + Z^2\sigma_{E_i}^2 \tag{11.28}$$

It should be pointed out at this stage that X, Y and Z are all dependent on β_1, β_2 and the value calculated for the free ligand concentration. Accordingly the calculation of the variances of the residuals must be repeated on each cycle of the calculation described in stage 2 (Section 11.4(ii)). Analysis of the data in Table 11.2 by this method, assuming that the error in the e.m.f. is $\pm 0.015\,\text{mV}$ and the errors in the silver(I) and allyl alcohol concentrations are both $\pm 1\%$, yields $K_1 = 17.82\ (0.20)\,\text{l.mol}^{-1}$ and $K_2 = 0.69\ (0.24)\,\text{l.mol}^{-1}$ where the values in parentheses are the standard deviations. These stability constants are very similar to those obtained, without weighting, in Section 11.4(i). Clearly weighting of the data points in this fashion has had little effect on the values calculated in this case. Quite often, though, weighting can have a profound effect on the calculations from potentiometric data.

11.5 USE OF A NON-LINEAR LEAST-SQUARES PROGRAM

An alternative to using an essentially simple linear calculation procedure based on an assumed two equilibria model (Reactions (11.1) and (11.2)), coupled with a demonstration that deviations from linearity are absent, is to carry out a non-linear analysis of the data. This can be done with a major computer program such as that described in detail in Appendix III. Such a program allows a more rigorous analysis of the system to be carried out.

The complete set of data (see Section 11.3) obtained for the present system was first analysed using the program DALSFEK [6] according to a model consisting of Equilibria (11.1) and (11.2). The resulting values for the stability constants were $K_1 = 17.84$ (0.05) l.mol^{-1} and $K_2 = 0.65$ (0.06) l.mol^{-1}, where the figures in parentheses are the standard deviations. The Hamilton R-factor calculated with this model was 0.00184 which is well within the limiting value of 0.00841, thus indicating that the model provides a good fit to the data (see Section 5.4). The limiting value of the Hamilton R-factor was obtained assuming that the errors in e.m.f. were ±0.015 mV and in the allyl alcohol and silver concentrations were ±1%. However, since a number of previous workers in the field have suggested that binuclear complexes $[Ag_2(al)]^{2+}$ may be formed, an alternative model involving Equilibria (11.1), (11.2) and (11.29) was examined with the program.

$$[Ag(al)]^+ + Ag^+ \xrightleftharpoons{K_{\frac{1}{2}}} [Ag_2(al)]^{2+} \tag{11.29}$$

The resulting stability constants, with standard deviations in parentheses, were $K_1 = 17.82$ (1.05) l.mol^{-1}, $K_2 = 0.66$ (2.9) l.mol^{-1} and $K_{\frac{1}{2}} = 0.09$ (2.8) l.mol^{-1}, and the limiting Hamilton R-factor had increased slightly to 0.00185. It is apparent that this model gives no improvement on the simpler model involving K_1 and K_2. The R-factor ratio test described in Section 5.4 can also be applied.

$$\frac{R_{K_1 K_2 K_{1/2}}}{R_{K_1 K_2}} = 1.0 \tag{11.30}$$

whereas $R_{3,18,0.01} = 1.36$, from tables [8], and hence the two models are unfortunately statistically indistinguishable because the observed ratio is less than this quantity. Generally, however, it is a conservative strategy to accept the simplest possible model that gives an acceptable fit to the data, as it is always possible to fit a model to a data set given enough parameters to adjust. In this case also $K_{\frac{1}{2}}$ is essentially zero, and it is the usual practice to reject the presence of a species if the value of the equilibrium constant is less than 2 or 3 times the standard deviation [8,9].

Thus, in conclusion, the use of a non-linear least-squares program has confirmed that the data is best described by a model involving Equilibria (11.1) and (11.2). In addition, it appears that in this simple case the linear Leden treatment is adequate as the calculated parameter values are very similar to those from the present non-linear treatment.

11.6 CONCLUSION

The equilibria present when silver perchlorate and allyl alcohol are mixed in aqueous solution at $25°C$ are given by Equilibria (11.1) and (11.2). At $1 \, mol.l^{-1}$ ionic strength the equilibrium constants, with their standard deviations in parentheses, are $K_1 = 17.84 \, (0.05) \, l.mol^{-1}$ and $K_2 = 0.65 \, (0.06) \, l.mol^{-1}$.

REFERENCES

[1] Searle, G. W. (1976). Ph.D. thesis, Southampton University.
[2] Hartley, F. R., Searle, G. W., Alcock, R. M., and Rogers, D. E. (1977). *J. Chem. Soc. (Dalton)*, 469.
[3] Brown, A. S. (1934). *J. Amer. Chem. Soc.*, **56**, 646.
[4] Hartley, F. R. and Venanzi, L. M. (1967). *J. Chem. Soc. (A).*, 333.
[5] Lansbury, R. C., Price, V. E., and Smeeth, A. G. (1965). *J. Chem. Soc.*, 1896.
[6] Alcock, R. M., Hartley, F. R., and Rogers, D. E. (1978). *J. Chem. Soc. (Dalton)*, 115.
[7] Sillén, L. G. (1964). *Acta. Chem. Scand.*, **18**, 1085.
[8] Hamilton, W. C. (1964). *Statistics in Physical Science.* New York: Ronald Press.
[9] Sillén, L. G. and Warnqvist, B. (1969). *Ark. Kemi.*, **31**, 341.

CHAPTER 12

Third Case Study: Qualitative and Quantitative Analysis of Spectrophotometric Data; the Copper(II)-Ethylenediamine-Oxalate System

12.1 INTRODUCTION

The copper(II)-ethylenediamine-oxalate system [1] will be used to illustrate the use to which spectrophotometry may be put in order to calculate both the number and nature of the species in the system and the various stability constants for the equilibria involved. The number and nature of the species in solution will be investigated using isosbestic point data, Job's method of continuous variations, and matrix rank analysis (see Chapter 2). These results will be used to propose a chemical model. Spectrophotometric data obtained at measured pH values will then be analysed by a classical approach using the linear functions described in Chapter 3 to evaluate the stability constants. Finally, the same data will be processed, using a non-linear least-squares approach. The computer program DALSFEK, described in Appendix III, will be used for this.

12.2 DEFINITION OF THE EQUILIBRIUM SYSTEM

The visible spectra of a series of solutions containing varying proportions of copper(II), oxalate ions (ox) and ethylenediamine (en) are shown in Figure 12.1. There are two 'isosbestic' points one at 600 nm and one at 700 nm. Not all the curves pass through these 'isosbestic' points notably curves 6, 7, 8 and 9. If the 'isosbestic' points are not accidental then it would indicate that there are at least three spectrophotometrically active species involved in the equilibrium process.

Copper(II) is known to form two stable and easily prepared complexes with ethylenediamine [2] and oxalate ions [3]. These may be isolated as $[Cu(en_2)]SO_4$ and $K_2[Cu(ox)_2]2H_2O$. Using these compounds in 0.01 mol.l^{-1} solution, it is possible to make a Job's plot (see Section 2.5(ii)). Based on Figure 12.1, suitable wavelengths are 500 nm, 600 nm, 650 nm, and 700 nm. The absorbance values for the pure $[Cu(en)_2]^{2+}$ and $[Cu(ox)_2]^{2-}$ ions are obtained as well as those for the mixed solutions. Corrected absorbance values, y_{ij}, are obtained by subtracting the calculated values for the combined absorbances due to the reactants assuming no reaction (see Equations (2.17) and (2.18)). The results are given in Table 12.1 and graphically in Figure 12.2.

From the position of the maxima and minimum in Figure 12.2, a 1:1 species is formed. If a restricted stoichiometry test is applied to these data (see Section 2.3(ii)) then a family of straight lines is found passing through the origin as shown in Figure 12.3. If 500 nm data had been included from Table 12.1 then negative values of y_{ij} or $y_{i'j}$ would have resulted, but the lines would still pass through the origin.

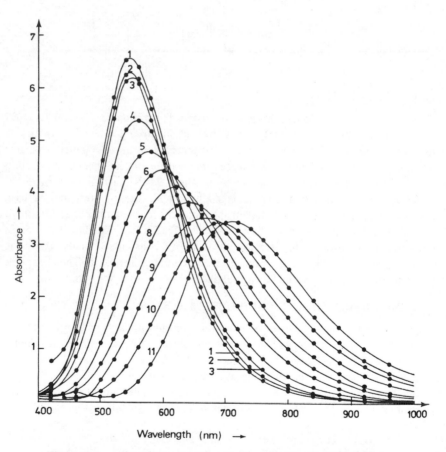

Figure 12.1 — Effect of varying the ratio of copper(II):ethylenediamine: oxalate by varying the amount of ethylenediamine added. All solutions contain 10^{-2} mol.l^{-1} CuSO$_4$, 0.25 mol.l^{-1} K$_2$C$_2$O$_4$, and the ionic strength adjusted to unity with NaNO$_3$; 1 cm cells. Ratios of copper(II):oxalate: ethylenediamine: (1) 1:250:3 (2) 1:0:3 (3) 1:250:2 (4) 1:250:1.75 (5) 1:250:1.5 (6) 1:250:1.25 (7) 1:250:1.00 (8) 1:250:0.75 (9) 1:250:0.5 (10) 1:250:0.25 (11) 1:250:0.

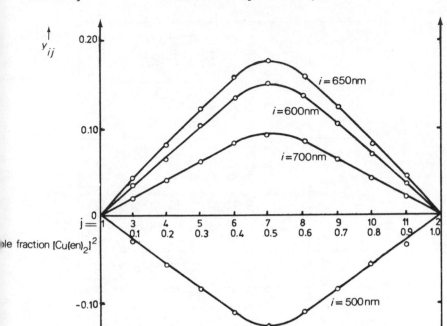

Figure 12.2 – Job's plots for the $[Cu(en)_2]^{2+}/[Cu(ox)_2]^{2-}$ system.

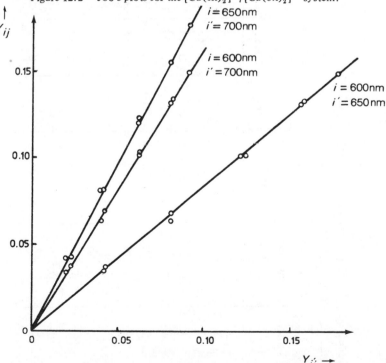

Figure 12.3 – Graphical rank matrix analysis – restricted stoichiometry for one species test using $[Cu(en)_2]^{2+}/[Cu(ox)_2]^{2-}$ corrected Job plot data.

Table 12.1 – Job's method data for the copper(II)-ethylenediamine-oxalate system.

Solution number (j)	Mole fraction $[Cu(en)_2]^{2+}$	Mole fraction $[Cu(ox)_2]^{2-}$	Absorbance measured (1 cm cell)				y_{ij}			
			$i=1$ 500 nm	$i=2$ 600 nm	$i=3$ 650 nm	$i=4$ 700 nm	$i=1$ 500 nm	$i=2$ 600 nm	$i=3$ 650 nm	$i=4$ 700 nm
1	0	1	0.006	0.115	0.259	0.346	0	0	0	0
2	1	0	0.414	0.468	0.249	0.117	0	0	0	0
3	0.100	0.900	0.017	0.184	0.300	0.342	−0.030	0.034	0.042	0.019
4	0.200	0.800	0.029	0.252	0.338	0.340	−0.058	0.064	0.081	0.040
5	0.300	0.700	0.043	0.323	0.377	0.339	−0.085	0.102	0.121	0.062
6	0.400	0.600	0.056	0.388	0.412	0.334	−0.113	0.132	0.156	0.080
7	0.500	0.500	0.082	0.442	0.431	0.323	−0.128	0.150	0.177	0.091
8	0.600	0.400	0.138	0.461	0.412	0.290	−0.113	0.134	0.158	0.080
9	0.700	0.300	0.206	0.465	0.376	0.249	−0.086	0.103	0.124	0.062
10	0.800	0.200	0.275	0.466	0.332	0.205	−0.057	0.069	0.081	0.042
11	0.900	0.100	0.347	0.470	0.293	0.162	−0.036	0.037	0.043	0.022

We could also use the 'raw' Job plot data and apply a restricted stoichiometry three-species test to it such that the function $(a_{2j} - a_{2j'})/(a_{1j} - a_{1j'})$ when plotted against $(a_{3j} - a_{3j'})/(a_{1j} - a_{1j'})$ will yield a straight line for all values where $j \neq j'$. The three values of i chosen, that is, 1, 2 and 3, correspond to 500 nm, 600 nm and 650 nm in Table 12.1. This calculation can be carried out for j values for the mixed solutions from 3 to 11. For example, taking $j = 3$ then

j'	$a_{23} - a_{2j'}$	$a_{13} - a_{1j'}$	$a_{33} - a_{3j'}$	$\left(\dfrac{a_{23} - a_{2j'}}{a_{13} - a_{1j'}}\right)$	$\left(\dfrac{a_{33} - a_{3j'}}{a_{13} - a_{1j'}}\right)$
4	−0.068	−0.012	−0.038	5.67	3.17
5	−0.139	−0.026	−0.077	5.35	2.96
6	−0.204	−0.039	−0.112	5.23	2.87
7	−0.258	−0.065	−0.131	3.97	2.02
8	−0.277	−0.121	−0.112	2.29	0.93
9	−0.281	−0.189	−0.076	1.49	0.40
10	−0.282	−0.258	−0.032	1.09	0.12
11	−0.286	−0.330	+0.007	0.87	−0.00(2)

The results for all values of j are plotted in Figure 12.4 again confirming that there are three absorbing species present. The same raw data when processed using the program TRIANG (see Appendix II) indicates three species for absorbance errors between 0.001 and 0.010. Hence the most likely species formed from these reactions is a neutral mixed ligand complex [Cu(en)(ox)].

Having established this, it is now possible to propose a reaction scheme for the equilibrium system if no appreciable amount of free copper(II) ions are present in the pH region being studied.

$$[Cu(en)_2]^{2+} + [ox]^{2-} \; \overset{K_1}{\rightleftharpoons} \; [Cu(en)(ox)] + en \tag{12.1}$$

$$[Cu(en)(ox)] + [ox]^{2-} \; \overset{K_2}{\rightleftharpoons} \; [Cu(ox)_2]^{2-} + en \tag{12.2}$$

$$en + H^+ \; \overset{K_4}{\rightleftharpoons} \; [enH]^+ \tag{12.3}$$

$$[enH]^+ + H^+ \; \overset{K_5}{\rightleftharpoons} \; [enH_2]^{2+} \tag{12.4}$$

In this scheme the protonation constants for (12.3) and (12.4) have been numbered K_4 and K_5 respectively to make them consistent with the same constants in Equilibria (10.4) and (10.5).

This model assumes that in the pH region of interest, pH5 to pH11, no un-ionised oxalic acid is present. This is reasonable as the pK values for oxalic acid are 1.14 and 3.85 and indicate that oxalic acid is effectively completely dissociated over the studied pH range.

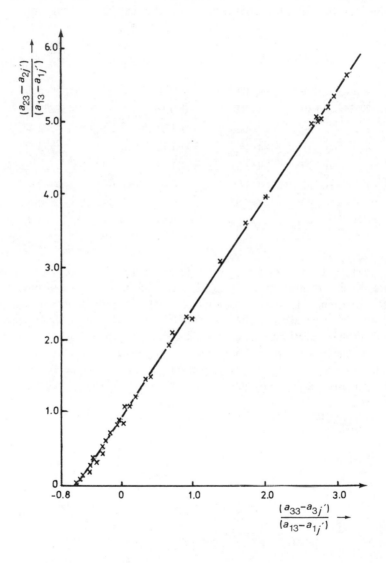

Figure 12.4 – Graphical rank matrix analysis – restricted stoichiometry three species test using Job plot data.

12.3 EXPERIMENTAL

In order to determine the stability constants, a series of solutions similar to those shown in Figure 12.1 are prepared, but the ratios of the total analytical concentrations of copper(II), ethylenediamine and oxalate ions are kept constant, the ratio of free ethylenediamine to oxalate being varied by adjusting the pH with nitric acid. All solutions must be adjusted to $1.0\,mol.l^{-1}$ with sodium nitrate to keep the ionic strength constant throughout the experiment. The solutions are thermostatted in a water bath at $25.0 \pm 0.05°C$. The pH of each solution is measured and the absorbances at six selected wavelengths obtained in thermostatted 1 cm cells. All solutions are protected from carbon dioxide using a nitrogen blanket, and the absorbance readings are obtained, observing the precautions outlined in Section 8.3.

Values of K_4 and K_5 at $25°C$ at $1\,mol.l^{-1}$ ionic strength are known from the work of Poulsen and Bjerrum [4] and extrapolated data of Everett and Pinsent [5]. Values of 1.514×10^{10} and 3.089×10^7 were chosen from these data. The total analytical concentrations of copper(II) ions, potassium oxalate, and ethylenediamine were $0.0100\,mol.l^{-1}$, $0.1000\,mol.l^{-1}$ and $0.1000\,mol.l^{-1}$ respectively. Suitable wavelengths for measurement are 480 nm, 600 nm, 640 nm, 646 nm, 700 nm and 800 nm, since these give maximum absorbance differences and data at the two 'isosbestic' wavelengths for ease of graphical data manipulation. These are not ideal from the viewpoint of numerical analysis of the system as there are insufficient absorbance measurements, and those at the 'isosbestic' wavelength ill-define the system. However, this example illustrates the graphical approach. The original data set is given in Table 12.2.

12.4 GRAPHICAL TREATMENT OF THE DATA

To simplify the calculation, data is used such that only Equilibrium (12.1) is involved. On examination of Figure 12.1 and Table 12.2, it is apparent that some solutions pass through the 'isosbestic' point at 600 nm. It will be assumed therefore that such solutions only contain $[Cu(en)_2]^{2+}$ and $[Cu(en)(ox)]$.

$$K_1 = \frac{[Cu(en)(ox)][en]}{[Cu(en)_2][ox]} \qquad (12.5)$$

As the concentrations of oxalate and ethylenediamine are such that the free copper ion concentration is negligible then,

$$[Cu]_T = [Cu(en)(ox)] + [Cu(en)_2] \qquad (12.6)$$

and from Beer's Law it follows that at wavelength, λ,

$$A_\lambda^{obs} = \epsilon_\lambda^{obs}[Cu]_T \qquad (12.7)$$

Table 12.2 — Effect of varying the ratio of ethylenediamine:oxalate concentration through pH adjustments made by adding nitric acid.

All solutions contain $0.01\,mol.l^{-1}$ copper(II), $0.1\,mol.l^{-1}$ potassium oxalate, $0.1\,mol.l^{-1}$ ethylenediamine; the nitric acid concentration varies; the ionic strength is made up to $1.0\,mol.l^{-1}$ using sodium nitrate; temperature $= 25.00 \pm 0.05°C$ (data from Reference [1]).

Solution number (*j*)	pH	Absorbances (in 1 cm cells)					
		480 nm ($i=1$)	600 nm ($i=2$)	640 nm ($i=3$)	646 nm ($i=4$)	700 nm ($i=5$)	800 nm ($i=6$)
1	11.21	0.273	0.460	0.285	0.265	0.119	0.030
2	7.28	0.256	0.460	0.294	0.271	0.124	0.029
3	7.14	0.247	0.459	0.296	0.275	0.127	0.030
4	6.92	0.235	0.461	0.315	0.293	0.147	0.039
5	6.85	0.224	0.461	0.320	0.298	0.155	0.039
6	6.73	0.202	0.460	0.333	0.312	0.172	0.047
7	6.66	0.187	0.460	0.346	0.326	0.192	0.056
8	6.56	0.162	0.460	0.365	0.349	0.207	0.069
9	6.47	0.140	0.455	0.380	0.364	0.230	0.080
10	6.37	0.112	0.450	0.402	0.387	0.260	0.096
11	6.28	0.087	0.432	0.400	0.390	0.271	0.107
12	6.19	0.070	0.414	0.400	0.392	0.288	0.119
13	6.08	0.045	0.376	0.390	0.386	0.310	0.142
14	5.90	0.034	0.327	0.369	0.370	0.329	0.170
15	5.81	0.020	0.285	0.343	0.345	0.327	0.181
16	5.72	0.014	0.250	0.320	0.327	0.332	0.195
17	5.61	0.015	0.225	0.302	0.312	0.336	0.202
18	5.50	0.012	0.179	0.275	0.285	0.337	0.225
19	5.29	0.007	0.142	0.250	0.265	0.335	0.235
20	5.20	0.008	0.135	0.246	0.264	0.341	0.250
21	5.12	0.010	0.129	0.244	0.256	0.345	0.244

hence,

$$A_\lambda^{obs} = \epsilon_\lambda^{en}[Cu(en)_2] + \epsilon_\lambda^{enox}[Cu(en)(ox)] \tag{12.8}$$

where ϵ_λ^{obs}, ϵ_λ^{en} and ϵ_λ^{enox} are the observed molar absorptivity, the molar absorptivity of $[Cu(en)_2]^{2+}$, and the molar absorptivity of $[Cu(en)(ox)]$ at wavelength λ respectively. Substituting for (12.6) in (12.8)

$$\epsilon_\lambda^{en}[Cu(en)_2] + \epsilon_\lambda^{enox}[Cu(en)(ox)] = \epsilon_\lambda^{obs}[Cu(en)(ox)] + \epsilon_\lambda^{obs}[Cu(en)_2] \tag{12.9}$$

Rearranging and collecting terms

$$\frac{[Cu(en)(ox)]}{[Cu(en)_2]} = \frac{\epsilon_\lambda^{obs} - \epsilon_\lambda^{en}}{\epsilon_\lambda^{enox} - \epsilon_\lambda^{obs}} \tag{12.10}$$

Rearranging (12.5) and substituting for (12.10)

$$\frac{[ox]}{[en]} = \frac{\epsilon_\lambda^{obs} - \epsilon_\lambda^{en}}{\epsilon_\lambda^{enox} - \epsilon_\lambda^{obs}} \frac{1}{K_1} \tag{12.11}$$

therefore

$$\frac{\dfrac{[ox]}{[en]}}{(\epsilon_\lambda^{en} - \epsilon_\lambda^{obs})} = -\frac{1}{(\epsilon_\lambda^{enox} - \epsilon_\lambda^{obs})K_1} \tag{12.12}$$

Extracting ϵ_λ^{obs} from (12.11)

$$\frac{[ox]}{[en]}\{\epsilon_\lambda^{enox} - \epsilon_\lambda^{obs}\}K_1 = \epsilon_\lambda^{obs} - \epsilon_\lambda^{en} \tag{12.13}$$

$$\frac{[ox]}{[en]}K_1\epsilon_\lambda^{enox} + \epsilon_\lambda^{en} = \epsilon_\lambda^{obs} + \frac{[ox]}{[en]}K_1\epsilon_\lambda^{obs} \tag{12.14}$$

Collecting terms

$$\frac{[ox]}{[en]}K_1\epsilon_\lambda^{enox} + \epsilon_\lambda^{en} = \epsilon_\lambda^{obs}\left\{1 + \frac{[ox]}{[en]}K_1\right\} \tag{12.15}$$

Substituting for ϵ_λ^{obs} from (12.15) in (12.12) right-hand side we get

$$\frac{\dfrac{[ox]}{[en]}}{(\epsilon_\lambda^{en} - \epsilon_\lambda^{obs})} = -\cfrac{1}{\left\{\cfrac{\epsilon_\lambda^{enox} - \left[\dfrac{[ox]}{[en]} K_1 \epsilon_\lambda^{enox} + \epsilon_\lambda^{en}\right]}{1 + K_1 \dfrac{[ox]}{[en]}}\right\}K_1} \tag{12.16}$$

Multiplying the numerator and denominator of the right-hand side of (12.16) by $\left(1 + K_1 \dfrac{[ox]}{[en]}\right)$,

$$\frac{\dfrac{[ox]}{[en]}}{\epsilon_\lambda^{en} - \epsilon_\lambda^{obs}} = \frac{-1 - K_1 \dfrac{[ox]}{[en]}}{\left\{\epsilon_\lambda^{enox} + \epsilon_\lambda^{enox} K_1 \dfrac{[ox]}{[en]} - \dfrac{[ox]}{[en]} K_1 \epsilon_\lambda^{enox} - \epsilon_\lambda^{en}\right\}K_1} \tag{12.17}$$

whence

$$\frac{\dfrac{[ox]}{[en]}}{\epsilon_\lambda^{en} - \epsilon_\lambda^{obs}} = \frac{1 + K_1 \dfrac{[ox]}{[en]}}{(\epsilon_\lambda^{en} - \epsilon_\lambda^{enox})K_1} \tag{12.18}$$

Separating terms and cancelling K_1 in the second term the equation finally becomes

$$\frac{\dfrac{[ox]}{[en]}}{(\epsilon_\lambda^{en} - \epsilon_\lambda^{obs})} = \frac{1}{(\epsilon_\lambda^{en} - \epsilon_\lambda^{enox})K_1} + \frac{\dfrac{[ox]}{[en]}}{(\epsilon_\lambda^{en} - \epsilon_\lambda^{enox})} \tag{12.19}$$

By a similar tortuous algebraic route, if Equilibrium (12.2) only is of importance, that is, the solutions chosen all pass through the 'isosbestic point' at 700 nm, then a second expression, (12.20), may be derived:

$$\frac{\dfrac{[en]}{[ox]}}{(\epsilon_\lambda^{ox} - \epsilon_\lambda^{obs})} = \frac{K_2}{(\epsilon_\lambda^{ox} - \epsilon_\lambda^{enox})} + \frac{\dfrac{[en]}{[ox]}}{(\epsilon_\lambda^{ox} - \epsilon_\lambda^{enox})} \tag{12.20}$$

where ϵ_λ^{ox} is the major absorptivity of the $[Cu(ox)_2]^{2-}$ complex at wavelength λ.

The importance of both (12.19) and (12.20) is that they are linear equations of the form $y = mx + c$ and both y and x are directly calculable from the experimental data. It should be noted that both x and y are calculated from the same experimental data. This can lead to correlated errors, and care must be taken in the interpretation of the calculated slope and intercept (see Section 4.6).

12.5 GRAPHICAL DETERMINATION OF K_1

The wavelength of choice is 480 nm as this represents a wavelength of maximum difference in absorbance between the $[Cu(en)_2]^{2+}$ ion and the neutral species. The free ethylenediamine concentration is directly determined by the pH of the solution as is shown more fully in the first case study (see Section 10.3(ii)(a)) if the bound ethylenediamine concentration is ignored. Likewise the concentration of oxalate bound to copper(II) is ignored, that is $[ox] \approx [ox]_T$. Hence

$$[en] \simeq \alpha_{en} [en]_T \tag{12.21}$$

where α_{en} is the fraction of the ethylenediamine present as free ethylenediamine. Since $[en]_T = [ox]_T \approx [ox]$, then

$$\frac{[ox]}{[en]} \simeq \frac{1}{\alpha_{en}} \tag{12.22}$$

which substituting for α_{en} from Equation (10.15) and taking K_4 and K_5 to be 1.514×10^{10} and 3.089×10^7 respectively (see Section 12.3) yields

$$\frac{[ox]}{[en]} = 1 + 1.514 \times 10^{10} [H^+] + 4.677 \times 10^{17} [H^+]^2 \tag{12.23}$$

ϵ_{480}^{en} is obtainable directly from solution 1 in Table 12.2, since if all the copper(II) is present as $[Cu(en)_2]^{2+}$ then the concentration is 0.01 mol.l^{-1}. Hence ϵ_{480}^{en} is equal to 27.3 l.mol^{-1}.cm^{-1}. ϵ_{480}^{obs} may be calculated similarly for each pH chosen, using Equation (12.7). A graphical solution to Equation (12.19) can now be accomplished, (Table 12.3). A plot of $\dfrac{[ox]}{[en]}\Big/(\epsilon_{480}^{en} - \epsilon_{480}^{obs})$ versus $\dfrac{[ox]}{[en]}$ yields the predicted straight line with a slope of 4.188×10^{-2} and an intercept of 1.897×10^3 (Figure 12.5a).

From Equation (12.19) a value for K_1 can be obtained by dividing the slope by intercept. A value of 2.208×10^{-5} is obtained, after neglecting to correct for the concentrations of ethylenediamine or oxalate bound to the copper. However,

Table 12.3 — Data for the graphical evaluation of Equation (12.19) for the copper(II)-ethylenediamine-oxalate system using solutions 5 to 10 in Table 12.2.

pH	$\dfrac{[ox]}{[en]} \times 10^{-4}$	ϵ_{480}^{obs}	$(\epsilon_{480}^{en} - \epsilon_{480}^{obs})$	$\dfrac{\dfrac{[ox]}{[en]}}{(\epsilon_{480}^{en} - \epsilon_{480}^{obs}) \times 10^{-3}}$
6.85	1.147	22.4	4.9	2.341
6.73	1.904	20.2	7.1	2.682
6.66	2.569	18.7	8.6	2.987
6.56	3.965	16.2	11.1	3.572
6.47	5.883	14.0	13.3	4.423
6.37	9.157	11.2	16.1	5.688

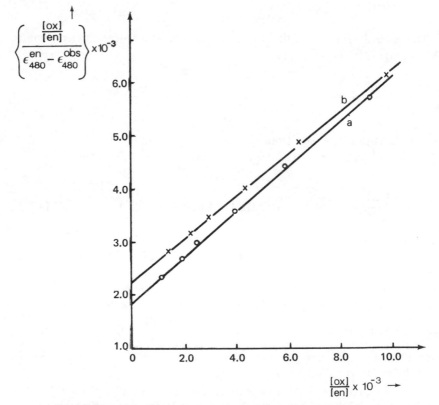

Figure 12.5 — Graphical solution of Equation (12.19) linear least-squares fit. (a) uncorrected data at 480 nm from Table 12.3, (b) corrected data at 480 nm from Table 12.4.

using this value, it is now possible to calculate these concentrations and recalculate a better approximation to the true value of K_1. The total ethylenediamine bound to copper(II), $[en]_B$ is given by:

$$[en]_B = 2[Cu(en)_2] + [Cu(en)(ox)] \qquad (12.24)$$

and the total oxalate bound to copper(II), $[ox]_B$, is given by

$$[ox]_B = [Cu(en)(ox)] \qquad (12.25)$$

hence

$$[ox] = [ox]_T - [Cu(en)(ox)] \qquad (12.26)$$

and

$$[en] = \{[en]_T - [en]_B\}\alpha_{en} \qquad (12.27)$$

The mass balance equation for copper(II) is known also:

$$[Cu]_T = [Cu(en)(ox)] + [Cu(en)_2] \qquad (12.28)$$

All that is required now to solve Equations (12.24) to (12.27) are the concentrations of $[Cu(en)_2]$ and $[Cu(en)(ox)]$. These may be obtained from Equation (12.1). Let the ratio $[ox]/[en]$ equal R then

$$K_1 R = \frac{[Cu(en)(ox)]}{[Cu(en)_2]} \qquad (12.29)$$

Combining this with (12.28) by substituting for $[Cu(en)(ox)]$,

$$RK_1[Cu(en)_2] + [Cu(en)_2] = [Cu]_T \qquad (12.30)$$

and hence,

$$[Cu(en)_2] = \frac{[Cu]_T}{\dfrac{[ox]}{[en]}K_1 + 1} \qquad (12.31)$$

The recalculation is summarised in Table 12.4. Plotting these data a straight line is obtained of slope 3.937×10^{-2} and intercept 2.270×10^3 (Figure 12.5b). A new value for K_1 is obtained by dividing the slope by the intercept to give a value of 1.734×10^{-5} and hence a pK_1 value of 4.76. This process, involving estimation of the bound ethylenediamine and oxalate concentrations, can be repeated until no significant change in K_1 occurs.

Table 12.4 — Data from Table 12.3 recalculated after correcting for the concentrations of ethylenediamine and oxalate bound to copper(II).

pH	$[Cu(en)_2]$ $\times 10^3$	$[Cu(en)(ox)]$ $\times 10^3$	$[en]_B$ $\times 10^2$	$[en]'$ $\times 10^6$	$[ox]'$	$\dfrac{[ox]'}{[en]'}$ $\times 10^{-4}$	$\dfrac{\dfrac{[ox]'}{[en]'}}{(\epsilon_{480}^{en} - \epsilon_{480}^{obs})}$ $\times 10^{-3}$
6.85	7.979	2.021	1.798	7.151	0.09798	1.370	2.796
6.73	7.040	2.960	1.704	4.358	0.09704	2.227	3.137
6.66	6.381	3.619	1.638	3.254	0.09638	2.962	3.444
6.56	5.332	4.668	1.533	2.137	0.09533	4.461	4.019
6.47	4.350	5.650	1.435	1.457	0.09435	6.476	4.869
6.37	3.309	6.691	1.331	0.947	0.09331	9.856	6.122

12.6 GRAPHICAL DETERMINATION OF K_2

In a similar manner to that described in Section 12.5, Equation (12.20) can be solved for K_2, only this time a wavelength of 800 nm is chosen as this represents a wavelength where a maximum spectral difference occurs between $[Cu(en)(ox)]$ and $[Cu(ox)_2]^{2-}$. In the first calculation, it is assumed again that bound concentrations of ethylenediamine and oxalate may be neglected. The calculation for the chosen pH region is summarised in Table 12.5. A value for the molar absorptivity of the $[Cu(ox)_2]^{2-}$ complex, ϵ_{800}^{ox} (24.71.mol^{-1}.cm^{-1}), is obtained directly

Table 12.5 — Data for the graphical solution of Equation (12.20) for the copper(II)-ethylenediamine-oxalate system using solutions 14 to 18 in Table 12.2.

pH	$\dfrac{[en]}{[ox]} \times 10^{7\dagger}$	ϵ_{800}^{obs}	$(\epsilon_{800}^{ox} - \epsilon_{800}^{obs})$	$\dfrac{\dfrac{[en]}{[ox]}}{(\epsilon_{800}^{ox} - \epsilon_{800}^{obs})} \times 10^7$
5.90	13.15	17.0	7.7	1.708
5.81	8.731	18.1	6.6	1.323
5.72	5.791	19.5	5.2	1.114
5.61	3.502	20.2	4.5	0.778
5.50	2.116	22.5	2.2	0.962

† These values are the reciprocals of those for $\dfrac{[ox]}{[en]}$ in Table 12.3.

from solutions 20 and 21 in Table 12.2 and the total copper(II) concentration. A plot of $\dfrac{[en]}{[ox]}\Big/(\epsilon_{800}^{ox} - \epsilon_{800}^{obs})$ against $[en]/[ox]$ gives a straight line with considerable scatter (Figure 12.6a). A value of 0.0777 is obtained for the slope and 6.60×10^{-8} for the intercept. K_2 is found by dividing the intercept by the slope as indicated by Equation (12.20); a value for K_2 of 8.494×10^{-7} is obtained.

The correction for the bound ligand concentrations can be carried out in a similar manner to that for K_1. However, as Equilibrium (12.2) is involved the equations for $[en]_B$ and $[ox]_B$ are different.

$$[en]_B = [Cu(en)(ox)] \tag{12.32}$$

$$[ox]_B = [ox]_T - [Cu(en)(ox)] - 2[Cu(ox)_2] \tag{12.33}$$

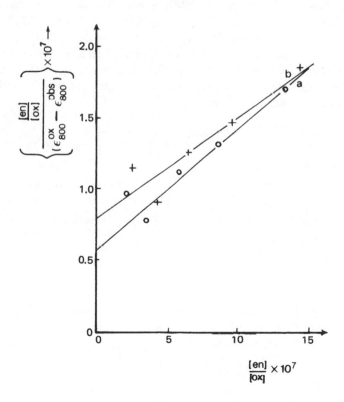

Figure 12.6 – Graphical solution of Equation (12.20) linear least-squares fit. (a) uncorrected data at 800 nm from Table 12.5, (b) corrected data at 800 nm from Table 12.6.

The concentrations can be calculated in a similar manner to that already described as the equation analogous to (12.31) becomes

$$[Cu(ox)_2] = \frac{[Cu]_T}{\dfrac{[en]/[ox]}{K_2} + 1}$$

(12.34)

The recalculation is summarised in Table 12.6. Replotting Equation (12.20) yields a straight line but with more scatter than before with a slope of 0.07134 and an intercept of 8.015×10^{-8} (Figure 12.6b). A value of 1.123×10^{-6} is obtained for K_2 and hence a pK_2 value of 5.95. As in the case of K_1 (Section 12.5), the calculation of K_2 is by iteration, involving estimation of the bound ethylenediamine and oxalate concentrations and should be carried out until no significant change in K_2 occurs.

The precision of this data is much worse than in the example of K_1. This is apparent on inspection of the graphs plotted in Figure 12.6. The cause is apparent if the column of $(\epsilon_{480}^{en} - \epsilon_{490}^{obs})$ values in Table 12.3 and the column of $(\epsilon_{800}^{ox} - \epsilon_{800}^{obs})$ values in Table 12.5 are compared. The latter values are smaller and in the last value approach the expected photometric error of the spectrophotometer. The former differences are much larger and hence yield much more consistent results.

12.7 ESTIMATION OF MOLE FRACTIONS OF THE COPPER(II) COMPLEXES AND STABILITY CONSTANTS FROM ISOSBESTIC POINT DATA

As the molar absorptivities of $[Cu(en)_2]^{2+}$ and $[Cu(en)(ox)]$ are the same at 600 nm it can be assumed that any decrease in absorbance is due to the $[Cu(ox)_2]^{2-}$ species. Hence the mole fraction of the $[Cu(ox)_2]^{2-}$ species present, x_{ox}, is given by

$$x_{ox} = \frac{\epsilon_{600}^{iso} - \epsilon_{600}^{obs}}{\epsilon_{600}^{iso} - \epsilon_{600}^{ox}}$$

(12.35)

The values ϵ_{600}^{iso} of 46.0 l.mol^{-1}.cm^{-1} and ϵ_{600}^{ox} of 12.9 l.mol^{-1}.cm^{-1} are readily obtainable from the first eight solutions and the last solution in Table 12.2. Hence Equation (12.35) becomes

$$x_{ox} = \frac{46.0 - \epsilon_{600}^{obs}}{33.1}$$

(12.36)

Similarly at the isosbestic wavelength of 700 nm the molar absorptivities of both the $[Cu(ox)_2]^{2-}$ complex and the $[Cu(en)(ox)]$ complex are equal. A value of ϵ_{700}^{iso} of 33.9 l.mol^{-1}.cm^{-1} is obtained from the last five solutions at 700 nm. The value of 11.9 $l.mol^{-1}.cm^{-1}$ for the molar absorptivity of the ethylenediamine complex at 700 nm, ϵ_{700}^{en}, is obtained from solution 1 in Table 12.2. Any decrease in absorbance at 700 nm can be attributed to the presence of the $[Cu(ox)_2]^{2-}$ complex. The mole fraction of this complex, x_{en}, may be calculated from (12.38).

$$x_{en} = \frac{\epsilon_{700}^{iso} - \epsilon_{700}^{obs}}{\epsilon_{700}^{iso} - \epsilon_{700}^{en}} \tag{12.37}$$

and hence

$$x_{en} = \frac{33.9 - \epsilon_{700}^{obs}}{22.0} \tag{12.38}$$

Using Equations (12.36) and (12.38), one can now calculate the mole fractions of the species present for selected solutions. If these are known the molar absorptivity of the mixed complex at another wavelength, for example 640 nm, can be calculated using (12.37):

$$\epsilon_{640}^{enox} = \frac{(\epsilon_{640}^{obs} - x_{en}\,\epsilon_{640}^{en} - x_{ox}\,\epsilon_{640}^{ox})}{(1 - x_{en} - x_{ox})} \tag{12.39}$$

These calculations are summarised in Table 12.7. Values for ϵ_{640}^{ox} and ϵ_{640}^{en} of 24.4 and 28.5 $l.mol^{-1}.cm^{-1}$ respectively are outlined from solutions 1 and 2 in Table 12.2. These values of x_{en} and x_{ox} can be used to calculate x_{enox} and hence the values for K_1 and K_2, but is better to take data from three wavelengths

Table 12.6 – Data from Table 12.5 recalculated after correcting for the concentrations of ethylenediamine and oxalate bound to copper(II).

pH	$[Cu(ox)_2]$ $\times 10^3$	$[Cu(en)(ox)]$ $\times 10^3$	$[ox]_B$ $\times 10^2$	$[en]'$ $\times 10^8$	$[ox]'$	$\dfrac{[en]'}{[ox]'}$ $\times 10^7$	$\dfrac{\dfrac{[en]'}{[ox]'}}{(\epsilon_{800}^{ox} - \epsilon_{800}^{obs})}$ $\times 10^7$
5.90	3.924	6.076	1.392	12.35	0.08608	14.35	1.863
5.81	4.891	5.109	1.489	8.285	0.08511	9.734	1.475
5.72	5.946	4.054	1.595	5.556	0.08405	6.610	1.271
5.61	7.081	2.919	1.708	3.400	0.08292	4.100	0.911
5.50	8.006	1.994	1.801	2.074	0.08199	2.530	1.150

to determine these more accurately, using the value of ϵ_{640}^{enox} found. From the slope of Equations (12.19) and (12.20) one obtains values for $\epsilon_{480}^{en} - \epsilon_{480}^{enox}$ and $\epsilon_{800}^{ox} - \epsilon_{800}^{enox}$ of 25.4 and $14.01.\text{mol}^{-1}.\text{cm}^{-1}$ respectively. As ϵ_{480}^{en} and ϵ_{800}^{ox} values are known from Table 12.2, the values of ϵ_{480}^{enox} and ϵ_{800}^{enox} are 1.9 and $10.41.\text{mol}^{-1}.\text{cm}^{-1}$ respectively.

We are now in a position to solve three equations containing three unknowns, that is, the mole fractions of $[Cu(en)_2]^{2+}$, $[Cu(en)(ox)]$, and $[Cu(ox)_2]^{2-}$, from data at three wavelengths, 480 nm, 640 nm, and 800 nm as we can write a general expression in accordance with Beer's Law.

$$\epsilon_\lambda^{en} x_{en} + \epsilon_\lambda^{enox} x_{enox} + \epsilon_\lambda^{ox} x_{ox} = \epsilon_\lambda^{obs} \tag{12.40}$$

This may be specified for our λ values

$$27.3 x_{en} + 1.9 x_{enox} + 1.0 x_{ox} = \epsilon_{480}^{obs} \tag{12.41}$$

$$28.5 x_{en} + 48.1 x_{enox} + 24.4 x_{ox} = \epsilon_{640}^{obs} \tag{12.42}$$

$$3.0 x_{en} + 10.4 x_{enox} + 24.4 x_{ox} = \epsilon_{800}^{obs} \tag{12.43}$$

In matrix notation we can express Equations (12.41) to (12.43) as

$$\mathbf{\epsilon} X = A \tag{12.44}$$

where $\mathbf{\epsilon}$ is a 3×3 matrix of molar absorptivities, X is a column vector of the mole fractions and A is a column vector of observed absorbances. Equation (12.44) is similar to Equation (3.54) which was solved using determinants. However, many small programmable calculators have programs to invert a 3×3 matrix and premultiply a column vector. Equation (12.44) can be solved for X in this matter.

$$X = \mathbf{\epsilon}^{-1} A \tag{12.45}$$

This is quite convenient as the inverse matrix $\mathbf{\epsilon}^{-1}$ has to be found only once by the method of determinants using the rule of Sarrus. The problem can be resolved as follows. Let the matrix $\mathbf{\epsilon}$ be represented as

$$\begin{bmatrix} \epsilon_{11} & \epsilon_{12} & \epsilon_{13} \\ \epsilon_{21} & \epsilon_{22} & \epsilon_{23} \\ \epsilon_{31} & \epsilon_{32} & \epsilon_{33} \end{bmatrix} = \begin{bmatrix} 27.3 & 1.9 & 1.0 \\ 28.5 & 48.1 & 24.4 \\ 3.0 & 10.4 & 24.4 \end{bmatrix} \tag{12.46}$$

the determinant, DET, is given by

Table 12.7 – Evaluation of x_{ox}, x_{en} and ϵ_{640}^{enox} from Equations (12.36), (12.38) and (12.39) respectively for solutions 5 to 10, 14 and 15 in Table 12.2.

pH	ϵ_{600}^{obs}	ϵ_{700}^{obs}	x_{ox}	x_{en}	ϵ_{640}^{obs}	$x_{en}\,\epsilon_{640}^{en}$	$x_{ox}\,\epsilon_{640}^{ox}$	ϵ_{640}^{enox}
6.85	46.1	15.5	0	0.836	32.0	23.8	0	50.0
6.73	46.0	17.2	0	0.759	33.3	21.6	0	48.5
6.66	46.0	19.2	0	0.668	34.6	19.0	0	47.0
6.56	46.0	20.7	0	0.600	36.5	17.1	0	48.5
6.47	45.5	23.0	0.015	0.496	38.0	14.1	0.4	48.1
6.37	45.0	26.0	0.030	0.359	40.2	10.2	0.7	48.0
5.90	32.7	32.9	0.402	0.046	36.9	1.3	9.8	46.7
5.81	28.5	32.7	0.529	0.055	34.3	1.6	12.9	47.6
							Mean	48.1
							Standard deviation	1.0

the determinant, DET, is given by

$$DET = \epsilon_{11}\epsilon_{22}\epsilon_{33} + \epsilon_{12}\epsilon_{23}\epsilon_{31} + \epsilon_{13}\epsilon_{32}\epsilon_{21} -$$
$$\epsilon_{13}\epsilon_{22}\epsilon_{31} - \epsilon_{23}\epsilon_{32}\epsilon_{11} - \epsilon_{33}\epsilon_{21}\epsilon_{12}$$

$$(12.47)$$

the value of which comes to 24082.6.

The elements of the inverse matrix $\boldsymbol{\mathcal{E}}^{-1}$ may be represented as

$$\boldsymbol{\mathcal{E}}^{-1} = \begin{bmatrix} \alpha_1 & \beta_1 & \gamma_1 \\ \alpha_2 & \beta_2 & \gamma_2 \\ \alpha_3 & \beta_3 & \gamma_3 \end{bmatrix} \qquad (12.48)$$

where
$$\alpha_1 = (\epsilon_{22}\epsilon_{33} - \epsilon_{32}\epsilon_{23})/DET = 0.0382$$
$$\alpha_2 = (\epsilon_{31}\epsilon_{23} - \epsilon_{21}\epsilon_{33})/DET = -0.0259$$
$$\alpha_3 = (\epsilon_{21}\epsilon_{32} - \epsilon_{31}\epsilon_{22})/DET = 0.0063$$
$$\beta_1 = (\epsilon_{32}\epsilon_{13} - \epsilon_{31}\epsilon_{22})/DET = -0.0015$$
$$\beta_2 = (\epsilon_{11}\epsilon_{33} - \epsilon_{31}\epsilon_{13})/DET = 0.0275$$
$$\beta_3 = (\epsilon_{31}\epsilon_{12} - \epsilon_{11}\epsilon_{32})/DET = -0.0116$$
$$\gamma_1 = (\epsilon_{12}\epsilon_{23} - \epsilon_{22}\epsilon_{13})/DET = -0.0001$$
$$\gamma_2 = (\epsilon_{21}\epsilon_{13} - \epsilon_{11}\epsilon_{23})/DET = -0.0265$$
$$\gamma_3 = (\epsilon_{11}\epsilon_{22} - \epsilon_{21}\epsilon_{12})/DET = 0.0523$$

All that now remains to be done to find the mole fraction vector, X, is to post-multiply the inverse matrix by the column vector A of observed absorbances.

$$X = \begin{bmatrix} \alpha_1 & \beta_1 & \gamma_1 \\ \alpha_2 & \beta_2 & \gamma_2 \\ \alpha_3 & \beta_3 & \gamma_3 \end{bmatrix} \begin{bmatrix} a_1 \\ a_2 \\ a_3 \end{bmatrix} \qquad (12.49)$$

Hence
$$X = \begin{bmatrix} \alpha_1 a_1 + \beta_1 a_2 + \gamma_1 a_3 \\ \alpha_2 a_1 + \beta_2 a_2 + \gamma_2 a_3 \\ \alpha_3 a_1 + \beta_3 a_2 + \gamma_3 a_3 \end{bmatrix} = \begin{bmatrix} x_{en} \\ x_{enox} \\ x_{ox} \end{bmatrix}$$

For example at pH 6.85, A $= \begin{bmatrix} 22.4 \\ 32.0 \\ 3.9 \end{bmatrix}$

resulting in $X = \begin{bmatrix} 0.808 \\ 0.199 \\ -0.024 \end{bmatrix}$

The obviously nonsensical negative value for x_{ox} arises from errors in the values used to generate ε^{-1}. As negative values have no chemical significance they are taken as zero for that species. The mole fractions found are summarised in Tables 12.8 and 12.9. The totals, x_T, in perfect error-free data would be unity, and in spite of the errors in the data set, the values of x_T found are within $\pm 4\%$ of unity.

Values of pK_1 and pK_2 can be obtained directly from Equation (12.1) and (12.2) using the ratios of the free ethylenediamine and oxalate concentrations as found in the graphical solutions. This procedure enables an estimate of the precision of the values found to be made.

12.8 CALCULATION USING A NON-LINEAR LEAST-SQUARES PROGRAM

The computer program DALSFEK (Appendix III) enables a non-linear least-squares analysis of stability constant data to be undertaken according to a defined chemical model (see Chapters 2 and 5). Having refined the parameters to fit the data to predetermined least-squares criteria the program can then calculate the values of the observables from the final determined constants according to the model chosen. In addition the concentrations of all species in solution are readily calculated, as shown in Table 12.10 for solution 5 from Table 12.2. The fourth place of decimals in the deviation column is included to show the mathematical variation only and is not of analytical significance. The mole fractions of the copper complexes are also available (see Table 12.11). The discrepancy between the values found for the mole fractions of the copper(II) species by DALSFEK and the method of determinants (Table 12.11) explains why the final values of K_1 and K_2 by the non-linear least-squares method do not coincide with those of the graphical or determinantal calculations.

The data in Table 12.2 is good and the fit is shown to be good, as the Hamilton R-factor is less than that of the R_{lim} factor, the values being 0.01186 and 0.01347 respectively (see Equations (5.5) and (5.6)). The goodness of fit of the data to the model is also indicated by the calculated molar absorptivity values (Table 12.12). The most interesting aspect of this table is the values found for the so-called 'isosbestic' wavelengths of 600 nm and 700 nm. The assumptions made in the graphical and determinantal methods were that $\epsilon_{600}^{en} = \epsilon_{600}^{enox}$ and $\epsilon_{700}^{enox} = \epsilon_{700}^{ox}$. It can now be seen that the values are only within 2 or 3 per cent of one another, and hence any values for stability constants derived by making these assumptions are only approximate.

Table 12.8 – Evaluation of the mole fractions of $[Cu(en)_2]^{2+}$, $[Cu(en)(ox)]$ and $[Cu(ox)_2]^{2-}$ and pK_1 for solutions 5 to 10 in Table 12.2 using Equation (12.50).

pH	ϵ_{480}^{obs}	ϵ_{640}^{obs}	ϵ_{800}^{obs}	mole fractions				$\dfrac{x_{enox}}{x_{en}}$	$\dfrac{[en]'}{[ox]'} \times 10^5$	pK_1
				x_{en}	x_{enox}	x_{ox}	x_T			
6.85	22.4	32.0	3.9	0.808	0.199	0	1.007	0.2463	7.298	4.75
6.73	20.2	33.3	4.7	0.722	0.271	0	0.993	0.3753	4.490	4.77
6.66	18.7	34.6	5.6	0.662	0.322	0.011	0.995	0.4864	3.376	4.79
6.56	16.2	36.5	6.9	0.564	0.404	0.041	1.009	0.7163	2.242	4.79
6.47	14.0	38.0	8.0	0.477	0.474	0.067	1.018	0.9937	1.544	4.81
6.37	11.2	40.2	9.6	0.367	0.564	0.108	1.039	1.5368	1.015	4.81
									Mean	4.79
									Standard deviation	0.02

Table 12.9 – Evaluation of the mole fractions of $[Cu(en)_2]^{2+}$, $[Cu(en)(ox)]$ and $[Cu(ox)_2]^{2-}$ and pK_2 for solutions 14 to 18 in Table 12.2 using Equation (12.50).

pH	ϵ_{480}^{obs}	ϵ_{640}^{obs}	ϵ_{800}^{obs}	mole fractions				$\dfrac{x_{ox}}{x_{enox}}$	$\dfrac{[en]'}{[ox]'} \times 10^7$	pK_2
				x_{en}	x_{enox}^1	x_{ox}	x_T			
5.90	3.4	36.9	17.0	0.074	0.479	0.484	1.037	1.0104	14.350	5.84
5.81	2.0	34.3	18.1	0.024	0.414	0.562	1.000	1.3575	9.734	5.88
5.72	1.4	32.0	19.5	0.004	0.329	0.658	0.991	2.0000	6.610	5.88
5.61	1.5	30.3	20.2	0.011	0.258	0.716	0.985	2.7752	4.100	5.94
5.50	1.2	27.5	22.5	0.003	0.131	0.866	1.000	6.6107	2.530	5.78
									Mean	5.86
									Standard deviation	0.06

Table 12.10 – Observed and calculated absorbances for Solution 5 in Table 12.2 using DALSFEK.

Wavelength	Absorbance		
	Observed	Calculated	Deviation
480 nm	0.224	0.223	0.0009
600 nm	0.461	0.461	0.0000
640 nm	0.320	0.320	0.0004
646 nm	0.298	0.300	−0.0018
700 nm	0.155	0.156	−0.0008
800 nm	0.039	0.043	−0.0036

Table 12.11 – Mole fractions of copper(II) species in Solution 5 in Table 12.2 obtained by the method of determinants and DALSFEK.

Complex	Mole fraction	
	Determinants	DALSFEK
$[Cu(en)_2]^{2+}$	0.808	0.726
$[Cu(en)(ox)]$	0.199	0.267
$[Cu(ox)_2]^{2-}$	0	0.007

12.9 SUMMARY

The values of pK_1 and pK_2 for Equilibria (12.1) and (12.2) obtained by the three methods described in this chapter are summarised in Table 12.13. Reasonable estimates of the values of pK_1 and pK_2 are obtainable using the graphical and determinantal methods although they are not as precise as those obtained by the non-linear least-squares treatment. This is, in part, because the apparent 'isosbestic' points in Figure 12.1 are not truly isosbestic as can be seen from the molar absorptivities in the boxes in Table 12.12.

Finally the distribution diagram as a function of pH for copper(II) complexes obtained from the data in Table 12.2 is shown in Figure 12.7.

Table 12.12 — Best fit molar absorptivities of copper(II) complexes (standard deviations are shown in parentheses) as determined using DALSFEK.

λ(nm)	$[Cu(en)_2]^{2+}$	$[Cu(en)(ox)]$	$[Cu(ox)_2]^{2-}$
480	26.90(0.19)	2.42(0.34)	0.73(0.19)
600	46.00(0.18)	47.07(0.35)†	11.53(0.23)
640	28.54(0.18)	46.63(0.35)	23.16(0.21)
646	26.23(0.18)	46.61(0.35)	24.82(0.20)
700	11.54(0.18)	33.10(0.32)	34.04(0.19)†
800	2.48(0.17)	11.84(0.29)	24.85(0.19)

† Attention is drawn to the two 'isosbestic' wavelengths and their calculated best fit molar absorptivities.

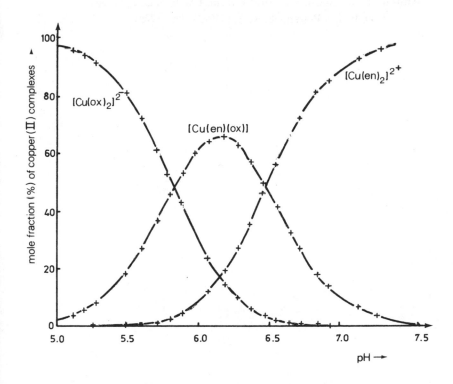

Figure 12.7 — Distribution of copper(II) complexes in the copper(II)-ethylenediamine-oxalate system.

Table 12.13 – Summary of the stability constants obtained for the copper(II)-ethylenediamine-oxalate system (standard deviations are shown in parentheses).

Method	pK_1	pK_2
Graphical (Sections 12.5 and 12.6)	4.76	5.95
Determinantal (Section 12.7)	4.79 (0.02)	5.86 (0.06)
DALSFEK (Section 12.8)	4.786 (0.022)	5.957 (0.019)

REFERENCES

[1] Dewitt, R. and Watters, J. I. (1954). *J. Amer. Chem. Soc.*, **76**, 3810.
[2] Werner, A. (1899). *Z. Anorg. Allgem. Chem.*, **21**, 200.
[3] Kirschner, S. (1960). *Inorg. Synth.*, **6**, 1.
[4] Poulsen, I. and Bjerrum J. (1955). *Acta. Chem. Scand.*, **9**, 1407.
[5] Everett, D. E. and Pinsent, B. R. W. (1952). *Proc. Roy. Soc. A.*, **215**, 416.

CHAPTER 13

Fourth Case Study: Model Building and Testing using a Computer; the Sodium Tetrachloropalladate(II)-Sodium Chloride System

13.1 INTRODUCTION

This case study illustrates the use of some of the model-building techniques described in Chapters 2, 4 and 5, applied to the sodium tetrachloropalladate(II)-sodium chloride system in glacial acetic acid. This system is studied spectrophotometrically [1] and the equilibria formed are sufficiently complicated as to make a conventional graphical treatment of the data very difficult. A number of chemical observations, both qualitative and quantitative, are used to infer a chemical model. This model is then used in conjunction with a non-linear least-squares program to analyse the data to calculate the stability constants. Several alternative models are tried and the effects of adjusting the systematic errors investigated.

13.2 EXPERIMENTAL METHOD

Stock solutions of sodium tetrachloropalladate(II) and sodium chloride are prepared by stirring excess of these compounds in glacial acetic acid and filtering off the precipitated sodium cloride in each case [2]. These solutions are then accurately standardised for palladium and chloride. The former is carried out gravimetrically using sodium iodide to precipitate palladium(II) iodide [3]. The latter is carried out by a Volhard titration [4], after pretreating with zinc to precipitate palladium so as not to obscure the end-point with the colour of palladium(II). The absorbances of a series of glacial acetic acid solutions, containing 1.51×10^{-4} mol.l^{-1} palladium(II) and chloride concentrations in the range 5.89×10^{-4} to 1.28×10^{-2} mol.l^{-1}, are determined at ten approximately equally spaced wavelengths in the range 260 to 375 nm, using a water-filled constant temperature cell-housing maintained at $25.00 \pm 0.01°$C.

13.3 BUILDING THE MODEL: THE NUMBER OF ABSORBING SPECIES IN SOLUTION

The first problem is to quantify the number of absorbing species in solution. This is done by rank analysis of the wavelength solution absorbance matrix, as described in Section 2.4. Thus running the computer program TRIANG (see Appendix II) on data derived from those solutions where the total chloride to total palladium ratio, $[Cl]_T:[Pd]_T$, was 20:1 or more, yields a rank of 2 for a

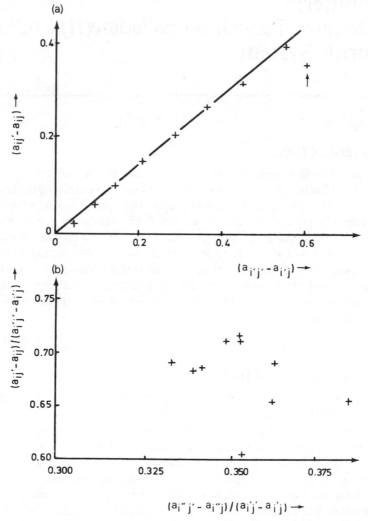

Figure 13.1 – Plots obtained using restricted stoichiometry graphical rank evaluation of the sodium tetrachloropalladate (II)-sodium chloride system: (a) two-species test where $i = 274$ and $i' = 282$ nm; (b) three-species test, where $i = 274, i' = 282$ and $i'' = 297$ nm.

reasonable absorbance error matrix of 0.003. A graphical method (see Section 2.3(ii)) of rank evaluation [5] supports this computer-based result. Thus a two-species restricted stoichiometry test gives a straight-line passing through the origin whereas a three-species restricted stoichiometry test merely gives a series of random points (Figure 13.1). It is particularly noticeable that the only point on the two-species plot that deviates significantly from the straight line is that (arrowed) which arises from a solution with a $[Cl]_T:[Pd]_T$ ratio of less than 20:1. Thus at low chloride concentrations it is likely that more than two absorbing species are present. This inference is supported by the program TRIANG, because inclusion of data from solutions with $[Cl]_T:[Pd]_T$ ratios of less than 20:1 results in a rank of 3 being obtained.

Further evidence in support of the number of species present in solution is obtained from the u.v. spectra of a series of sodium tetrachloropalladate(II) solutions in glacial acetic acid, with varying amounts of sodium chloride added. These show two sharp isosbestic points for those solutions whose $[Cl]_T:[Pd]_T$ ratios are 20:1 or more (Figure 13.2). Whilst this observation cannot provide

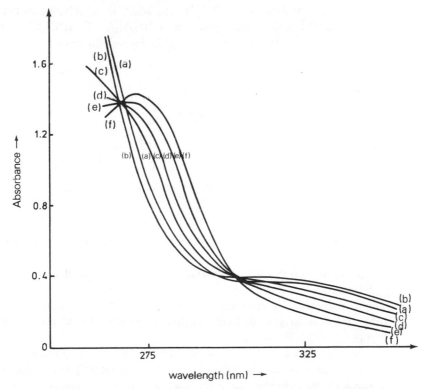

Figure 13.2 — U.v. spectra of a series of chloropalladium(II) solutions in glacial acetic acid: $[Pd]_T = 1.51 \times 10^{-4}$ mol.l^{-1}; $[Cl]_T = 5.90 \times 10^{-4}$ (a), 1.98×10^{-3} (b), 3.38×10^{-3} (c), 6.17×10^{-3} (d), 8.96×10^{-3} (e), and 1.31×10^{-2} mol.l^{-1} (f).

absolute proof of the presence of only two absorbing species, as discussed in Section 2.2, this evidence is consistent with that from the absorbance matrix rank analysis. Solution (a) in Figure 13.2 clearly does not pass through the isosbestic points, suggesting the existence of at least one further species at low chloride concentrations, in agreement with the absorbance matrix rank analysis.

13.4 BUILDING THE MODEL: THE NATURE OF THE SPECIES IN SOLUTION

Having obtained some idea of how many species are present the next step is to attempt to determine their chemical formulae. To do this we make use of some further experimental observations. These are:

(a) At high $[Cl]_T:[Pd]_T$ ratios it is possible to isolate $(C_3H_5NH_3^+)_2[PdCl_4]^{2-}$ and $(C_3H_7NH_3^+)_2[PdCl_4]^{2-}$ from glacial acetic acid solution by addition of allyl- and n-propyl-ammonium chlorides respectively [6]. This suggests that one of the species present at high chloride concentration is Na_2PdCl_4. At low $[Cl]_T:[Pd]_T$ ratios addition of allylammonium perchlorate [6] leads to the formation of $Na[Pd_2Cl_5(C_3H_5NH_3Cl)]$, an olefin complex containing the dimeric palladium-olefin species I.

I

This strongly suggests that another of the palladium species present is $Na_2Pd_2Cl_6$.

(b) When sodium tetrachloropalladate(II) is dissolved in glacial acetic acid, sodium chloride is precipitated.

(c) The dimerisation of inorganic chlorides in glacial acetic acid and in other solvents of low dielectric constant has been found previously [7,8].

(d) Spectral changes are observed in the visible region when chloride ions are added to a solution of sodium tetrachoropalladate(II) ions in glacial acetic acid. Since in this region the spectra of $[PdCl_4]^{2-}$ and $[Pd_2Cl_6]^{2-}$ are very similar [9], this observation implies the existence of a solvo-species.

All of the qualitative evidence described so far is consistent with the presence of Equilibrium (13.1) together with either (13.2) or (13.3), or all three. To proceed further requires quantitative data.

$$2Na_2PdCl_4 \xrightleftharpoons{K_1} Na_2Pd_2Cl_6 + 2NaCl \tag{13.1}$$

$$Na_2Pd_2Cl_6 \xrightleftharpoons{K_2} Na[Pd_2Cl_5(CH_3COOH)] + NaCl \tag{13.2}$$

$$Na_2PdCl_4 \xrightleftharpoons{K_3} Na[PdCl_3(CH_3COOH)] + NaCl \tag{13.3}$$

13.5 BUILDING THE MODEL: EVALUATION OF THE STABILITY CONSTANTS

Qualitative data has shown that Equilibria (13.2) and (13.3) can be ignored when the $[Cl]_T:[Pd]_T$ ratio is greater than 20:1. Hence it is possible to derive an estimate for K_1 using data from solutions satisfying this criterion. Values for K_1 and the molar absorptivities of the Na_2PdCl_4 and $Na_2Pd_2Cl_6$ species can be obtained [1,2] using the program DALSFEK (see Appendix III). The input data for this calculation are the absorbances of each solution with $[Cl]_T:[Pd]_T$ ratios of greater than 20:1, $[Pd]_T$, $[Cl]_T$ and initial estimates of both K_1 and the molar absorptivities of Na_2PdCl_4 and $Na_2Pd_2Cl_6$. Whilst not absolutely necessary for convergence, good intitial estimates of these latter parameters can be obtained in the following way.

(i) Initial estimates of the molar absorbtivities of Na_2PdCl_4 and $Na_2Pd_2Cl_6$

It is, of course, not possible to prepare glacial acetic acid solutions of either Na_2PdCl_4 or $Na_2Pd_2Cl_6$, since immediately this is attempted equilibria that we are trying to evaluate are established. The molar absorptivity of $Na_2Pd_2Cl_6$ can, however, be estimated by plotting the absorbances of a series of solutions of constant palladium(II) concentration and decreasing chloride concentrations at the required wavelengths and extrapolating to obtain the absorbance at a $[Cl]_T:[Pd]_T$ ratio of 3:1. Such a series of plots is shown in Figure 13.3. As expected, the points at the lowest $[Cl]_T:[Pd]_T$ ratios deviate from the smooth curves owing to the presence of the solvo-species. The validity of the estimates so obtained can be established by plotting them out as spectra, including the known molar absorptivities at the isosbestic points, and checking that a smooth curve is obtained. When this done the solid (estimated) line in Figure 13.4a is obtained.

Estimates of the molar absorptivitites of Na_2PdCl_4 cannot be obtained from the sodium tetrachloropalladate(II)-sodium chloride data used in this study, because even at the highest chloride concentration obtainable using sodium

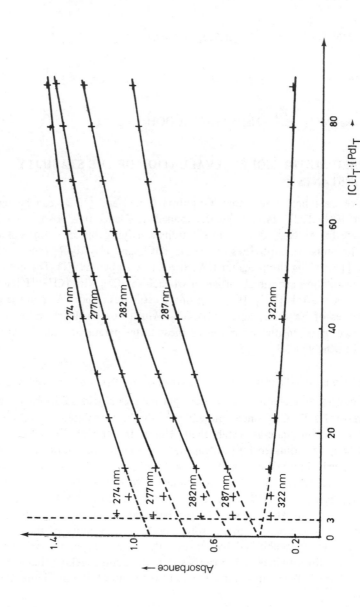

Figure 13.3 — Plots of absorbance against $[Cl]_T : [Pd]_T$ ratio at 274 nm, 277 nm, 282 nm, 287 nm and 322 nm.

chloride (ca. $0.013\ mol.l^{-1}$), only approximately 65% of the palladium is present as Na_2PdCl_4. However, using the more soluble lithium chloride, solutions with $[Cl]_T:[Pd]_T$ ratios in excess of 1000:1 can be obtained. At these concentrations the spectra are virtually independent of chloride concentration, suggesting that Li_2PdCl_4 is the only palladium(II) species present in significant amount. The required molar absorptivities can then be obtained on the assumption that Li_2PdCl_4 and Na_2PdCl_4 have similar spectra, an assumption that can be shown to be valid at the isosbestic wavelengths. The resulting spectrum is shown as the solid (estimated) line in Figure 13.4b.

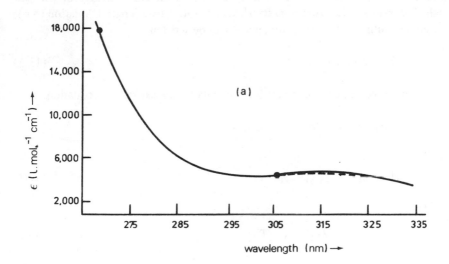

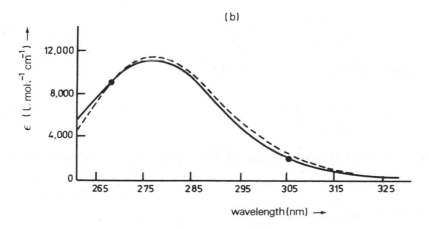

Figure 13.4 – Estimated (———) and computed (- - - - -) spectra of (a) $Na_2Pd_2Cl_6$ and (b) Na_2PdCl_4; ● represent molar absorptivities determined at the isosbestic wavelengths.

(ii) *Initial estimate of the stability constant K_1*

From Equation (13.1) it follows that,

$$K_1 = \frac{[Na_2Pd_2Cl_6][NaCl]^2}{[Na_2PdCl_4]^2} \tag{13.4}$$

By algebraic manipulation it is possible to derive an equation to estimate K_1. Let c_1, c_2 and c_3 be the equilibrium concentrations of Na_2PdCl_4, $Na_2Pd_2Cl_6$ and NaCl respectively and ϵ_1 and ϵ_2 be the molar absorptivities of the two palladium(II) species. Applying Beer's Law for unit path length (Equation (8.6)) to Equilibrium (13.1), the absorbance A can be written,

$$A = \epsilon_1 c_1 + \epsilon_2 c_2 \tag{13.5}$$

from which we can eliminate c_2 using the palladium mass-balance equation,

$$[Pd]_T = c_1 + 2c_2 \tag{13.6}$$

whence

$$A = \epsilon_1 c_1 + \tfrac{1}{2}\epsilon_2([Pd]_T - c_1) \tag{13.7}$$

therefore

$$A = c_1(\epsilon_1 - \tfrac{1}{2}\epsilon_2) + \tfrac{1}{2}\epsilon_2[Pd]_T \tag{13.8}$$

from which,

$$c_1 = \frac{A - \tfrac{1}{2}\epsilon_2[Pd]_T}{\epsilon_1 - \tfrac{1}{2}\epsilon_2} \tag{13.9}$$

Equation (13.4) can be written as (13.10).

$$K_1 = \frac{c_2 c_3^2}{c_1^2} = c_2 \left(\frac{c_3}{c_1}\right)^2 \tag{13.10}$$

We can obtain an expression for $(c_3/c_1)^2$ from the chloride mass-balance equation,

$$[Cl]_T = 4c_1 + 6c_2 + c_3 \tag{13.11}$$

which on rearrangement yields,

$$(c_3/c_1)^2 = \left(\frac{[Cl]_T}{c_1} - 4 - \frac{6c_2}{c_1}\right)^2 \tag{13.12}$$

Substituting for $(c_3/c_1)^2$ from (13.12) and c_2 from (13.6), Equation (13.10) becomes

$$K_1 = \tfrac{1}{2}([Pd]_T - c_1)\left\{\frac{[Cl]_T}{c_1} - 4 - \frac{6\{\tfrac{1}{2}([Pd]_T - c_1)\}}{c_1}\right\}^2 \qquad (13.13)$$

therefore

$$K_1 = \frac{\tfrac{1}{2}([Pd]_T - c_1)}{}\left\{\frac{[Cl]_T}{c_1} - \frac{3[Pd]_T}{c_1} - 4 + 3\right\}^2 \qquad (13.14)$$

therefore

$$K_1 = \frac{([Pd]_T - c_1)}{2}\left\{\frac{[Cl]_T - 3[Pd]_T - 1}{c_1}\right\}^2 \qquad (13.15)$$

c_1 can be calculated from the values of A, $[Pd]_T$, ϵ_1 and ϵ_2 using Equation (13.9) and an estimate of K_1 obtained from Equation (13.15).

(iii) *Refinement of initial estimates*

The initial estimates of K_1 and the molar absorptivities obtained above are then input into the computer program DALSFEK, and final refined values of the parameters and their standard deviations printed out. The results from four sets of data are shown in Table 13.1. In every case the fit between the experimental data and that calculated from the best estimates of the parameters was found to be satisfactory. K_1 and its standard deviation, obtained [10] from Equation (13.16) and (13.17), are 0.601 ± 0.019.

$$K_{\text{(weighted mean)}} = \frac{1}{\sigma_a^{-2} + \sigma_b^{-2} + \sigma_c^{-2} + \sigma_d^{-2}}\left(\frac{K_a}{\sigma_a^2} + \frac{K_b}{\sigma_b^2} + \frac{K_c}{\sigma_c^2} + \frac{K_d}{\sigma_d^2}\right) \qquad (13.16)$$

$$\sigma_{\text{(weighted mean)}}^{-2} = \sigma_a^{-2} + \sigma_b^{-2} + \sigma_c^{-2} + \sigma_d^{-2} \qquad (13.17)$$

Table 13.1 – Values of K_1 calculated from DALSFEK.

Data set	$[Cl]_T:[Pd]_T$ (range)[†]	K_1 (mol.l^{-1})	σ_{K_1}	$n-m$[††]
1	22.4–87.2	0.565	0.035	31
2	22.4–87.2	0.614	0.043	55
3	22.4–87.2	0.562	0.038	59
4	22.4–87.2	0.666	0.036	59

† The range shown is from the smallest to largest ratio of $[Cl]_T:[Pd]_T$.

†† $n-m$ = number of degrees of freedom of the system, where n is the number of data points and m is the number of parameters determined from them.

It is notable that the final standard deviation of 0.019 is less than that of any data set in Table 13.1. This is a consequence of Equation (13.17) and arises because the reliability of the mean of all four data sets is greater than that of any one.

Having obtained estimates in this way for some of the parameters of our model, the next step is to include Equilibrium (13.2). For this purpose all the data, including that at low $[Cl]_T:[Pd]_T$, ratios is used. An initial estimate of the value of K_2 of about 10^{-5} mol.l^{-1} can be obtained from the values of the parameters estimated so far and the qualitative observations already made. The results, obtained when the complete data sets 1–4 of Table 13.1 and two further data sets are analysed by DALSFEK using a model involving both Equilibria (13.1) and (13.2), are shown in Table 13.2. For every data set, the inclusion of the K_2 step brings about a significant reduction in the sum of squares of the errors, and in the goodness of fit as measured by the Hamilton R-factor (see Section 5.4), over that when only the K_1 equilibrium was considered. As well as calculating the stability constants shown in Table 13.2, the molar absorptivities of the three absorbing species are evaluated from the data. The evaluated spectral curves for Na_2PdCl_4 and $Na_2Pd_2Cl_6$ can be compared with those estimated as described above in Section 13.5(i) to provide another check on the performance of the model. It is apparent from Figure 13.4 that the agreement between the estimated spectra and those calculated by DALSFEK is good, $\pm1\%$ and $\pm5\%$ for $Na_2Pd_2Cl_6$ and Na_2PdCl_4 respectively, and further that both the estimated and calculated spectra agree well with the accurately known molar absorptivities at the isosbestic wavelengths. The final best estimates of K_1 and K_2 from the data in Table 13.2, averaged using Equations (13.16) and (13.17), are 0.56 ± 0.2 mol.l^{-1} and $(2.9 \pm 0.6) \times 10^{-5}$ mol.l^{-1} respectively.

Despite the good overall fit of the model it is apparent that data sets 5 and 6 give significantly poorer results in terms of the Hamilton R-factor than the other four. This is reflected in the very high standard deviations in the evaluated parameters. The $[Cl]_T:[Pd]_T$ range is much narrower for these data sets and the data inadequately defines the proposed model (see Section 5.11). The next stage is to examine a model based on Equilibria (13.1) and (13.3). When this is attempted, the improvement over a model involving Equilibrium (13.1) only is slight, and is significantly less than a model involving Equilibria (13.1) and (13.2).

13.6 TESTING THE MODEL: ADJUSTMENT OF SYSTEMATIC ERRORS

In order to test the model further, the facilities in DALSFEK for adjusting the possible systematic errors can be used. The importance of this technique was described in Section 5.10 and was pioneered by Sillén and coworkers [11–13]. It can lead to both the inclusion of minor species in the model and to species elimination.

Table 13.2 — Analysis of the sodium tetrachloropalladate(II)-sodium chloride data by a two equilibria model (K_1 and K_2).

Data set	$[Cl]_T:[Pd]_T$ (range)	K_1 (mol.l^{-1})	σ_{K_1}	K_2 (mol.l^{-1})	σ_{K_2}	$R^\dagger$	$R_{lim}^{\dagger\dagger}$
1	3.9–87.2	0.542	0.064	3.16×10^{-5}	2.27×10^{-5}	0.00283	0.0307
2	3.9–87.2	0.572	0.029	2.49×10^{-5}	6.39×10^{-6}	0.00316	0.0322
3	3.9–87.2	0.531	0.038	7.61×10^{-5}	3.55×10^{-5}	0.00382	0.0325
4	3.9–87.2	0.595	0.053	7.25×10^{-5}	2.99×10^{-5}	0.00382	0.0321
5	3.7–23.6	0.440	0.960	7.68×10^{-6}	3.32×10^{-6}	0.00858	0.0261
6	2.7–17.7	0.499	0.332	3.67×10^{-4}	2.84×10^{-4}	0.00548	0.0517

$\dagger\ R = \left[\left\{ \sum_{i=1}^{i=n} (a_i^{calc.} - a_i^{obs})^2 \right\} \middle/ \left\{ \sum_{i=1}^{i=n} (a_i^{obs})^2 \right\} \right]^{\frac{1}{2}}$ where a_i = absorbance at wavelength i.

$\dagger\dagger\ R_{lim} = \left[\left\{ \sum_{i=1}^{i=n} \epsilon_i^2 \right\} \middle/ \left\{ \sum_{i=1}^{i=n} (a_i^{obs})^2 \right\} \right]^{\frac{1}{2}}$, where ϵ_i is the residual in the ith equation calculated from the following pessimistic estimates

of errors: absorbance ± 2%, total chloride concentration ± 1%, total palladium concentration ± 1%.

On rerunning the model based on Equilibria (13.1) and (13.2) on one of the close-fitting data sets (4 in Table 13.1), allowing the total concentrations of chloride and palladium to vary, it becomes apparent that the computer is attempting to improve the fit by assuming unreasonable errors in the total chloride concentrations ($> 20\%$), especially at low $[Cl]_T : [Pd]_T$ ratios (Table 13.3). Accordingly further equilibria must now be added to the model to see if an improved fit to the data can be obtained. Possible equilibria in addition to (13.1) and (13.2) are (13.3) and (13.18–13.20).

$$Na[Pd_2Cl_5(CH_3COOH)] \overset{K_4}{\rightleftharpoons} [Pd_2Cl_4(CH_3COOH)_2] + NaCl \quad (13.18)$$

$$Na_2PdCl_4 + NaCl \overset{K_5}{\rightleftharpoons} Na_3PdCl_5 \quad (13.19)$$

$$Na_2Pd_2Cl_6 + NaCl \overset{K_6}{\rightleftharpoons} Na_3Pd_2Cl_7 \quad (13.20)$$

Of these equilibria, (13.3) and (13.18) are the most likely, as the data at high chloride concentrations, when (13.19) and (13.20) might be expected to become important, has already been shown to be well represented by Equilibrium (13.1) alone. With a computer-based treatment, though, it is a simple matter to try other chemically possible models in this fashion. When this done it is found that only the inclusion of Equilibrium (13.3) to the model involving (13.1) and (13.2) gives rise to a small reduction in the sum of the squares of the errors. The others either fail to converge to a minimum variance value at all, or give unacceptable values of the R-factor as compared to the R_{lim} value. Failure to converge to some sort of minimum variance value only appears to occur with DALSFEK if the model is apparently completely unacceptable. Those models converging but giving unacceptable fits to the data also give instances of unreasonable spectra, that is, either non-smooth spectral curves or negative molar absorptivities. This provides a further check on the validity of the model.

Whilst the reduction in the variance by the inclusion of Equilibrium (13.3) is small, further support for its existence is provided on readjusting the systematic errors. Much more acceptable corrections ($< 3\%$) are now made to the total chloride concentrations (Table 13.4). However, the stability constant of Equilibrium (13.3) (K_3) is not well-defined by the data so that its standard deviation is close to the estimated value itself; $K_3 = (3.5 \pm 3.9) \times 10^{-4}$ mol.l^{-1}. The existence of Equilibrium (13.3) must therefore be regarded as only tentative. If it does exist the reason why it is ill-defined can be seen from Figure 13.5 which indicates that if K_3 does have the value 3.5×10^{-4} mol.l^{-1}, there is no concentration range in which more than 3.35% of the palladium is present as $Na[PdCl_3(CH_3COOH)]$.

Table 13.3 — Adjustment of systematic (concentration) errors for data set 4 in Table 13.1 using a model based on Equilibria (13.1) and (13.2) only.

Solution	$[Cl]_T:[Pd]_T$	$[Pd]_T$			$[Cl]_T$		
		Exptl $\times 10^4$	Adjusted $\times 10^4$	% Adjust	Exptl $\times 10^4$	Adjusted $\times 10^4$	% Adjust
1	3.89	1.476	1.470	−0.41	5.74	6.72	17.1
2	7.59	1.476	1.456	−1.35	11.20	15.39	37.4
3	13.14	1.476	1.447	−1.96	19.40	23.45	20.9
4	22.41	1.476	1.455	−1.42	33.06	37.02	12.0
5	31.65	1.476	1.468	−0.54	46.72	49.86	7.3
6	40.82	1.476	1.455	−1.42	60.38	63.48	0.5
7	50.47	1.476	1.464	−0.81	74.04	75.82	2.4
8	59.41	1.476	1.473	−0.21	87.70	88.49	0.9
9	68.69	1.476	1.472	−0.25	101.4	101.8	0.2
10	78.86	1.476	1.486	0.74	116.4	113.6	−2.4
11	87.20	1.476	1.487	0.74	128.7	123.7	−3.9

Table 13.4 — Adjustment of systematic (concentration) errors for data set 4 in Table 13.1 using a model based on Equilibria (13.1), (13.2) and (13.3).

Solution	$[Cl]_T : [Pd]_T$	$[Pd]_T$				$[Cl]_T$		
		Exptl $\times 10^4$	Adjusted $\times 10^4$	% Adjust		Exptl $\times 10^4$	Adjusted $\times 10^4$	% Adjust
1	3.89	1.476	1.476	0.00		5.738	5.683	−0.96
2	7.59	1.476	1.480	0.27		11.20	11.85	−1.34
3	13.14	1.476	1.471	−0.34		19.40	19.97	2.85
4	22.41	1.476	1.474	−0.14		33.06	33.76	2.12
5	31.65	1.476	1.484	0.54		46.72	47.06	0.73
6	40.82	1.476	1.466	−0.68		60.38	61.33	1.57
7	50.47	1.476	1.471	−0.34		74.04	74.31	−0.04
8	59.41	1.476	1.477	0.01		87.70	87.66	0.29
9	68.69	1.476	1.474	−0.14		101.7	101.7	−1.80
10	78.86	1.476	1.485	0.61		116.4	114.3	−1.80
11	87.20	1.476	1.485	0.61		128.7	125.0	−2.87

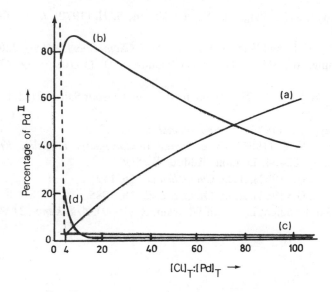

Figure 13.5 — Percentage of palladium (II) present in each form as a function of the $[Cl]_T : [Pd]_T$ ratio: (a) Na_2PdCl_4, (b) $Na_2Pd_2Cl_6$, (c) $Na[PdCl_3(CH_3COOH)]$ and (d) $Na[Pd_2Cl_5(CH_3COOH)]$.

13.7 CONCLUSION

This case study shows how it is possible to objectively construct a chemical model for spectrophotometrically studied systems. This is carried out using qualitative information derived from the spectrophotometric data, supplemented by chemical observations concerning both the systems under study and related systems. A non-linear least-squares program such as DALSFEK then allows the proposed and competing models to be objectively tested comparatively easily. The best estimates of the parameter values, along with their standard deviations, are obtained as the final product of this stage of the analysis.

REFERENCES

[1] Alcock, R. M., Hartley, F. R., Rogers, D. E., and Wagner, J. L. (1975). *J. Chem. Soc. (Dalton)*, 2189.

[2] Wagner, J. L. (1974). Ph.D. thesis, Southampton University.

[3] Beamish, F. E. and Dale, J. (1938). *Ind. and Eng. Chem. (Anal. Ed.)*, **10**, 697.

[4] Vogel, A. I. (1961). *A Textbook of Quantitative Inorganic Analysis*, 3rd ed., p. 266. London. Longmans.

[5] Coleman, J. S., Varga, L. P., and Mastin, S. H. (1970). *Inorg. Chem.*, **9**, 1015.

[6] Hartley, F. R. and Wagner, J. L. (1972). *J. Chem. Soc. (Dalton)*, 2282.

[7] Kitching, W., Moore, G. J., and Doddrell, D. (1970). *Inorg. Chem.*, **9**, 541.

[8] Popov, A. I. (1970). *The Chemistry of Non-Aqueous Solvents* (ed. Lagowski, J. J.), 3, 241.

[9] Hartley, F. R. (1970). *J. Organometal. Chem.*, **21**, 227.

[10] Barford, N. C. (1967). *Experimental Measurements: Precision, Error and Truth*, pp. 63–64. London: Addison-Wesley.

[11] Sillén, L. G. (1962). *Acta. Chem. Scand.*, **16**, 159.

[12] Sillén, L. G. (1964). *Acta. Chem. Scand.*, **18**, 1085.

[13] Braunar, P., Sillén, L. G. and Whitekar, R. (1969). *Ark. Kemi.*, **31**, 365.

CHAPTER 14

The Interpretation of Stability Constant Data

14.1 INTRODUCTION

In this chapter we shall consider in outline some of the more successful theories that have been developed to explain why a given metal ion prefers to bond to one ligand rather than another. What is presented is an account of such theories as have been shown to be of widespread value; no attempt has been made to provide a comprehensive account of the subject partly because it would require an unreasonable amount of space and partly because many rationalisations have been either of limited validity or merely alternatives to those described in the present chapter.

There is a great temptation to many chemists, having once obtained a few stability constants, to attempt to find an explanation for the trends they observe. Most, although by no means all, chemists tend to first think of an explanation involving trends in the relative abilities of a series of ligands to bond to metal ions. Whilst such explanations will be correct in some cases, there are several factors that need to be considered.

As has already been emphasised (Section 1.10) stability constants are related to thermodynamic functions by Equations (14.1) and (14.2). Thus in order to

$$\Delta G = -RT \ln K \qquad (14.1)$$

$$\Delta G = \Delta H - T \Delta S \qquad (14.2)$$

understand why one particular stability constant is larger or smaller than another it is necessary to determine both the enthalapy and the entropy change that corresponds to that particular stability constant. Having obtained the enthalpy and entropy terms, it is important to recognise that these themselves are the product of many separate terms. Two broad approaches have been used to subdivide them further. One starts from the experimental point of view and divides them into temperature dependent and temperature independent terms and then examines these to see what further deductions can be made from this division. The other, which is the more theoretical in approach, attempts to split the observed entropies and enthalpies into two parts, that due to solvation and that due to metal ligand bonding. Let us consider each of these approaches in turn.

14.2 TEMPERATURE DEPENDENCE OF THERMODYNAMIC TERMS

In Section 1.10 we noted that neither the enthalpy nor the entropy of complex formation are independent of temperature. As a result, the free energy of complex formation is not linearly dependent on the reciprocal of the absolute temperature but varies non-linearly. Accordingly we might expect to find systems for which a plot of free energy against temperature shows a maximum, and indeed this is observed for the pKa's of a number of carboxylic acids (see Figure 14.1) [1,2]. Such maxima in the free energies imply corresponding

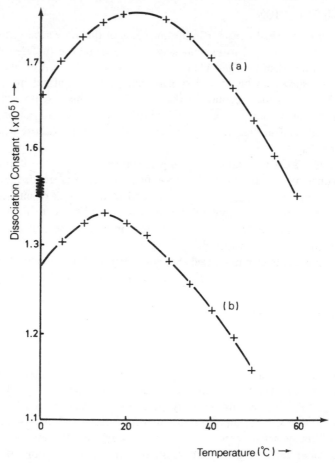

Figure 14.1 – The temperature dependence of the dissociation constants of (a) acetic and (b) propionic acids (data from references [1] and [2]).

maxima in the enthalpies, and again these have been confirmed experimentally. The observation of such maxima has been ascribed to two different types of forces between the particles in solution [3–6]. The first of these is an essentially temperature independent interaction. This is thought to arise from short-range, quantum mechanical exchange forces that are not broken by thermal agitation, and which are normally described as covalent bonding. The temperature dependent interaction is thought to arise from electrostatic interactions which vary with temperature in essentially the same way as the macroscopic dielectric constant of the medium. The mutual effect of these two forces leads to three special cases being observed:

(a) When the covalent interaction is very much greater than the electrostatic interaction, the minimum in the stability constant will lie well below ambient temperature and the enthalpy change observed at ambient temperature will be positive.

(b) When covalent and electrostatic interactions are comparable in importance, the minimum stability constant will lie around ambient temperature and the enthalpy change observed at ambient temperature will be close to zero.

(c) When the electrostatic interaction is very much greater than the covalent interaction, the minimum in the stability constant will lie well above ambient temperature and the enthalpy change observed at ambient temperature will be negative.

14.3 DIVISION OF THERMODYNAMIC TERMS INTO SOLVATION AND BONDING COMPONENTS

For a reaction such as

$$[M(H_2O)_n].aq + L.aq \rightleftharpoons [M(H_2O)_{n-1}L].aq + H_2O \qquad (14.3)$$

it is possible to consider the observed entropy and enthalpy changes as arising from two major sources: solvation of all the species present and the breaking and making of bonds.

(i) Solvation terms

We can consider the solvation changes in a reaction such as (14.3) schematically as involving complete desolvation of each of the species on the left and solvation of each of those on the right. This solvation and desolvation will give rise to both an enthalpy ($\Delta H_{solv.}$) and an entropy ($\Delta S_{solv.}$) term. Powell-Latimer [7], Born [8] and more recent [9,10] models for ion-solvent interaction lead to the reasonable conclusion that $\Delta H_{solv.}$ is proportional to $\Delta S_{solv.}$ (that is, $\Delta H_{solv.} = \beta \Delta S_{solv.}$). Evaluation of β for a number of systems has shown that it is generally within about $\pm 25°$K of the absolute temperature of the system, indicating that to a first approximation the solvation enthalpy and entropy terms mutually oppose one another [11,12]. They can often, therefore, be neglected in considering the overall free energy of a reaction but not, of course, when considering the component enthalpy and entropy terms.

(ii) *Bonding terms*

Bonding terms arise from both metal-solvent and metal-ligand interactions. The resultant bond energy is a consequence of the interplay of both steric and electronic factors. Clearly the more bulky a ligand the more steric opposition to coordination it is likely to experience from the other ligands present, and accordingly the lower will be the enthalpy of formation of the complex. Electronic effects can be broadly divided into σ-bonding, π-bonding and, for transition metals, crystal field effects. The greater the σ-donor ability of a ligand (that is, the more basic it is), the greater will be the strength of the metal-ligand σ-bond. Similarly the greater the electron acceptor ability of a metal, the stronger will be the complexes that it forms. Electron acceptance is promoted by high electropositivity, high oxidation state, and for a given metal ion in a given oxidation state as high a positive charge on the complex as possible. π-back donation from filled orbitals of suitable symmetry on a metal ion to empty orbitals of the same symmetry on the ligand also promotes high enthalpies of formation. However, π-back donation does not affect basicity since basicity reflects the ability of the donor to bond to protons which, having no filled p-orbitals, cannot take part in π-bonding. For a transition metal ion, the effect of the ligand on the energies of the metal d-orbitals must also be considered. Thus the energies of the five d-orbitals, which in a free metal ion are all equal, are split in the presence of a ligand field. Let us consider bringing up a group of six negatively charged ligands to a metal ion and leaving their charge smeared out evenly on the surface of a sphere around the metal ion. This raises the energies of all the d-orbitals as a result of the electrostatic repulsion between the negatively charged sphere and the negatively charged d-electrons (Figure 14.2a). If these six ligands are then moved to become point charges lying in an octahedral arrangement around the metal ion then the energies of the d-orbitals will be altered again. If the point charges are considered to lie on the x, y and z axes then the two d-orbitals whose lobes lie along these axes (d_{z^2} and $d_{x^2-y^2}$) will be further raised in energy, whilst the three d-orbitals whose lobes lie between the axes will be lowered in energy owing to their being less affected by repulsion (Figure 14.2b). If the difference between the two sets of orbitals, known as the e_g and t_{2g} set respectively, is Δ then the t_{2g} set will lie $2/5 \Delta$ below and the e_g set $3/5 \Delta$ above the energy of the five d-orbitals in Figure 14.2a. If now we have an excess of electrons in the t_{2g} level there will be a net gain in energy known as a crystal field stabilisation energy (Table 14.1). The value of Δ depends on the ligand present. The ability of ligands to influence Δ can be determined from the electronic spectra of complexes. It is found that for virtually all metal ions the relative ability of ligands to influence Δ is the same, decreasing in the order $CO > CN^- > NO_2^- > 1,10$-phenanthroline $> \alpha,\alpha'$-bipyridyl $>$ ethylenediamine $>$ $NH_3 \sim$ pyridine $> \underline{N}CS^- > H_2O > C_2O_4^{2-} > OH^- > F^- > NO_3^- > Cl^- > \underline{S}CN^-$ $> S^{2-} > Br^- > I^-$, which is known as the spectrochemical series. If for a metal ion that has a positive crystal field stabilisation a ligand higher in the spectro-chemical series, such as an amine, replaces one that is lower, such as water, then there is a favourable crystal field stabilisation contribution to the net enthalpy change. This effect is partly responsible for the Irving-Williams series of metal ions (see Section 14.5(i)). Similarly metal ions with more than three and less than eight d-electrons can exist in high spin and low spin forms (Table 14.1). A change from high spin to low spin is usually accompanied by a favourable enthalpy change (see below Section 14.4).

14.4 RATIO OF SUCCESSIVE STABILITY CONSTANTS

One very useful way not only of checking the reliability of stability constant data, but also of using stability constant data to obtain insight into metal-ligand complex formation, is to look at the ratio of successive stability constants [13, 14]. In general $K_1 > K_2 > K_3 >$ etc. (see Table 14.2), and any reversal of this order implies some specific electronic or steric phenomenon. The total ratio of two successive stability constants is made up of three parts, a statistical part, which has already been discussed in Section 3.4, a ligand part and a metal part. Typical experimental ratios are smaller than the statistical ratio.

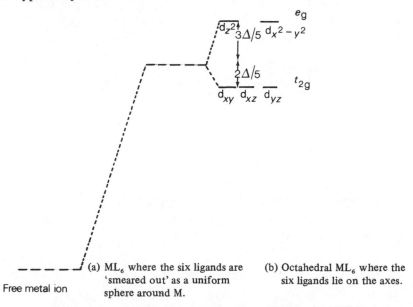

(a) ML_6 where the six ligands are 'smeared out' as a uniform sphere around M.

(b) Octahedral ML_6 where the six ligands lie on the axes.

Free metal ion

Figure 14.2 – The influence of ligands on the energies of d-orbitals.

The effect of ligands can be subdivided into their electrostatic and steric effects. The *electrostatic effect* takes account of the fact that in, for example, the chromium(III)-thiocyanate system, the first thiocyanate sees a tripositive metal ion, the second a dipositive and so on until the sixth sees a dinegative anion where the repulsion will obviously be considerable. The *effect of steric size* on the ratio of successive constants will depend on whether the entering ligand is bulkier or less bulky than the ligand it is replacing; bulkier entering ligands will obviously suppress the higher stability constants, whereas less bulky ligands will enhance the earlier stability constants. An example of a

Table 14.1 – Crystal field stabilisation energies for octahedral ML_6 complexes.

No. of d-electrons	Crystal field stabilisation energy		Example of metal ions
0	0		Sc^{III}, Ti^{IV}
1	$2\Delta/5$		Ti^{III}, V^{IV}
2	$4\Delta/5$		V^{III}
3	$6\Delta/5$		V^{II}, Cr^{III}
	high spin	low spin	
4	$3\Delta/5$	$8\Delta/5$	Cr^{II}, Mn^{III}
5	0	2Δ	Mn^{II}, Fe^{III}
6	$2\Delta/5$	$12\Delta/5$	Fe^{II}, Co^{III}
7	$4\Delta/5$	$9\Delta/5$	Co^{II}
8	$6\Delta/5$		Ni^{II}
9	$3\Delta/5$		Cu^{II}
10	0		Cu^{I}, Zn^{II}

d^4 high spin $(t_{2g}^3 e_g^1)$ d^5 high spin $(t_{2g}^3 e_g^2)$ d^6 high spin $(t_{2g}^4 e_g^2)$ d^7 high spin $(t_{2g}^5 e_g^2)$

d^4 low spin (t_{2g}) d^5 low spin (t_{2g}^5) d^6 low spin (t_{2g}^6) d^7 low spin $(t_{2g}^6 e_g^1)$

Table 14.2 – Stability constants for the formation of successive complexes.

Metal ion	Ligand	Temperature	Solvent	Ionic medium	Stability constants	Reference
Pd^{2+}	Cl^-		Water	1M $HClO_4$	K_1 7.59×10^3 K_2 1.07×10^3 K_3 1.51×10^2 K_4 21.9	[15]
$PdCl_4^{2-}$	Br^-		Water	4.5 M, $LiClO_4$ + $HClO_4$ + $LiCl$ + $LiBr$	K_1 35.5 K_2 12.3 K_3 8.9 K_4 3.5	[16]
Pb^{2+}	Cl^-		Water	3M $NaClO_4$	K_1 14.5 K_2 3.5 K_3 1.9 K_4 0.05	[17]
La^{3+}	CH_3COO^-	25	60% ethanol in water	2M $NaClO_4$	K_1 389 K_2 115 K_3 51 K_4 10	[18]
Pb^{2+}	CH_3COO^-	25	Water	3M $NaClO_4$	K_1 214 K_2 19 K_3 1 K_4 0.2	[19]
Co^{2+}	$(CH_2NH_2)_2$	20	Water	2.7M	K_1 1.8×10^5 K_2 1.2×10^4 K_3 3.7×10^2	[20]
Cd^{2+}	Maleic acid	25	Water	0.2M $MaClO_4$	K_1 158 K_2 25 K_3 1.6	[21]

very bulky ligand is 6,6'-dimethyl-2,2'-bipyridyl ((I), R = CH_3), and many metals that form tris-complexes with bipyridine ((I), R = H) form only mono- or bis-complexes or in some cases no isolatable complexes at all with the dimethyl-substituted ligand ((I), R = CH_3) owing to the steric interference of the methyl groups with the other ligands present.

The influence of the metal ion in giving rise to abnormal ratios of successive stability constants can usually be traced to an electronic effect such as a high-spin to low-spin change or a change in hybridisation. Thus, for example, iron(II) with 2,2'-bipyridyl [22] ((I), R = H) and 1,10-phenanthroline (II) [23] gives $K_3 > K_2$, owing to the tris-complexes being diamagnetic low-spin (t_{2g}^6), whereas the mono- and bis-, like the hexaquo-iron(II), are high-spin ($t_{2g}^4 e_g^2$). This high-spin to low-spin change causes the enthalpy change for the addition of the third ligand to be anomalously large and favourable. In the reaction of ammonia with silver(I), K_2 is greater than K_1 probably because in $[Ag(NH_3)_2]^+$ silver attains a favourable linear sp-hybridisation whereas with $[Ag(NH_3)(H_2O)_n]^+$, where $n = 3$ or 5, this is not possible [24]. Hybridisation changes can give rise not only to anomalously high ratios of K_{n+1}/K_n but also anomalously low ratios. Thus in the copper(II)-ammonia system successive stability constants of 2.04×10^4 (K_1), 4.68×10^3 (K_2), 1.10×10^3 (K_3), 1.99×10^2 (K_4) and 0.35 (K_5) are observed, indicating the strong preference of copper(II) for 4-coordination as opposed to a higher coordination number [25]. Similarly, in the mercury(II)-halide systems K_3/K_2 values are anomalously low because mercury(II) prefers the linear coordination (sp-hybridisation) of HgX_2 [26]. The very low value of K_3/K_2 suggests that the hybridisation change from sp to sp^3 occurs on going from HgX_2 to HgX_3^-.

14.5 CLASSIFICATION OF METALS AND LIGANDS

Once a considerable body of stability constant data had been built up chemists began to examine it to see what generalisations could be made. The object of this was twofold: firstly by analysing the trends in the known stability constants it was hoped that it might be possible to predict the values of unknown stability constants, and secondly, it was hoped to obtain an insight into why a particular metal ion shows a preference for one ligand rather than another. In this section only five of the many classification schemes that have been proposed are considered.

(i) *Irving-Williams series*

A large number of stability constants for various ligands with divalent high-spin transition metal ions have been reported. For ligands that lie above water in the spectrochemical series (see Section 14.3(ii)) the stability constants for a given ligand vary with the metal ion in the order $Mn^{II} < Fe^{II} < Co^{II} < Ni^{II} < Cu^{II} > Zn^{II}$ (see Table 14.3) which is known as the Irving-Williams order after its initial discoverers [29]. The Irving-Williams order largely reflects the changes in heats of complex formation across the series (see Table 14.3), and it arises from a combination of the influence of the polarising ability of the metal ions, as measured by the ratio of charge to ionic radius, which varies in the sequence $Mn^{II} < Fe^{II} < Co^{II} < Ni^{II} \sim Cu^{II} > Zn^{II}$, and the crystal field stabilisation energies which vary in the order $Mn^{II} < Fe^{II} < Co^{II} < Ni^{II} > Zn^{II}$ (see Table 14.1) [30].

Table 14.3 – Thermodynamic data [27,28] at 25°C for the equilibrium $M(H_2O)_6^{2+} + en \rightleftharpoons M(en)(H_2O)_4^{2+} + 2H_2O$ (en = $NH_2CH_2CH_2NH_2$).

M^{2+}	$\Delta G^\dagger$	$\Delta H^\dagger$	$T\Delta S^\dagger$
Mn	−15.7 (−3.8)	−11.7 (−2.8)	+4.0 (+1.0)
Fe	−24.7 (−5.9)	−21.2 (−5.1)	+3.5 (+0.8)
Co	−33.9 (−8.1)	−28.9 (−6.9)	+5.0 (+1.2)
Ni	−44.1 (−10.5)	−37.2 (−8.9)	+6.9 (+1.6)
Cu	−61.2 (−14.6)	−54.5 (−13.0)	+6.7 (+1.6)
Zn	−33.1 (−7.9)	−27.8 (−6.6)	+5.3 (+1.3)

† The values listed are in $kJ.mol^{-1}$ with $kcal.mol^{-1}$ in parentheses.

(ii) *Class 'a' and class 'b' metals*

The first major classification of metal ions was produced by Chatt, Ahrland and Davies [31] who, after examining a considerable range of *free energy* data, suggested that metal ions could be divided into two classes, class 'a' and class 'b'. The first group, class 'a', comprised metal ions that formed more stable complexes with ligands in which the coordinating atom came from the first row of the periodic table (N, O, F) than with analogous ligands in which the donor atom came from the second row of the periodic table. The class 'b' metal ions were opposite to this in that they formed their more stable complexes with second row donors. Thus class 'a' metal ions exhibited the following stability constant preferences:

$$F^- \gg Cl^- > Br^- > I^-$$

$$O \gg S > Se > Te$$

$$N \gg P > As > Sb > Bi$$

whereas with class 'b' metal ions the following preferences were observed:

$$F^- \ll Cl^- < Br^- < I^-$$

$$O \ll S \sim Se \sim Te$$

$$N \ll P > As > Sb > Bi$$

A number of metal ions were found to be borderline, not showing either class of behaviour uniquely. The class 'b' metal ions were

Rh	Pd	Ag	
Ir	Pt	Au	Hg

and the borderline metal ions were those that surround them, namely:

Mn	Fe	Fe	Co	Ni	Cu				
Mo	Tc	Ru				Cd			
W	Re	Os					Tl	Pb	Bi	Po

The remainder of the metal ions in the Periodic Table together with the proton behave as class 'a' acceptors. It is for this reason that many authors have been able to demonstrate a close correlation between the pK_a values of ligands and the stability constants of those ligands with both class 'a' as well as with many borderline metal ions.

Before looking further into the origins of class 'a' and 'b' behaviour it must be emphasised firstly that this classification is purely empirical and secondly that class 'b' character is only exhibited in very polar solvents such as water. In less polar solvents the class 'b' characteristics become less pronounced, and in the gas phase all metals exhibit class 'a' character. This is well illustrated by taking one of the most class 'b' metal ions, namely platinum(II), and comparing the enthalpies and free energies of formation of its chloro- and bromo-complexes in aqueous solution and in the gas phase as is done in Table 14.4. Both the two extreme bonding models, namely ionic and covalent, can readily account for the fact that all metals exhibit class 'a' character in the gas phase. On an ionic model the smaller the anion to which the metal is bound the greater will be the force of attraction, and on a covalent model the smaller the atom to which the metal atom is bound the greater will be the overlap between the orbitals of the two atoms.

Table 14.4 – Enthalpies and free energies of formulation of $[PtX_4]^{2-}$ in aqueous solution and in the gas-phase [32,33].

Complex	$\Delta G_{aq}^{\dagger}$	$\Delta H_{aq}^{\dagger}$	$\Delta H_{gas}^{\dagger}$
$[PtCl_4]^{2-}$	+144.0 (+34.4)	+159.2 (+38.0)	−1508 (−360.3)
$[PtBr_4]^{2-}$	+133.0 (+31.8)	+111.1 (+26.5)	−1376 (−328.7)

† The values listed are in kJ.mol⁻¹ with kcal.mol⁻¹ in parentheses.

What makes a given metal ion class 'a' or class 'b' in solution? A detailed analysis of the available thermodynamic data suggests that class 'a' metal complex formation is dominated whilst that of class 'b' is enthalpy dominated [34]. Consider first the class 'a' iron(III) reacting with fluoride and chloride ions [35,36].

$$[Fe(H_2O)_6]^{3+}.aq + X^-.aq \rightleftharpoons [FeX(H_2O)_5]^{2+}.aq + H_2O \qquad (14.4)$$

$$X = F, \quad \Delta G = -29.5 \text{ kJ.mol}^{-1}, \quad \Delta H = +9.7 \text{ kJ.mol}^{-1},$$
$$(-7.0 \text{ kcal.mol}^{-1}) \qquad (+2.3 \text{ kcal.mol}^{-1})$$
$$T\Delta S = +39.2 \text{ kJ.mol}^{-1} \text{ at } 25°C$$
$$(+9.3 \text{ kcal.mol}^{-1})$$

$$X = Cl, \quad \Delta G = -2.6 \text{ kJ.mol}^{-1}, \quad \Delta H = +17.6 \text{ kJ.mol}^{-1},$$
$$(-0.6 \text{ kcal.mol}^{-1}) \qquad (+4.2 \text{ kcal.mol}^{-1})$$
$$T\Delta S = +20.2 \text{ kJ.mol}^{-1} \text{ at } 25°C$$
$$(+4.8 \text{ kcal.mol}^{-1})$$

When X is fluoride the overall free energy change is favourable owing to a very favourable entropy change and in spite of an unfavourable enthalpy change. The favourable entropy change arises from the large number of water molecules that are liberated from the fluoride ion when it coordinates to iron(III). The less solvated chloride ion, having rather fewer water ligands around it (a consequence of its larger size), gives a correspondingly lower entropy change on complex formation. The observed enthalpy change on complex formation is, of course, the net effect of a number of enthalpy changes† including the enthalpies of solvation of all the species present together with the enthalpies of the iron(III)-water bond broken and the iron(III)-halide bond formed. The slightly more

† The same, of course, is true for the entropy term.

unfavourable enthalpy change in the chloride case is probably due to the weaker bonding between the iron(III) and the larger chloride than the smaller fluoride ion.

Complex formation by class 'b' metal ions is an enthalpy dominated process with the entropy change making a small contribution sometimes in support of complex formation and sometimes opposing it. This is because the class 'b' metal ions and the larger ligands, such as iodide, that they favour are structure breaking in water so that when two of these groups are brought together there is a net making of structure which leads to an unfavourable entropy change. Consider the reaction between mercury(II) and halide ions [37–39].

$$[Hg(H_2O)_4]^{2+}.aq + X^-.aq \rightleftharpoons [HgX(H_2O)_3]^+ \ aq + H_2O \qquad (14.5)$$

$$X = Cl, \quad \Delta G = -38.5 \ kJ.mol^{-1}, \qquad \Delta H = -23.0 \ kJ.mol^{-1},$$
$$(-9.2 \ kcal.mol^{-1}) \qquad (-5.5 \ kcal.mol^{-1})$$
$$T\Delta S = +15.5 \ kJ.mol^{-1} \ at \ 25°C$$
$$(+3.7 \ kcal.mol^{-1})$$

$$X = Br, \quad \Delta G = -51.5 \ kJ.mol^{-1}, \qquad \Delta H = -42.7 \ kJ.mol^{-1},$$
$$(-12.3 \ kcal.mol^{-1}) \qquad (-10.2 \ kcal.mol^{-1})$$
$$T\Delta S = +8.8 \ kJ.mol^{-1} \ at \ 25°C$$
$$(+2.1 \ kcal.mol^{-1})$$

$$X = I, \quad \Delta G = -73.2 \ kJ.mol^{-1}, \qquad \Delta H = -75.3 \ kJ.mol^{-1},$$
$$(-17.5 \ kcal.mol^{-1}) \qquad (-18.0 \ kcal.mol^{-1})$$
$$T\Delta S = -2.1 \ kJ.mol^{-1} \ at \ 25°C$$
$$(-0.5 \ kcal.mol^{-1})$$

As the halides increase in atomic weight the equilibrium lies progressively further to the right, and this is due to the steadily increasing enthalpy term. The entropy term becomes less favourable with increasing size of the halide ion corresponding to the increasing structure breaking ability of the larger halide ions. The increasingly favourable enthalpy change with the heavier halides is a consequence of the decreasing energy of solvation of the halide ions as their size increases. This is more than sufficient to compensate for the reduction in the mercury(II)-halide bond energy as the halide ion increases in size.

Thus the class 'a'/class 'b' character of metal ions is basically an empirical observation of free energy data. It can be understood in terms of the thermo-dynamic driving force for the reaction. Further, it should be appreciated that the overall enthalpy and entropy change in a particular reaction is a complex result of many terms. However, when several reactions are being compared a number of these terms will be common and so may be neglected. A further lesson that is brought out by the above analyses is that it is extremely dangerous to attempt to explain the relative stability constants (or free energies) of two reactions without a knowledge of the component enthalpy and entropy terms.

(iii) *Principle of Hard and Soft Acids and Bases*

Pearson [40,41] has suggested that the interaction of metals and ligands can be understood in terms of their 'hardness' or 'softness'. This is formalised in the Principle of Hard and Soft Acids and Bases, in which an acid is any electron acceptor (Lewis acid), a base is any electron donor (Lewis base), and acids and bases are considered to bond by sharing at least one pair of electrons. We might expect the equilibrium constant of Reaction (14.6)

$$A + :B \rightleftharpoons A:B \tag{14.6}$$

to be given by

$$\log K = S_A S_B \tag{14.7}$$

where S_A and S_B are strength factors for the acid and base respectively. However, when a series of bases are tested against a number of acids it is found that the order of base strength obtained is a function of the reference acid. Accordingly the two-parameter Equation (14.7) was extended to a four-parameter equation:

$$\log K = S_A S_B + \sigma_A \sigma_B \tag{14.8}$$

where σ is a parameter that measures some characteristic other than strength — this is known as 'softness'. Values of the parameters are set by (a) measuring K, (b) setting the value of σ for the proton arbitrarily at zero, which turns out to be reasonable since σ values appear to be related to the polarisability of the species, and (c) setting the intrinsic strength of the proton arbitrarily at 1. In this way σ values for a series of acids and bases can be evaluated. These values suggest that non-polarisable, which we may may call 'hard', species give low σ values, and polarisable, 'soft', species give higher σ values. By looking at the hard and soft acids and bases so obtained it is apparent that in addition to polarisability there are a number of other factors that make an acid hard or soft (see Table 14.5) and for this reason it has been suggested that the terms 'hard' and 'soft' are misleading [42]. However, the names are unlikely to be altered after seventeen years of use. The division of acids and bases on the basis of experimentally determined stability constants into hard, soft and borderline is shown in Table 14.6. It is apparent by comparing Table 14.6 with Section 14.5 (ii) that class 'a' metal ions are hard acids and class 'b' metal ions are soft acids. Furthermore it is interesting to note that the borderline elements in the class 'a'/class 'b' approach tend to be harder in their higher oxidation states and softer in their lower oxidation states (for example, Fe, Co, Cu and Sn).

Table 14.5 – Properties of Hard and Soft Acids and Bases.

Acid (electron acceptor)

Property	Hard	Soft
Polarisability	low	high
Electropositivity	high	low
Positive charge or oxidation state	high	low
Size	small	large
Type of bond usually associated with the acid	ionic, electrostatic	covalent, π
Outer electrons on acid	few and not easily excited	several, easily excited

Base (electron donor)

Property	Hard	Soft
Polarisability	low	high
Electronegativity	high	low
Negative charge	high	low
Size	small	large
Type of bond usually associated with the base	ionic, electrostatic	covalent, π
Available empty orbitals on the base	high energy, inaccessible	low lying, accessible

Table 14.6 – Hard and Soft Acids and Bases.[†]

Acids[††]

Hard	Soft
H^+, Li^+, Na^+, K^+	Cu^+, Ag^+, Au^+, Tl^+, Hg^+
Be^{2+}, Mg^{2+}, Ca^{2+}, Sr^{2+}, Mn^{2+}	Pd^{2+}, Cd^{2+}, Pt^{2+}, Hg^{2+}, CH_3Hg^+
	$Co(CN)_5^{2-}$, Pt^{4+}, Te^{4+}
Al^{3+}, Sc^{3+}, Ga^{3+}, In^{3+}, La^{3+}	Tl^{3+}, $Tl(CH_3)_3$, BH_3, $Ga(CH_3)_3$
N^{3+}, Cl^{3+}, Gd^{3+}, Lu^{3+}	$GaCl_3$, GaI_3, $InCl_3$
Cr^{3+}, Co^{3+}, Fe^{3+}, As^{3+}, CH_3Sn^{3+}	RS^+, RSe^+, RTe^+
Si^{4+}, Ti^{4+}, Zr^{4+}, Th^{4+}, U^{4+}	I^+, Br^+, HO^+, RO^+
Pu^{4+}, Ce^{3+}, Hf^{4+}, WO^{4+}, Sn^{4+}	
UO_2^{2+}, $(CH_3)_2Sn^{2+}$, VO^{2+}, MoO^{3+}	I_2, Br_2, ICN, etc.
$BeMe_2$, BF_3, $B(OR)_3$	trinitrobenzene etc.
$Al(CH_3)_3$, $AlCl_3$, AlH_3	chloranil, quinones, etc.
RPO_2^+, $ROPO_2^+$	tetracyanoethylene, etc.
RSO_2^+, $ROSO_2^+$, SO_3	O, Cl, Br, I, N, $RO\cdot$, $RO_2\cdot$
I^{7+}, I^{5+}, Cl^{7+}, Cr^{6+}	$M°$ (metal atoms)
RCO^+, CO_2, NC^+	bulk metals
HX (hydrogen bonding molecules)	CH_2, carbenes
Borderline	
Fe^{2+}, Co^{2+}, Ni^{2+}, Cu^{2+}, Zn^{2+}, Pb^{2+}, Sn^{2+}, Sb^{3+},Bi^{3+}, Rh^{3+}, Ir^{3+}, $B(CH_3)_3$, SO_2, NO^+, Ru^{2+}, Os^{2+}, R_3C^+, $C_6H_5^+$, GaH_3	

Bases[††]

Hard	Soft
H_2O, OH^-, F^-	R_2S, RSH, RS^-
$CH_3CO_2^-$, PO_4^{3-}, SO_4^{2-}	I^-, SCN^-, $S_2O_3^{2-}$
Cl^-, CO_3^{2-}, ClO_4^-, NO_3^-	R_3P, R_3As, $(RO)_3P$
ROH, RO^-, R_2O	CN^-, RNC, CO
NH_3, RNH_2, N_2H_4	C_2H_4, C_6H_6
	H^-, R^-
Borderline	
$C_6H_5NH_2$, C_5H_5N, N_3^-, Br^-, NO_2^-, SO_3^{2-}, N_2	

[†] From Pearson, R. G. (1968). *J. Chem. Ed.*, 45, 581.
[††] R = alkyl or aryl.

The Principle of Hard and Soft Acids and Bases as originally put forward states that "Hard acids prefer to bind to hard bases and soft acids prefer to bind to soft bases". Hard-soft interactions tend to be weak. This principle gives a qualitative prediction of what will happen when an acid and a base meet. Unfortunately from a quantitative point of view Equation (14.8) is not exact or even nearly exact, because it is too simple to represent the complexity of changes that occur when electron donating groups combine with electron-acceptors. Part of the difficulty in providing a quantitative scale for predicting free energy changes is shown by the phenomenon of *symbiosis*. Symbiosis, which means "the flocking together of kindred spirits", is a process whereby once a borderline metal has been coordinated by a hard ligand it becomes harder; if the first ligand is a soft ligand then the borderline metal becomes softer [43]. For example cobalt(III) in $[Co(NH_3)_5(H_2O)]^{3+}$ behaves as a hard or class 'a' metal ion showing a halide preference of $Cl^- > Br^- > I^-$; in 1 M aqueous ammonium perchlorate solution at 45°C, stability constants for Reaction (14.9) are 1.25 (X = Cl), 0.48 (X = Br) and 0.21 (X = I) [44].

$$[Co(NH_3)_5(H_2O)]^{3+} + X^- \rightleftharpoons [Co(NH_3)_5X]^{2+} + H_2O \tag{14.9}$$

By contrast $[Co(CN)_5(H_2O)]^{2-}$ behaves as a soft or class 'b' metal ion showing a halide preference of $I^- > Br^- > Cl^-$ [43]. Symbiosis is particularly important in biological systems where a number of the important metal ions are borderline and can thus become hard or soft according to their environment. For example in aqueous solution zinc(II) shows a halide preference $F^- > Cl^- > Br^- > I^-$, whereas in the metalloenzyme carbonic anhydrase in which zinc is coordinated to three soft imidazole groups (III) of histidine residues it shows the reverse preference, $I^- > Br^- > Cl^- > F^-$ [45].

III

The origin of the phenomenon of symbiosis can be understood in a qualitative manner by reference to the orbital energy diagram in Figure 14.3.

(iv) *Other classification schemes*

The class 'a'/class 'b' approach provides a valuable qualitative method for classifying metal ions. The principle of Hard and Soft Acids and Bases extends this somewhat, and as a qualitative method is excellent; however, it has limitations when attempts are made to obtain quantitative predictions. A large number of alternative schemes have been put forward for classifying metals and ligands, but here we will restrict mention to only two, both of which attempt to be quantitative. Drago, after noting the difficulties involved in studying donor/acceptor systems in polar solvents where interactions with the solvent mask the weak donor/acceptor interactions, proposed a four parameter equation (14.10) for correlating the enthalpies of formation of Lewis acid/base adducts in the gas-phase and in poorly solvating solvents [46, 47].

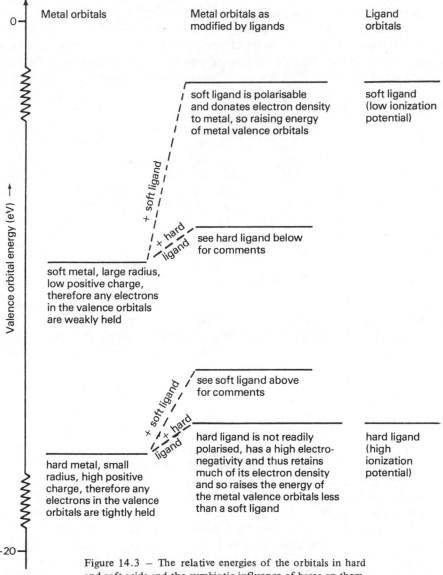

Figure 14.3 – The relative energies of the orbitals in hard and soft acids and the symbiotic influence of bases on them.

$$-\Delta H = E_A E_B + C_A C_B \qquad (14.10)$$

E_A and E_B are described as parameters that measure the electrostatic bond forming ability of the acid and base respectively, whilst C_A and C_B measure their covalent bond forming ability. Both Equations (14.10) and (14.8) are four parameter equations, and although at first sight they appear very different it must be remembered that neither possesses a unique solution for the parameters. At least four values must be set before use. Two of these simply set the scale, (E_A and C_A for iodine are arbitrarily set at 1) while the other two are selected with some physical model in mind and automatically bias all the other values to fit that model. Because of this, recent attempts to show the relationship between E and C of Equation (14.10) and σ and S of Equation (14.8) and to demonstrate that one approach is superior to the other are clearly futile [48-50]. As can be anticipated for such a system which depends on bonding ability, the E and C classification is only really successful when the donor atoms are of similar size to the metal ion [51]. Where the sizes are widely disparate, steric effects begin to dominate. Thus with large ligands such as chloride ions or sulphur donors, the E and C approach gives very poor predictions concerning interactions with small metal ions such as copper(II) or nickel(II), but fairly good predictions with large metal ions such as silver(I) and lead(II).

Nieboer and McBryde [52] define a parameter Q for metal ions (Equation (14.11) such that plots of Q against log K_{ML} are linear with a slope (ρ) that is a function of the ligand.

$$Q = (a\delta Z\chi_M + b\chi_M^2)/(a + b) \qquad (14.11)$$

χ_M is the Allred electronegativity of the metal ion, δ is a parameter calculated with the aid of Slater atomic shielding constants and for certain elements compensates for an effective increase in electronegativity due to small size or extra covalent bonding character, Z is the ionic charge, and a and b are integral (0, 1, 2 ...) weighting factors that are chosen to give the best straight line plots of Q against log K_{ML}. For some metal ions a and b are dependent on the ligand. Two further functions are obtained from plots of Q against log K_{ML}, the slope (ρ) and the intercept (Q_{int}). Both are characteristic of the ligand, and they increase in numerical value with increasing softness of the ligand. The results obtained using Nieboer and McBryde's approach are in broad agreement with the class 'a'/class 'b' and hard and soft classifications of donors and acceptors.

To summarise, there are a number of qualitative approaches for predicting which ligands will interact preferentially with which metals. Some of these are semi-quantitative in nature, but there is still a great deal of work to be done before it will be possible to predict accurately the thermodynamic parameters for an unknown donor/acceptor interaction in a particular solvent. However, both the class 'a'/class 'b' and hard and soft classifications do give some insight into those factors which make for strong interactions as well as suggesting factors such as symbiosis which are bound to make any precise quantitative predictions extremely difficult.

14.6 THE CHELATE EFFECT

The chelate effect is manifest in the experimentally observed preference of metal ions to form complexes with chelating ligands in preference to non-chelating ligands if both can form bonds of similar strength. For example, at 25°C Equilibrium (14.12) lies well to the right for a number of metal ions (for M = Co, Ni, Cu, Zn, Cd; ΔG = −13.1, −13.2, −18.0, −6.48, −5.05 kJ.mol^{-1} or −3.1, −3.15, −4.3, −1.5, −1.2 kcal.mol^{-1} respectively) [53].

$$[M(NH_3)_2(H_2O)_n]^{2+} + NH_2CH_2CH_2NH_2 \rightleftharpoons$$
$$[M(NH_2CH_2CH_2NH_2)(H_2O)_n]^{2+} + 2NH_3$$

$$(14.12)$$

The preference of metal ions for chelating as opposed to non-chelating ligands is exploited in many fields including the widespread use of EDTA in analytical chemistry, the use of chelating ligands to remove poisonous metal ions from the body, the use of chelating ligands as sequestering agents for calcium in detergents, and many other applications which are described in Chapter 15.

In order to determine the origins of the chelate effect it is vital to split the observed free energy changes up into separate enthalpy and entropy terms and then examine each of these in some detail.

(i) *Enthalpy contributions to the chelate effect*

In addition to the enthalpy terms present when complex formation by mono-dentate ligands is being considered, three further enthalpy terms must be considered when chelate ligands are being discussed.

(a) *Ligand repulsion.* When two ligands, either charged or neutral, are brought up to a single metal ion they repel one another by electrostatic and/or dipolar forces, giving rise to an unfavourable enthalpy change on complex formation. With a chelate ligand some of this repulsion has already been built into the ligand during its synthesis [54]. Clearly more repulsion will have been overcome during synthesis when a rigid ligand such as IV is used than with the more 'floppy' aliphatic analogue V.

$$Me_2AsCH_2CH_2AsMe_2$$

IV   V

(b) *Ligand distortion.* When a chelate ligand bonds to a metal ion some distortion of the ideal bond angles within the ligand is almost always necessary. This produces an unfavourable enthalpy change which tends to oppose the chelate as compared to monodentate complex formation. Clearly the more rigid the ligand the greater will this enthalpy term be unless the 'bite' of the ligand, which is essentially the distance between the donor atoms, is ideally suited to the metal. Furthermore, this term tends to favour the formation of complexes with 5- or 6-membered rings, since bond distortions are generally at a minimum in such rings.

(c) *Crystal field stabilisation energy.* A chelate ligand generates a larger crystal field splitting than do a pair of otherwise very similar monodentate ligands [55]. As a result metal ions that are susceptible to crystal field stabilisation effects (see Table 14.1) form stronger complexes with chelate ligands than monodentate ligand in part due to the greater crystal field stabilisation effects of the chelate ligand [56].

(ii) *Entropy contributions to the chelate effect*

There are four main entropy contributions to the chelate effect.

(a) *A statistical factor.* A statistical factor which disfavours the chelate relative to monodentate complex formation arises because not all the coordination sites around a metal atom are available to the chelate ligand. This is because except for a few rather special ligands [57,58] such as $Bu_2^tP(CH_2)_{9 \text{ or } 10}PBu_2^t$ and VI, chelate ligands normally only span *cis*-positions.[†] Thus once one end of the chelate ligand has co-ordinated to a particular site on the metal, only those sites *cis* to the first site are available to the other donor atoms of the chelate ligand. Except for ligands which have very strong influences on the *trans*-position [59] no such restraint applies to monodentate ligands.

CH$_2$PPh$_2$ CH$_2$PPh$_2$

VI

[†] Although in the last couple of years several *trans*-chelating ligands have been reported, *trans*-chelation is still the exception and *cis*-chelation the norm.

(b) *An activity factor.* Schwarzenbach [60] considered the formation of a chelate complex as a stepwise process involving coordination of one end of a bidentate ligand first and then subsequent coordination of the other end. The chance of coordination of the second end would be proportional to its effective local concentration around the metal ion. In dilute solution this would be much higher than the average ligand concentration because the second end is restrained in a relatively small volume of solution immediately surrounding the metal ion. Clearly this effect will decrease with chain length, since the longer the chain the greater is the effective volume in which the second end is constrained and hence the lower is its activity around the metal ion.

(c) *Internal entropy factor.* A further factor that is related to the chain length of the chelate ligand is the internal entropy of that ligand. The greater the chain length the greater the internal entropy of the ligand. Furthermore on coordination much of this internal entropy will be lost, which will oppose complex formation. A rigid ligand such as *o*-phenylenebis(dimethylarsine) (IV) will have much less internal entropy than the corresponding aliphatic ligand ethylenebis(dimethylarsine) (V), so that the internal entropy losses will disfavour complex formation by the latter more than the former.

(d) *Translational entropy.* The gain in translational entropy on replacing two or more monodentate ligands (often solvent molecules) by one multidentate ligand is often quoted as being the main source of the chelate effect. Adamson has pointed out [61] that if we compare Equilibria (14.13) and (14.14), then if we write the stability constants

$$[Ni(H_2O)_6]^{2+} + 2NH_3 \xrightleftharpoons{\beta_{2NH_3}} [Ni(NH_3)_2(H_2O)_4]^{2+} + 2H_2O$$

$$(14.13)$$

$$[Ni(H_2O)_6]^{2+} + en \xrightleftharpoons{K_{en}} [Ni(en)(H_2O)_4]^{2+} + 2H_2O$$

$$(14.14)$$

$$en = NH_2CH_2CH_2NH_2$$

in the normal way, that is,

$$\beta_{2NH_3} = [Ni(NH_3)_2(H_2O)_4^{2+}] / [Ni(H_2O)_6^{2+}][NH_3]^2 \quad (14.15)$$

the ratio of K_{en}/β_{2NH_3} will be 2.76 l.mol^{-1}. If, however, we reject our apparently arbitrary decision to follow convention in expressing all the concentrations in mol.l^{-1} and instead express them in mole fractions, so that the concentration of each species is divided by 55.5, which is the concentration of water in mol.l^{-1}, then the ratio K_{en}/β_{2NH_3} drops to 0.05.

One might perhaps think that this problem could be obviated by studying the thermodynamics of the direct replacement of two ammonia ligands by one ethylenediamine. However, this is not so because the stability constant for Reaction (14.16) has dimensions.

$$[Ni(NH_3)_2(H_2O)_4]^{2+} + en \rightleftharpoons [Ni(en)(H_2O)_4]^{2+} + 2NH_3$$
$$pqrs$$

$$(14.16)$$

Let the equilibrium concentrations of the species be $p, q,$ r and s mol.l^{-1} as indicated. Then the stability constant on the molar scale, K_M, will be given by:

$$K_M = \frac{rs^2}{pq} \tag{14.17}$$

However, if the concentrations had been expressed on the millimolar scale, K_{MM}, then since the concentration of $[Ni(NH_3)_2(H_2O)_4]^{2+}$ in mmol.l^{-1} will be $10^3 p$, and so on for the other species it follows that:

$$K_{MM} = \frac{10^3 r (10^3 s)^2}{10^3 p \, 10^3 q} \tag{14.18}$$

Thus

$$K_{MM} = \frac{10^3 rs^2}{pq} = 10^3 K_M \tag{14.19}$$

Thus the stability constant for Reaction (14.16), which is a measure of the chelate effect, is dependent on our arbitrary choice of standard state, molar as by convention or millimolar as in this example. How then do we get a true measure of the chelate effect for Equilibrium (14.16)? The answer to this lies in expressing the concentration in mole fractions since this gives rise to dimensionless stability constants. It also shows that the translational entropy contribution to the chelate effect is much smaller than it was at one time thought to be, and furthermore, that the magnitude of the chelate effect increases as the concentration decreases, which is a well-known experimental observation.

(iii) *Summary of the chelate effect*

Recent literature discussions of the origin and magnitude of the chelate effect have tended on occasions to throw doubt on its very existence. It should, therefore, be clearly remembered that it is an experimentally observable phenomenon which finds application in the widespread use of chelating agents in analytical chemistry, medicine, and bioinorganic chemistry, to mention only a few fields.

Furthermore, whatever standard state is chosen the chelate complex becomes increasingly favoured relative to the monodentate complex as the solutions become more dilute. Conversely the chelate effect slowly decreases in magnitude as the solutions become more concentrated and is virtually non-existent in the solid state. It does, however, exist in the gas phase, and recent analyses in this phase have indicated that enthalpy contributions are certainly as important and sometimes more important than entropy contributions in giving rise to the chelate effect [62].

14.7 THE MACROCYCLIC OR SUPER-CHELATE EFFECT

Macrocyclic ligands such as cyclam (VII) from far more stable complexes than the corresponding open-chain ligand such as tetraamine (VIII). This effect, which is known as the macrocyclic or super-chelate effect [63], manifests itself in both the enthalpy and entropy terms [64–66] (see Equation (14.20)).

VII

VIII

$$[Ni(H_2O)_6]^{2+} + L \rightleftharpoons [NiL]^{2+} + 6H_2O \tag{14.20}$$

L = cyclam, $K = 1.5 \times 10^{22}$, $\Delta H = -130 \, kJ.mol^{-1}$ ($-31 \, kcal.mol^{-1}$),
$\Delta S = -8.4 \, joule.°K^{-1}.mol^{-1}$ ($-2.0 \, cal.°K^{-1}.mol^{-1}$).
L = tetraamine, $K = 2.5 \times 10^{15}$, $\Delta H = -70 \, kJ.mol^{-1}$ ($-16.7 \, kcal.mol^{-1}$),
$\Delta S = +58.5 \, joule.°K^{-1}.mol^{-1}$ ($+14.0 \, cal.°K^{-1}.mol^{-1}$).

The most important factor that gives rise to the macrocyclic effect is the influence of complex formation on the solvation terms. Thus although the metal complexes of the macrocyclic and open-chain ligands are similarly solvated, the free macrocyclic ligand is not able to accommodate as many hydrogen-bonded water molecules as its open-chain counterpart, and thus less desolvation of the macrocyclic ligand occurs on complex formation [64–67]. Since the macrocyclic effect arises largely from ligand solvation effects the effect is largely independent of metal ion so long as the macrocyclic ligand does not attempt to impose a geometry different from that of the open-chain ligand. In addition the macrocyclic effect decreases in magnitude in solvents which only weakly solvate dissolved species. An understanding of the origins of the macrocyclic effect should be of value in unravelling the complexities of the interaction of metal ions with large biological molecules, such as proteins and enzymes where solvation terms play a very important role in determining the nature and extent of complex formation.

14.8 SUMMARY

Let us conclude this chapter by summarising the factors that influence the stabilities of metal-ligand complexes in solution [62,68].

Enthalpy effects

(a) Variation of bond strength with the donor/acceptor abilities of the ligand and metal ion.
(b) Ligand field effects.
(c) Steric and electrostatic repulsion between ligand and donor groups in the complex.
(d) Enthalpy effects related to the conformation of the free ligand.
(e) Other coulombic forces involved in chelate ring formation.
(f) Enthalpy of solution of metal ions, ligands and complexes.

Entropy effects

(a) Entropy of solution of metal ions, ligands and complexes.
(b) Difference in configurational entropy between free and coordinated ligand.
(c) Number, size and arrangement of chelate rings.

REFERENCES

[1] Harned, H. S. and Ehlers, R. W. (1933). *J. Amer. Chem. Soc.*, **55**, 652.
[2] Harned, H. S. and Ehlers, R. W. (1933). *J. Amer. Chem. Soc.*, **55**, 2379.
[3] Gurney, R. W. (1953). *Ionic Processes in Solution.* New York: McGraw-Hill.
[4] Nancollas, G. H. (1960). *Quart. Rev.*, **14**, 402.
[5] Anderegg, G. (1968). *Helv. Chim. Acta.*, **51**, 1856.
[6] Degischer, G. and Nancollas, G. H. (1970). *J. Chem. Soc. (A)*, 1125.
[7] Powell, R. E. and Latimer, W. M. (1951). *J. Chem. Phys.*, **19**, 1139.
[8] Born, M. (1920). *Z. Physik*, **1**, 45.
[9] Lewis, G. N. and Randall, M. (1961). *Thermodynamics* (2nd ed. revised by Pitter, K. S. and Brewer, L.) Chapter 32. New York: McGraw-Hill.
[10] Guggenheim, E. A. and Stokes, R. H. (1969). *Equilibrium Properties of Aqueous Solutions of Single Strong Electrolytes*, Chapter 10. Oxford: Pergamon.

[11] Hepler, L. G. (1963). *J. Amer. Chem. Soc.*, **85**, 3089.

[12] Brown, R. F. (1962). *J. Org. Chem.*, **27**, 3015.

[13] Burkin, A. R. (1951). *Quart. Rev.*, **5**, 1.

[14] Ahrland, S. (1973). *Structure and Bonding*, **15**, 167.

[15] Burger, K. and Dyrssen, D. (1963). *Acta Chem. Scand.*, **17**, 1489.

[16] Srivastava, S. C. and Newman, L. (1966). *Inorg. Chem.*, **5**, 1506.

[17] Mironov, V. E., Kul'ba, F. Ya., Fedorov, V. A., and Tikhomirov, O. B. (1963). *Russ. J. Inorg. Chem.*, **8**, 1328.

[18] Migal', P. K. and Chebotar', N. G. (1967). *Russ. J. Inorg. Chem.*, **12**, 630.

[19] Gobom, S. (1963). *Acta. Chem. Scand.*, **17**, 2181; (1963) *Nature*, **197**, 283.

[20] Konrad, D. and Vleck, A. A. (1963). *Coll. Czech. Chem. Comm.*, **28**, 595.

[21] Nozaki, T., Mise, T., and Higaki, K. (1967). *Nippon Kagaku Zasshi.*, **88**, 1168.

[22] Baxendale, J. H. and George, P. (1950). *Trans. Faraday Soc.*, **46**, 55.

[23] Irving, H. and Mellor, D. H. (1962). *J. Chem. Soc.*, 5222.

[24] Bjerrum, J. (1950). *Chem. Rev.*, **46**, 381.

[25] Bjerrum, J. (1931). *Kgl Danske Videnskab Selskab, Math-fys Medd.*, **11**, No. 5, 82.

[26] Sillén, L. G. (1949). *Acta. Chem. Scand.*, **3**, 539.

[27] Ciampolini, M., Paoletti, P., and Sacconi, L. (1960). *J. Chem. Soc.*, 4533.

[28] Poulsen, I. and Bjerrum, J. (1955). *Acta Chem. Scand.*, **5**, 1407.

[29] Irving, H. M. N. and Williams, R. J. P. (1953). *J. Chem. Soc.*, 3192.

[30] Phillips, C. S. G. and Williams, R. J. P. (1966). *Inorganic Chemistry*, Vol. 2, pp. 268–269. Oxford.

[31] Chatt, J., Ahrland, S., and Davies, N. R. (1958). *Quart. Rev.*, **12**, 265.

[32] Hartley, F. R. (1973). *The Chemistry of Platinum and Palladium*, p. 15. London: Applied Science.

[33] Hartley, F. R. (1972). *Nature*, **236**, 75.

[34] Ahrland, S. (1967). *Helv. Chim. Acta.*, **50**, 306.

[35] Connick, R. E., Helper, L. G., Hugus, Z. Z., Kury, J. M., Latimer, W. M., and Tsao, M. S. (1956). *J. Amer. Chem. Soc.*, **78**, 1827.

[36] Woods, M. J. M., Gallagher, P. K., and King, E. L. (1962). *Inorg. Chem.*, **1**, 55.

[37] Sillén, L. G. (1949). *Acta Chem. Scand.*, **3**, 539.

[38] Hansen, L. D., Izatt, R. M., and Christensen, J. J. (1963). *Inorg. Chem.*, **2**, 1243.

[39] Christensen, J. J., Izatt, R. M., Hansen, L. D., and Hale, J. D. (1964). *Inorg. Chem.*, **3**, 130.

[40] Pearson, R. G. (1963). *J. Amer. Chem. Soc.*, **85**, 3533; (1966) *Science*, **151**, 172; (1967) *Chem. in Britain*, **3**, 103; (1968) *J. Chem. Ed.*, **45**, 581, 643.

[41] *Benchmark Papers in Inorganic Chemistry: Hard and Soft Acids and Bases*, (1973). Ed. Pearson, R. G. Chichester: Wiley.

[42] Myers, R. T. (1974). *Inorg. Chem.*, **13**, 2040.

[43] Jørgensen, C. K. (1964). *Inorg. Chem.*, **3**, 1201.

[44] Yalman, R. G. (1962). *Inorg. Chem.*, **1**, 16.

[45] Pocker, Y. and Stone, J. T. (1967). *Biochemistry*, **6**, 668.

[46] Drago, R. S. and Wayland, B. B. (1965). *J. Amer. Chem. Soc.*, **87**, 3571.

[47] Drago, R. S. (1967). *Chem. in Britain*, **3**, 516; (1973) *Structure and Bonding*, **15**, 73.

[48] Drago, R. S. and Kabler, R. A. (1972). *Inorg. Chem.*, **111**, 3144.

[49] Pearson, R. G. (1972). *Inorg. Chem.*, **11**, 3146.

[50] Drago, R. S. (1973). *Inorg. Chem.*, **12**, 2211.

[51] Hancock, R. D. and Marsicano, F. (1978). *Inorg. Chem.*, **17**, 560.

[52] Nieboer, E. and McBryde, W. A. E. (1973). *Can. J. Chem.*, **51**, 2512.

[53] *Stability Constants* (1964, No. 17; 1971, No. 25). Ed by Sillén, L. G. and Martell, A. E., Chem. Soc. Spec. Publns. London: Chemical Society.

[54] Williams, R. J. P. (1954). *J. Phys. Chem.*, **58**, 121.

[55] Jørgensen, C. K. (1962). *Absorption Spectra and Chemical Bonding in Complexes*, London: Pergamon.

[56] Atkinson, G. and Bauman, J. E. (1963). *Inorg. Chem.*, **2**, 64.

[57] Pryde, A. J., Shaw, B. L., and Weeks, B. (1973). *J. C. S. Chem. Commun.*, 947.

[58] DeStefano, N. J., Johnson, D. K., and Venanzi, L. M. (1974). *Angew Chem. Int. Ed.*, **13**, 133.

[59] See for example Hartley, F. R. (1973). *Chem. Soc. Rev.*, **2**, 163.

[60] Schwarzenbach, G. (1952). *Helv. Chim. Acta.*, **35**, 2344.

[61] Adamson, A. W. (1954). *J. Amer. Chem. Soc.*, **76**, 1578.

[62] Myers, R. T. (1978). *Inorg. Chem.*, **17**, 952.

[63] Cabbiness, D. K. and Margerum, D. W. (1969). *J. Amer. Chem. Soc.*, **91**, 6540.

[64] Hinz, F. P. and Margerum, D. W. (1974). *J. Amer. Chem. Soc.*, **96**, 4993.

[65] Anichini, A., Fabbrizzi, L., Paoletti, P. and Clay, R. M. (1978). *J. C. S. (Dalton)*, 577.

[66] Kodama, M. and Kimura, E. (1978). *J. C. S. (Dalton)*, 1081 and refs therein.

[67] Dei, D. and Gori, R. (1975). *Inorg. Chim. Acta*, **14**, 157.

[68] Martell, A. E. (1967). *Adv. Chem. Ser.*, **62**, 272.

CHAPTER 15

The Applications of Stability Constants

15.1 INTRODUCTION

Wherever metal ions and ligands are present, equilibria between them will be established. Accordingly the applications of stability constants are ubiquitous and clearly cannot all be described in a book of this size. Instead we shall consider only a number of illustrations from life sciences, both animal and plant, medicine, pollution, electrochemistry, analytical chemistry, geochemistry and photography.

15.2 LIFE

Both plants and animals contain significant quantities of both metal ions and ligands [1-5]. The essential metal ions for man together with a brief summary of their roles are given in Table 15.1 where the word 'essential' is limited to those metal ions that are present in all healthy tissues, that have a fairly constant concentration range across species, and whose exclusion causes reproducible physiological abnormalities that are reversed upon readmitting the metal ion. The principle ligands present in man are summarised in Table 15.2. Combining Tables 15.1 and 15.2, it is apparent that life involves a large number of metal-ligand complex equilibria. The amount of metal that a given ligand binding site, which we will call B because it may be either monodentate or multidentate, can absorb is given by:

$$\text{Amount of M complexed} \propto [M]K_{MB} \qquad (15.1)$$

Whilst Equation (15.1) enables binding sites to discriminate between two metal ions on the basis of both the local concentration of free metal and the metal-binding site stability constant, it does not always discriminate sufficiently. Further selectivity can be introduced kinetically by the introduction of two

Table 15.1 − Essential metals in man.

Metal	Role	Preferred donor	Comments
Na	Charge transfer, nerve transmission	0	Controls osmotic pressures and membrane potentials; largely excluded from cells.
K	charge transfer, nerve transmission	0	Similar to Na, but particularly important within cells; as such, an important cofactor for some intracellular enzymes.
Mg	Structure forming (cell walls), trigger reactions, hydrolysis, phosphate transfer	0	Stabilises internal structure of cells by bridging between neighbouring carboxylate groups in lipoproteins. Helps to maintain membrane potentials and transmit nerve signals. Essential for DNA replication. (In plants essential for photo-synthetic conversion of carbon dioxide into carbohydrates).
Ca	Structure forming (bones and cell walls), trigger reactions, hydrolysis, phosphate transfer	0	Present in bones and other structural situations, stiffens cell walls (cf. Mg^{2+}). Antagonises the activating effect of Mg^{2+} in many enzymic processes, so providing a control mechanism.
V	?	?	Function unknown, possibly involved in lipid metabolism, it may prevent dental caries.
Cr	Carbohydrate metabolism	0	Works in conjunction with insulin in carbohydrate utili-sation. Bound to phosphates of nucleic acids; influences nucleic acid, lipid and cholesterol syntheses.
Mo	Redox reagent	N, S	Participates in redox reactions. (In plants is involved in nitrogen fixation).

Table 15.1 — *continued*

Metal	Role	Preferred donor	Comments
Mn	Redox reagent, hydrolysis	O, N, S	Replaces magnesium in certain enzyme reactions. Possibly a cofactor in respiratory enzymes.
Fe	Redox reagent, O_2 transporter	N, S	O_2 transport effected by hemoglobin. Widely involved in redox reactions.
Co	H and CH_3 group transfer, redox reagent	N, S	Present in vitamin B_{12} which is involved in synthesis of DNA and hemoglobin, metabolism of amino-acids, hydride and methyl group transfer. Involved in redox reactions.
Ni	?	N, S	Unknown role, but nickel deficiency does impair iron absorption.
Cu	Redox reagent	N, S	Involved in redox reactions of about 12 enzymes; concerned in iron utilisation and skin pigmentation.
Zn	Hydrolysis, pH control	N, S	pH buffer involved in phosphate hydrolysis and RNA synthesis.

binding sites (B^1 and B^2) and kinetic control of the release of metal ions from site B^1.

$$M + B^1 \xrightleftharpoons{K_{MB^1}} MB^1 \xrightarrow[+B^2]{k} MB^2 \tag{15.2}$$

The application of Equation (15.2) is best considered by way of a real example. There is no known ligand which has a higher stability constant for magnesium than zinc. Thus the protein that inserts magnesium into chlorophyll preferentially coordinates zinc, thus K_{ZnB^1} in Equation (15.1) is much greater than K_{MgB^1}. In part the amount of zinc complexed by this protein (B^1) is limited by the smaller amounts of zinc relative to magnesium present in nature. In this way about 1% of the transfer protein is complexed to zinc and 99% to magnesium. However, chlorophyll is a porphyrin-like molecule which will complex zinc about 10^{10} times more strongly than magnesium, so that at equilibrium only zinc chlorophyll will be formed. However, by using kinetic control by having an irreversible k_{MB^2} step as in Equation (15.2) it is possible for the rate of conversion of MgB^2 to be many orders of magnitude faster than for ZnB^1 to ZnB^2 conversion [6]. In this way magnesium can form a chlorophyll complex (B^2 = chlorophyll), and if magnesium complex formation is irreversible this would prevent the entrance of zinc.

Table 15.2 – Principal ligands found in man.

Simple ligands
  H_2O, OH^-, Cl^-, HCO_3^-, phosphates, SO_4^{2-}, F^-, Br^-, I^-

More complex ligands

Proteins, based on amino-acids linked through a peptide $-\overset{\displaystyle O}{\overset{\|}{C}}-\underset{\underset{H}{|}}{N}-$

  backbone; the side-chains have nitrogen, sulphur and oxygen donors as well as aromatic rings.

Carbohydrates and carboxylic acids have oxygen donors.

Nucleic acids have nitrogen and oxygen donors as well as phosphate groups.

Lipids have oxygen and olefinic donors.

Steroids have oxygen and olefinic donors.

Since it is not possible to demonstrate the application of stability constants to all the metal ions involved in life in a book of this size, we shall limit further discussion to the sodium-potassium ion pump and the role of iron complexes in oxygen transport and storage.

(i) *Sodium-potassium ion pump*

In the body the concentration of potassium ions inside cells is much greater than in the medium outside, and the reverse is true for sodium. These concentration gradients do three things. Firstly they give rise to potential gradients across cell walls which form the basis of our senses of smell, touch, pain etc. Secondly they represent a store of free energy which can be used either in exchange reactions so as to reject or accumulate chemicals such as amino-acids or in conjunction with other chemical reactions. Thirdly the distribution of ions can be used as a basis for controlling enzymes located inside or outside the cell, since the level of enzyme activity depends on the local concentration of particular metal ions.

The high concentration of sodium outside and potassium inside cells is surprising since both ions can diffuse through cell walls. As a result the natural tendency would be for sodium to diffuse in and potassium to diffuse out of the cell until the concentrations of each ion were equal inside and out. This does occur, but is counteracted by a chemical reinstatement process called a 'sodium-potassium ion pump' which pumps these ions from regions of low concentration to regions of higher concentration. If the ion pump is switched off, by the shock that follows a severe burning, or by freezing its enzymes for example in low temperature surgery or in blood transfusion vessels stored under refrigeration, then the normal Donnan membrane equilibrium prevails. On rewarming, the ion-pump restarts and the normal ion imbalance is reestablished. The ion-pump depends upon the coordination chemistry of sodium and potassium ions [7,8]. In general there are two stability constant sequences for alkali metal complexes:

(a) $Li^+ > Na^+ > K^+ > Rb^+ > Cs^+$ exhibited with anions of small simple weak acids such as hydroxide and acetate.

(b) $Li^+ < Na^+ < K^+ < Rb^+ < Cs^+$ exhibited with anions of large strong acids such as nitrate and sulphate.

In addition a ligand that is more selective for a cation in the middle of the series can be obtained by changing the nature of the coordinating atom to some intermediate type or by designing a ligand which is only able to coordinate ions of a specific size. Macrocyclic polyethers and polyketones show such a property. For example polyether I coordinates preferentially to potassium, ($\log_{10}K = 0.6$ (Li), 1.7 (Na), 2.18 (K), 1.25 (Cs)) [9]. By varying the size of the 'hole' in the centre of the ligand it is possible to vary the coordination preference of the ligand. In addition to 'hole' size it must be remembered that coordination to such a ligand involves the equilibrium

I

$$M^+(aq) + L(aq) \rightleftharpoons ML^+ + aq \tag{15.3}$$

so that the stability constant will depend in part in the ability of the metal ion to lose its hydration. In general, potassium ions lose their hydration and enter into a hydrophobic medium more easily than sodium ions. All cells are surrounded by membranes which are thin hydrophobic phases into which cations can partition, so that the equilibrium

$$M^+(aq) \rightleftharpoons M^+(membrane) \tag{15.4}$$

is set up. This equilibrium will lie further to the right for potassium than for sodium. Thus potassium is transported into the cell through complex formation by multidentate ligands of optimum 'hole' size located in a hydrophobic environment. Sodium is transported from the less hydrophilic inside of the cell to the more hydrophilic outside via small, more polar sites such as phosphate ($ROPO_3^{2-}$) groups in the cells walls. This pump, then, depends on the inside of the cell being more hydrophobic and the outside more hydrophilic, together with a supply of free energy which is provided by the hydrolysis of adenosine triphosphate.

It is important in biological systems that reagents that have selectivities $K^+ > Na^+$ and $Na^+ > K^+$ should exclude calcium and magnesium, since these are dipositive ions which will form stronger complexes than the unipositive alkali metal ions and which will therefore become saturated with calcium and magnesium. Such selectivity is easy to build into potassium selective ligands, because the relative sizes of the cations are $K^+ > Na^+ \sim Ca^{2+} > Mg^{2+}$. However, such ligands should be blocked by barium, thallium(I), rubidium and cesium ions, which is why these ions are so very poisonous.[†] Both calcium and lithium ions do compete with sodium sites, possibly accounting for the use of controlled amounts of lithium in the treatment of certain mental disorders.

(ii) Oxygen transport and storage [10-12]

Oxygen is transported from the lungs to the muscles by hemoglobin and is stored in the muscles by myoglobin. Both hemoglobin and myoglobin are complexes of iron in which the heme group (II) is the iron-containing unit.

II

---

† Note that 'barium meals' are safe to take because the barium is in the form of its extremely insoluble sulphate.

A fifth coordination position is occupied by an imidazole nitrogen which provides the sole covalent link between the heme group and the polypeptide chain of the protein, so that the iron in hemoglobin can be shown schematically as (III).

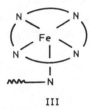

III

In deoxyhemoglobin (III) the iron is in the +2 oxidation state and the iron atom lies 0.8Å out of the porphyrin plane on the side remote from the histidine [13]. This displacement occurs because the iron(II) is in the high-spin state (see Section 14.3(ii) and Table 14.1), the two e_g electrons making it too 'big' to fit into the porphyrin square-plane.

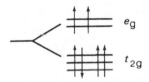

In this position it is readily available for coordination to oxygen, a situation that has been described [14] as 'entatic'. As soon as an oxygen molecule coordinates to iron, the iron drops down into the low-spin state which has empty e_g orbitals and is thus smaller so that the iron now fits into the plane of the

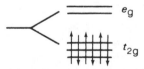

porphyrin ring. Thus the iron atom moves about 0.8Å when deoxyhemoglobin is oxygenated. Since all the time it is coordinated to the main protein chain through the histidine this motion is transmitted to various parts of the protein. In hemoglobin there are four heme units per molecule, and the small movements of the chain have the effect of increasing the ability of the other heme groups to pick up oxygen.

The process of oxygen transport from the lungs to the muscles occurs as follows. In the lungs the partial pressure of oxygen is high and so oxygen co-ordinates to hemoglobin. It is then transported in the blood to a tissue where the oxygen pressure is low when it is split off from the hemoglobin and becomes attached to myoglobin. Myoglobin is similar to hemoglobin in having a protein chain with iron coordinated to a heme group. But myoglobin has only one heme unit per molecule in contrast to the four in hemoglobin. For myoglobin (Mb), oxygen uptake [15] can be represented as:

$$Mb + O_2 \; \underset{}{\overset{K_{Mb}}{\rightleftharpoons}} \; MbO_2 \qquad\qquad (15.5)$$

$$K_{Mb} = [MbO_2]/[Mb][O_2] \qquad\qquad (15.6)$$

If f is the fraction of myoglobin molecules carrying oxygen and p is the partial pressure of oxygen, then

$$K_{Mb} = \frac{f}{(1-f)p} \quad \text{or} \quad f = \frac{K_{Mb}p}{1 + K_{Mb}p} \qquad\qquad (15.7)$$

This is the equation of a hyperbolic curve (as in Figure 15.1(a)). The uptake of oxygen by hemoglobin (Hb) with its four iron atoms is more complex and approximately follows the equation [15]

$$f = \frac{K_{Hb}p^n}{1 + K_{Hb}p^n} \qquad\qquad (15.8)$$

where n is pH dependent and of the order of 2.7. Equation (15.8) gives rise to curves (b) and (c) in Figure 15.1. The greater than unity value of n is a consequence of the 0.8Å shift of the iron, the transmission of which motion depends on the nature of the charged side groups of the protein chain; the charges on the side groups are themselves pH-dependent.

Thus hemoglobin is about as good an oxygen binder as myoglobin at high oxygen partial pressure, but is much poorer at the lower oxygen partial pressures prevailing in the muscles, and so it passes its oxygen on to myoglobin as required. The need for oxygen will be greatest in tissues that have already consumed oxygen and produced carbon dioxide. This carbon dioxide will lower the pH thus causing hemoglobin to release even more oxygen to myoglobin. The pH-sensitivity as well as the progressive increase of oxygen binding constants in hemoglobin both result from the interactions between the subunits. Myoglobin behaves more simply because it consists of only one unit.

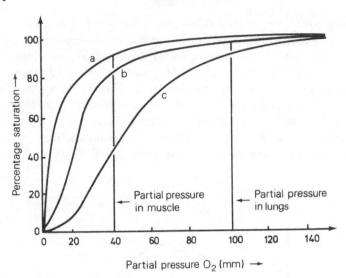

Figure 15.1 — The uptake of oxygen by myoglobin and hemoglobin.
(a) myoglobin, (b) hemoglobin at pH 7.6, (c) hemoglobin at pH 6.8.

Compounds such as carbon monoxide, hydrogen cyanide and trifluorophosphine are all toxic when inhaled because they bind to hemoglobin more strongly than oxygen; their effect is one of competitive inhibition (Equation (15.9)).

$$[Hb-CO] + O_2 \xrightleftharpoons{K^*} [Hb-O_2] + CO \qquad (15.9)$$

For mammalian myoglobins K^* has values ranging between 0.025 and 0.05 at 20°C, whereas for hemoglobins K^* has values between 0.0033 and 0.0066 at 37°C [15]. The standard treatment for carbon monoxide poisoning is to place the patient in an oxygen tent to drive the equilibrium over to the right-hand side by increasing the partial pressure of oxygen and decreasing the partial pressure of carbon monoxide in the lungs. Cyanide ions can act in a similar way to carbon monoxide. When they have been swallowed one treatment is to swallow a solution of ferrous sulphate buffered with citric acid and sodium carbonate. The ferrous ions rapidly react with the cyanide to form a very stable ferrocyanide complex which can be eliminated from the body.

15.3 MEDICINE

(i) Removal of unwanted metal ions

A total analysis of the body would show the presence of most of the elements of the Periodic Table; however, many of these have been introduced accidentally. When the physiological effects of elements are examined it is found that as a function of concentration they follow one or other of two broad curves (Figure 15.2). It is apparent that excess of any element, whether essential or not, is harmful; the degree of harm being rather dependent on the element. A preliminary classification of the degree of toxicity (Table 15.3) shows that the heavier elements are generally the more toxic [16–18]. In terms of the class 'a'/'b' or hard and soft classifications introduced in Sections 14.5 (ii) and 14.5 (iii) the essential elements are all either borderline or hard/class 'a', whereas the class 'b'/soft elements are all very toxic. We obtain trace metals from drinking water, unwashed vegetables and fruit, cooking pots, dental fillings and many other

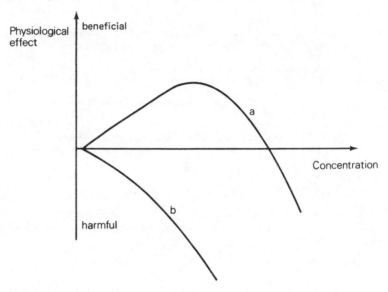

Figure 15.2 – The physiological effects of elements according to dosage: (a) essential elements, (b) poisons.

Table 15.3 – The toxicity of elements (adapted from reference [15]).

Non-critical
     H, Li, Na, K, Rb, Mg, Ca, Sr, Al, Fe, C, Si, N, P, O, S, F, Cl, Br

Very toxic and relatively accessible
     Be, Sn, Pb, As, Sb, Bi, Se, Te, Co, Ni, Cu, Zn, Tc, Pd, Ag, Cd, Pt, Au, Hg

Toxic, but very insoluble or very rare
     Ba, Ge, Ti, Zr, Nb, Ru, Rh, La, Hf, Ta, W, Re, Os, Ir

sources. The principal features of a suitable reagent for removing unwanted metal ions are [1, 5, 19, 20]:

(a) The ideal reagent will be a multidentate chelate that coordinatively saturates the metal ion and gives a water-soluble, easily excreted complex.

(b) The reagent must be sufficiently small to get through to the metal ion.

(c) The reagent must not be destroyed by the method of introduction.

(d) The donor groups in the ligand are chosen according to the hard or soft character of the metal ion to be removed.

(e) The steric requirements of the metal ion must be considered. Thus iron(III) forms octahedral whereas silver(I) forms linear complexes so that each will require a totally different ligand geometry if it is to form a chelate complex.

(f) If the ligand or its complex have to pass through a cell membrane, which will behave as a non-aqueous phase, then both should have a low or zero charge.

(g) The stoichiometry of the metal ligand system must be considered. Thus iron(III) forms mono-, bis- and tris-complexes with 8-hydroxyquinoline yet only the latter is non-toxic and being uncharged can penetrate cell walls.

(h) Both the ligand and its complex must be non-toxic. Thus for example, 2,3-dimercaptopropanol should not be used to remove zinc or cadmium because the complexes that it forms with these metal ions are more poisonous than the free metal ions!

Let us look then at some specific metal ions:

Iron is a well-known tonic and is used in treating anaemia. However, excess iron causes giddiness, diarrhoea and cardiac collapse — conditions found amongst people such as the Bantus of South Africa who cook and brew their beer in iron pots. Excess iron can be removed by using desferrioxamine (IV), a naturally occurring polyhydroxamic acid that is found as an iron complex in certain microorganisms, an observation which itself indicates high specificity. The stability constant for the interaction of desferrioxamine with iron(III) is 10^{31} which is 10^{17} time greater than for its interaction with any other metal ion [21].

$$NH_2(CH_2)_5\overset{\displaystyle |}{\underset{\displaystyle OH}{N}}-\overset{\displaystyle O}{\overset{\displaystyle \|}{C}}-(CH_2)_2-\overset{\displaystyle O}{\underset{\displaystyle \|}{C}}-\overset{\displaystyle H}{N}-(CH_2)_5-\overset{\displaystyle O}{\underset{\displaystyle \|}{N}}-\overset{\displaystyle \|}{C}-(CH_2)_2-\overset{\displaystyle O}{\underset{\displaystyle \|}{C}}-\overset{\displaystyle H}{N}-(CH_2)_5-\overset{\displaystyle |}{\underset{\displaystyle OH}{N}}-\overset{\displaystyle O}{\overset{\displaystyle \|}{C}}-CH_3$$

(IV)

Copper. Small quantities of copper are normally present in the body. Excess copper arises from Wilson's disease in which the copper control mechanism is deranged and copper is then deposited in the liver, brain and kidneys as well as other parts of the body [22]. It may be seen as brown or green rings in the cornea. Excess copper leads to liver and nervous disorders and ultimately to death. For some time penicillamine (V) has been used to remove copper from patients suffering from Wilson's disease. Some patients respond well, some are allergic to it and some lose zinc as well. Accordingly work is currently being carried out to design a ligand that mimics the copper binding site in human albumin (VI). At present glycylglycylhistamide appears promising, but a great deal of work remains to be done before it can be given to patients [22-24].

Arsenic. Since the poison gas Lewisite (VII) contains arsenic which binds to the —SH groups of certain enzymes and renders them inactive, an intensive search for a ligand to remove arsenic was mounted. This led to dimercaprol (VIII) or British Anti Lewisite BAL. In addition to removing arsenic, BAL is very useful for removing Al, Hg, Cd, Au, Tl, Bi, Sb, Te and V. Its major drawback is apparent from this list, namely lack of specificity.

Uranium. Uranium initially becomes bound to the bone but is later carried to the kidney as bicarbonate complexes where it kills the kidney cells. It can be removed by EDTA. However, EDTA is not only a very non-specific ligand that chelates to most metal ions and hence removes them, but it is also a very powerful chelating agent for calcium. Accordingly EDTA must be administered in the form of $Na_2Ca[EDTA]$ so that it carries its own calcium atom which prevents its robbing the body of calcium. The calcium atom can be displaced by many metal ions including U^{IV} and U^{VI} so that treatment must be carried out with care.

Lead [25]. Lead, in common with mercury and arsenic, displaces copper and zinc from their normal binding sites, hence giving rise to poisoning. In adults most of the toxic effects of lead are substantially reversible once the lead has been removed by using either penicillamine (V) or $Na_2Ca[EDTA]$.

Calcium. The body contains large quantities of calcium both in solution and as a precipitate, in bones. A number of ailments result when calcium salts precipitate in the wrong places. Thus cataract is a precipitate of calcium salts which forms over the cornea of the eye and gradually prevents light entering it. Cataract can be treated either by bathing the eye in EDTA solution or allowing the precipitate to build up into a hard crust which can then be lifted off in a minor operation. Gall stones and hardening of the arteries leading to the heart (atherosclerosis) both involve the precipitation of calcium salts of cholesterol (IX), an oxygen donor. Although gall stones are generally removed by surgery this is not readily possible with atherosclerosis since the precipitation has occurred in the middle layer of the arterial walls. Both conditions have been treated with EDTA with some measure of success.

IX

(ii) *Medical research*

During the 1950s it was discovered that a number of metal chelates were active anti-viral agents [26]. This, coupled with the discovery that many cancers appear to be virus dependent, led to an interest in metal complexes as therapeutic agents [27]. There are several approaches to the development of new therapeutic agents that influence the concentrations of the metal ions and ligands present in the body. One is to make a very wide range of agents and try them out. This a very costly particularly in the trials part of the work. Another is to calculate what the effect of adding a particular reagent will be on the other reagents already present. This approach has been developed by Perrin in Canberra [28] and Williams in Cardiff [29]. The approach is first of all to list all the metal ions and ligands of interest, which are usually taken as those in the bloodstream. Then each metal-ligand interaction is examined *in vitro* to determine its stability constants. A computer is used to combine all these reactions and to calculate the concentration of each complex present at equilibrium. There are two main programs for doing this, COMICS (Concentration of Metal Ions and Complexing Species) [30] and HALTAFALL (Concentrations and Precipitates − in Swedish) [31].

When a new drug is synthesised its proton and metal ion stability constants are determined. It is then possible to determine the effect of administering a given dose of that drug on all the other components of the bloodstream. At present more than 9000 species can be considered at once. The end result is to prepare plots of drug concentration administered versus the concentrations of each of the species formed at equilibrium in the blood. By studying those plots of interest to the particular application concerned, for example, the removal of copper in Wilson's disease [28], it is possible to optimise the amount of drug required and to determine how much drug is required relative to its toxicity.

There has recently been an increasing interest in the possible use of metal complexes in the treatment of cancer [32–36] following the initial report that *cis*-[Pt(NH$_3$)$_2$Cl$_2$] was an effective anti-tumour agent in the case of certain tumours [37]. Cancer may be defined as "a disease of multicellular organisms which is characterised by the seemingly uncontrolled multiplication and spread within the organism of apparently abnormal forms of the organism's own cells" [38]. As already mentioned, certain cancers appear to be virus dependent. Viruses are made up of a core of nucleic acid encased in a layer of protein, lipid or polysaccharide. Viruses can only reproduce inside living cells where they take over the chemical and energy supplies to the cell and use them to produce more viruses. It has been suggested that antiviral action involves at least two aspects: (i) interaction between the virus's host cell and the metal complex so that viral growth and propagation is inadequately supported, and (ii) direct reaction between virions and the metal complex. Platinum complexes only seem to be effective *in vivo* against viruses that require DNA replication such as Rous Sarcoma Virus and Fowl Pest Virus. Thus it is suggested that *cis*-[Pt(NH$_3$)$_2$Cl$_2$] may selectively inhibit the synthesis of new DNA polymers within the cancer cells by reaction with two of the nitrogen-containing bases of DNA.

15.4 POLLUTION [39–41]

One of the major applications of metal complex formation that has recently been causing problems is the use of phosphates, such as sodium triphosphate $Na_5P_3O_{10}$, as 'builders' in detergent powders. The function of the sodium triphosphate is, firstly to complex the calcium and magnesium present in hard water so keeping them in solution [40] and preventing their reacting with the anionic groups of the detergent, and secondly to react with water to produce hydroxide ions (Reaction (15.11)) so keeping the water slightly alkaline and

$$[P_3O_{10}]^{5-} + 2H_2O \rightarrow HP_2O_7^{3-} + H_2PO_4^- + OH^- \qquad (15.11)$$

thus helping to emulsify the grease [41]. The evironmental disadvantage of this use of phosphates is that phosphates promote the growth of certain algae which can give rise to 'eutrophication' in sluggish water [42] and 'red tide' in warm coastal waters [43]. In the USA this has, in some cases, gone so far as to convert lakes into marshes or even dry land. Whilst detergents are only one source of the phosphates that find their way into rivers — humans and animals produce considerable amounts, and phosphate fertilisers account for quite a bit more — attempts have been made to find alternative cheap sequestering agents for calcium and magnesium. However, the problem is not easy, partly because of cost and partly because alternative compounds such as EDTA or NTA, nitrilotriacetic acid (X), which might otherwise be ideal, could conceivably decompose to yield

$$\begin{array}{c} CH_2COOH \\ \diagup \\ N \!\!-\!\!-\!\!-\!\! CH_2COOH \\ \diagdown \\ CH_2COOH \end{array}$$

X

undesirable products such as cyanide. However, to date only ammonia, carbon dioxide and traces of amino acids have been detected during the degradation of NTA in cells. In addition NTA has recently been linked with cancer and deformed offspring in laboratory animals.

15.5 ELECTROCHEMISTRY

There are two main applications of coordination complexes in electrochemistry [44, 45]. These are in electroplating and in anticorrosion liquids. Electroplating is generally carried out in solution by making the object to be electroplated the cathode and depositing a film of the coating metal on it. All metal ions in solution are coordinated by ligands, and the nature of the ligands has a profound effect on the type of surface deposit that is obtained. In order to obtain an even surface the concentration of metal ions is solution should be low since this will inhibit crystal growth. If the concentration of metal ion is too high then deposition is too rapid and a course grained, uneven, dendritic deposit will be formed. Accordingly, cyanide ions are the commonest ligands added, particularly for elements to the right of the transition series, Cu, Ag, Au, Zn and Cd, but many other ligands such as amines, ethylenediamine, sulphamic acid, phosphate, sulphate and chloride are also used.

In the electroplating of copper from a cyanide bath, the copper is present as a number of complex ions including $[Cu(CN)_2]^-$, $[Cu(CN)_3]^{2-}$ and $[Cu(CN)_4]^{3-}$, although copper is only actually deposited from $[Cu(CN)_2]^-$. Thus the cyanide reduces the concentration of available copper to about 10^{-18} mol.l^{-1}, so helping to obtain a slow, even growth of deposited copper.

Anti-corrosion liquids, pickling agents and 'rust-eaters' generally involve phosphoric acid in one form or another. A typical 'rust-eater', for example, is a mixture of phosphoric acid, water and ethanol. The phosphoric acid dissolves the oxide that forms the rust until the bare metal is exposed. The ethanol then raises the hydrogen overpotential so that the free metal, generally iron, does not dissolve in the acid. It does, however, react with the phosphate ions, which being very strong ligands for iron form an inert protective layer, which not only protects the iron from further attack but also acts as a very good primer, ensuring that the paint really sticks on firmly [46].

Phosphates are often added to anodising baths in which a surface layer of phosphate is deposited on the metal (15.12). Metals that can be treated in this way

$$M + PO_4^{3-} \rightarrow MPO_4 + 3\epsilon \tag{15.12}$$

include iron and steel and Zn, Cd, Al and their alloys. In addition to preventing corrosion, phosphatising is used to provide electrical insulation, antifriction between sliding metal surfaces, and as a lubricant in drawing iron and steel into wire. It depends on the high affinity of the highly charged phosphate ligand for each of these metals.

Traditional solutions for cleaning silver involve a mild abrasive which is used to remove the surface layer of silver atoms which have become tarnished by reaction with sulphide, together with ammonia which reacts with the exposed silver atoms to yield a silver ammonia complex. This is more resistant to further sulphide attack than is uncoordinated silver.

15.6 ANALYTICAL CHEMISTRY

The formation of complexes in solution is widely used in analytical chemistry [47,48] in such areas as complexometric titrations, metal-ion indicators, colorimetric analysis, precipitants and reagents for extracting specific metal ions from solution.

(i) *Complexometric titrations* [49]

In order that a complexometric reaction can be used as the basis for a titration procedure it must fulfil three criteria: it must be fast, proceed stoichiometrically and be quantitative. Non-transition and many transition metal ions with the notable exceptions of Cr^{III}, Co^{III}, Rh^{III}, Ir^{III}, Pt^{II} and Au^{III} react with ligands within the time of mixing. The requirement that the reaction occurs stoichiometrically to form only one complex, namely ML, eliminates many ligands which form ML_2 and higher complexes. If higher complexes are formed then in order to completely coordinate all the metal ion an excess of ligand will be required and a sharp end-point will not be obtained. Figure 15.3 illustrates the problem for three different ligands, all of which give overall stability constants of 10^{20}. It is apparent that the ligand that forms a single ML complex is the most satisfactory. Thus the ligands used in complexlometric titrations are polydentate ligands that form 1:1 complexes. The requirement that a complexometric

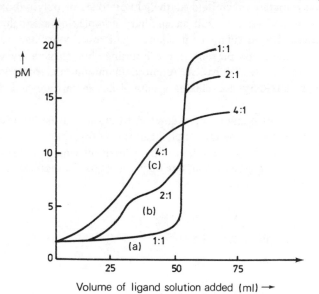

Figure 15.3 – Curves for the titration of a $0.02\,\mathrm{mol.l^{-1}}$ solution of a metal ion (50 ml) against

(a) $0.02\,\mathrm{mol.l^{-1}}$ ligand solution where $\mathrm{M} + \mathrm{L} \xrightleftharpoons{K} \mathrm{ML}$ $K = 10^{20}$

(b) $0.04\,\mathrm{mol.l^{-1}}$ ligand solution where $\left.\begin{array}{l}\mathrm{M} + \mathrm{L} \xrightleftharpoons{K_1} \mathrm{ML} \\ \mathrm{ML} \xrightleftharpoons{K_2} \mathrm{ML_2}\end{array}\right\}$ $\begin{array}{l}K_1 = 10^{12}, K_2 = 10^8 \\ \text{i.e. } \beta_2 = 10^{20}\end{array}$

(c) $0.08\,\mathrm{mol.l^{-1}}$ ligand solution where $\left.\begin{array}{l}\mathrm{M} + \mathrm{L} \xrightleftharpoons{K_1} \mathrm{ML} \\ \mathrm{ML_3} \xrightleftharpoons{K_4} \mathrm{ML_4}\end{array}\right\}$ $\begin{array}{l}K_1 = 10^8, K_2 = 10^6, \\ K_3 = 10^4, K_4 = 10^2\end{array}$

i.e. $\beta_4 = 10^{20}$

reaction be quantitative can, of course, never be met in the strict sense of the word, since all complex forming reactions are equilibrium processes. However, if an x mol.l^{-1} solution of a metal ion is to be titrated then if $K > 10^5/x$, the titration error due to the incompleteness of the reaction will be less than 1% [50].

The first type of complexometric reagents to be used were polyamines such as $(H_2NCH_2CH_2)_2NCH_2CH_2N(CH_2CH_2NH_2)_2$. However, these are only successful with metal ions such as Co, Ni, Cu, Zn, Cd and Hg which form strong complexes with basic nitrogen atoms. A more versatile reagent is EDTA which forms strong complexes with all metal ions except those of the alkali metals. EDTA may be written as H_4Y, and on complex formation the four carboxylic protons are displaced by the metal ion, so that the stability constant for metal-EDTA complex formation will be pH-dependent and will be greatest at high pH. As a result most EDTA titrations are carried out in solutions buffered at high pH, and since many metals precipitate as their hydroxides or polyhydroxo species at high pH it is necessary to add an auxiliary complexing agent during most EDTA titrations. The auxiliary complexing agent must coordinate sufficiently strongly to the metal to prevent it precipitating, but sufficiently weakly to release the metal ion to the EDTA. Ammonia/ammonium chloride buffers are the commonest auxiliary complexing agents although tartrate and citrate are also used.

The specificity of many complexometric titrations can be improved by the use of masking agents. These are simply ligands that form very stable complexes with potential interfering metal ions thereby effectively removing them from the titration. In addition to the proton, one of the most useful masking agents is the cyanide ion which prevents the cations of

	Co	Ni	Cu	Zn
Ru	Rh	Pd	Ag	Cd
Os	Ir	Pt	Au	Hg

from reacting with EDTA. Zn^{2+} and Cd^{2+} can, if desired, be subsequently demasked by treating the solution with formaldehyde (15.13).

$$[Cd(CN)_4]^{2-} + 4H^+ + 4HCHO \rightarrow 4HOCH_2CN + Cd^{2+}.aq \qquad (15.13)$$

(ii) *Metal-ion indicators*

One of the ways of detecting the sharp change in metal-ion concentration that occurs in a complexometric titration is to use a metal-ion indicator. This is a dyestuff that forms a coloured metal complex at some characteristic range of pM values, exactly as an acid-base indicator forms a hydrogen ion complex over a characteristic range of pH. Since most metal-ion indicators are also hydrogen ion indicators it is necessary to consider their acid-base equilibria as well. Consider Eriochrome Black T (XI) which is one of the most widely used

XI

indicators and which we will abbreviate to H_2In^-. It undergoes acid-base equilibria (15.14) and also reacts with many ions including Mg, Ca, In, Pb, Ti, Fe, Co, Ni, Ru, Rh, Pd, Os, Ir, Pt, Cu, Zn, Cd, Hg and the rare earths to form a red complex (15.15).

$$H_2In^- \xrightleftharpoons{pK\ 6.3} HIn^{2-} \xrightleftharpoons{pK\ 11.5} In^{3-} \qquad (15.14)$$
$$\ \ \text{red}\qquad\qquad \text{blue}\qquad\qquad \text{yellow-orange}$$

$$HIn^{2-} + M^{2+} \rightleftharpoons MIn^- + H^+ \qquad (15.15)$$
$$\ \text{blue}\qquad\qquad\quad \text{red}$$

It is apparent from Equilibrium (15.14) that the indicator should only be used between pH 7 and 11. To be suitable as an indicator and give a minimum titration error the metal-indicator formation constant (K_{MIn}) at the pH of the titration should be large ($>10^4$). However, K_{MIn} must be much smaller than the metal-EDTA formation constant (K_{MY}) at the pH of the titration and in the presence of auxiliary ligand, or a premature end-point will be observed. In practice K_{MY}/K_{MIn} should be greater then 10^4, but if it is too large a late end-point will result [51]. Finally, to get an accurate end-point the ratio of indicator to metal ion concentration should be less than 0.01 which in practice means that the indicator must be very strongly coloured.

(iii) Colorimetric analysis [52]

In a colorimetric or spectrophotometric method of analysis a ligand is added to the metal ion solution to form a deeply coloured complex. The solution containing this complex is then put into the u.v.-visible spectrophotometer and its absorbance measured. From a previously prepared calibration curve of absorbance against metal ion concentration the metal ion concentration in the sample can be read off. A number of points need to be considered for a satisfactory colorimetric analysis:

(a) *Specificity*. Very few ligands are completely specific for one metal ion, although by designing the ligand carefully and paying attention to the type of donor atom present, using the principle of hard and soft acids and bases (see Section 14.5(iii)) and, in a chelate ligand, the 'bite' of the ligand (see Section 14.6), ligands that are fairly selective for a small group of metal ions can often be obtained. Since many ligands form complexes by loss of a proton (as in Reaction (15.16)) it is often possible to increase the selectivity by carefully controlling the pH.

$$+2H^+ + 3H_2O \qquad (15.16)$$

Further specificity can be achieved by using masking agents (see Section 15.6(i)), which preferentially complex with interfering metal ions.

(b) *Proportionality between absorbance and concentration*. Ideally the solutions should obey Beer's law (see Section 8.2) although this is not absolutely essential provided that a calibration curve is used.

(c) *Stability of the colour*. The stability of the colour is a very important feature of any colorimetric analysis and is generally the factor that causes the most difficulty. The colour should ideally be indefinitely stable, but in practice stability for an hour or so is often all that can be achieved.

(d) *Intensity of the colour*. The intensity of the colour that is required depends on the amount of metal ion present. If only small amounts of metal ion are present, then the absorptivity should be as high as possible, and in practice this means that a charge transfer band is necessary. However, sometimes fairly large samples are available, perhaps because of sampling difficulties as in the case of mineral exploration where too small a sample would be unrepresentative, and in such cases large absorptions can be a positive disadvantage because of the need to dilute the sample, with its attendant errors.

(e) *Position of absorption*. It is highly desirable that the coloured complex should absorb in the visible rather than in the u.v. region of the spectrum, because interference by other compounds in the u.v. is more pronounced. For example colourless compounds such as benzene, acetone and metal nitrates all absorb significantly in the u.v.

Colorimetric analysis has been extended to the determination of anionic species (X^-) using basic dyes (D^+) which form ion-pairs (DX) that can be extracted into a suitable organic solvent before analysing them spectrophotometrically [54]. Anionic species that can be determined in this way include anionic metal-ligand complexes as well as ClO_4^-, PO_4^{3-}, SO_4^{2-} and NO_3^-. The dyestuffs include the xanthene (XII) and triphenylmethane dyes (XIII).

XII   XIII

(iv) *Precipitation of metals*

Most metals form an insoluble product with one or more inorganic ligands such as sulphate or iodide. However, these ligands precipitate many metal ions, and accordingly analysts have often turned to organic reagents to obtain greater selectivity. Two examples will be considered. 8-Hydroxyquinoline (oxine), illustrated in Reaction (15.17), is a rather non-specific reagent that forms precipitates with about two dozen cations although their solubilities differ somewhat.

$$(15.17)$$

Selectivity can be introduced by suitably controlling the pH, since proton displacement occurs on complex formation, and by the addition of competing ligands such as EDTA. The concentration of metal ion remaining in solution after precipitation can be determined [55] from Equation (15.18) where m and n are the number of M and L groups in the precipitate M_mL_n, K is the solubility product of M_mL_n, and $\alpha_{L(H)}$ and α_M are defined by Equations (15.19) and (15.20) in which Y is the competing ligand (for example, EDTA).

$$\log [M] = -\log \alpha_M - m/n \log \alpha_{L(H)} - 1/n \, (pK + m\log[L]) \qquad (15.18)$$

$$\alpha_{L(H)} = \frac{[L]}{[L] + [HL] + [H_2L] + \dots} \qquad (15.19)$$

$$\alpha_M = \frac{\alpha_{Y(H)}}{\alpha_{Y(H)} + K_{ML}[Y]} \qquad (15.20)$$

In contrast to oxine, dimethylglyoxime exhibits great specificity in that it will only precipitate palladium from acid solutions and only nickel from weakly alkaline solutions (Reaction (15.21)).

$$(15.21)$$

The insolubility of the complexes depends upon the planar structure which allows vertical stacking of the planar units in the crystal with weak axial metal-metal interactions.

(v) *Extraction of metals* [56, 57]

Organic ligands are valuable for extracting metal ions out of aqueous solutions into organic solvents such as chloroform, carbon tetrachloride or benzene. Since the organic reagent is usually put in the organic phase initially it should be uncharged, but if aquated metal ions are to be extracted, the ligand should be capable of losing protons in such a way that it attains the charge of the metal and so gives a neutral complex. Selectivity is incorporated into the reagent (a) by choosing the donor atom according to the principle of hard and soft acids and bases (see Section 14.5(iii)), (b) with chelate ligands by choosing one with a 'bite' of a suitable size for the metal ion involved (see Section 14.6), (c) by suitably adjusting the pH, and (d) by altering the organic phase into which the complex is to be extracted. Examples of extraction reagents that have been used are:

8-hydroxyquinoline (oxine)

Diphenylthiocarbazone (dithizone)

$$HS-C\begin{smallmatrix}N-NHPh\\\\N=NPh\end{smallmatrix} \longleftrightarrow S=C\begin{smallmatrix}NH-NHPh\\\\N=NPh\end{smallmatrix}$$

Acetylacetone

$$CH_3-C-CH_2-C-CH_3 \longleftrightarrow CH_3-C-CH=C-CH_3$$
$$\quad\;\overset{\|}{O}\quad\;\overset{\|}{O} \qquad\qquad \overset{\|}{O}\quad\;\overset{|}{OH}$$

Tri-n-octylphosphine oxide (used particularly to extract uranium (VI))

$(n\text{-octyl})_3 P = O$

8-Hydroxyquinoline has been widely studied in aqueous solution as it exists in three forms,

$$\begin{array}{ccccc} (H_2L) & \xrightarrow[\;pK_1 = 5.09\;]{-H^+} & (HL) & \xrightarrow[\;pK_2 = 9.82\;]{-H^+} & (L) \end{array} \qquad (15.22)$$

but only the neutral molecule, HL, and any neutral complexes formed are extracted into organic solvents such as chloroform [58]. The concentration of the neutral species HL that is present in chloroform at equilibrium is given by

$$[HL]_{CHCl_3} = \{[H_2L]_{H_2O} + [HL]_{H_2O} + [L]_{H_2O}\} K_{D,L} \alpha_{HL} \qquad (15.23)$$

where $K_{D,L}$ is the distribution ratio of 8-hydroxyquinoline between chloroform and water (720) [58], and α_{HL} is the fraction of 8-hydroxyquinoline that is present in aqueous solution as the neutral molecule (15.24).

$$\alpha_{HL} = \frac{K_1[H]}{[H]^2 + K_1[H] + K_1K_2} \qquad (15.24)$$

In order to determine [50] how much metal will be extracted by a weakly basic ligand such as 8-hydroxyquinoline it is necessary to consider a reaction such as

$$(M^{n+})_{aq} + n(HL)_{org} \xrightleftharpoons{K_{ex}} (ML_n)_{org} + n(H^+)_{aq} \tag{15.25}$$

which has an 'equilibrium constant' K_{ex} (15.26).

$$K_{ex} = \frac{[H]_{aq}^n [ML_n]_{org}}{[M]_{aq} [HL]_{org}^n} \tag{15.26}$$

In practice several species ML_1, ML_2 ... may be extracted so that it is convenient to define a conditional constant K'_{ex} given by,

$$K'_{ex} = \frac{[H]_{aq}^n [ML'_n]_{org}}{[M']_{aq} [HL']_{org}^n} \tag{15.27}$$

where $[ML'_n]_{org}$ represents the various species ML_1, ML_2 ... in the organic phase, $[M']_{aq}$ the various forms of M in the aqueous phase, and $[HL']_{org}$ represents the species L, HL, H_2L in the organic phase. $[ML'_n]$ can then be defined in terms of a function $\theta_{ML_n(L)}$:

$$\theta_{ML_n(L)} = \frac{\{[M] + [ML] + [ML_2] + \ldots\}}{[ML_n]} \tag{15.28}$$

Similar functions $\theta_{MY_n(Y)}$ and $\theta_{MZ_n(Z)}$ can be defined for the formation of complexes between the metal and any other competing ligands Y and Z. These can be combined to give an overall θ_M (for θ_M, n in Equation (15.28) is zero):

$$\theta_M = 1 + \alpha_{M(L)} + \alpha_{M(Y)} + \ldots -P \tag{15.29}$$

where P is the number of competing ligands. Thus

$$K'_{ex} = \frac{K_{ex} (\theta_{ML_n})_{org}}{(\theta_M)_{aq} (\theta_{HL}{}^n)_{org}} \tag{15.30}$$

If the volumes of the two phases are equal, the extraction coefficient E, which is defined as the ratio of the total metal concentration in the organic phase to the total metal concentration in the aqueous phase, is given by:

$$E = \frac{[ML'_n]_{org}}{[M']_{aq}} \tag{15.31}$$

Combining Equations (15.27) and (15.31).

$$E = \frac{K'_{ex}[HL']^n_{org}}{[H]^n_{org}} \qquad (15.32)$$

This can be rewritten in logarithmic form:

$$\log E = \log K'_{ex} + n \log [HL']_{org} + n\text{pH} \qquad (15.33)$$

By evaluating K'_{ex} from K_{ex} using Equation (15.30) and obtaining $[HL']_{org}$ from Equation (15.23), plots of the amount of metal extracted against pH can be prepared and used for determining the optimal conditions for extracting one metal from a solution containing several.

The technique of solvent extraction of metals has been developed extensively in recent years, spurred on particularly by its value in the purification of uranium for nuclear fuel purposes as well as its applications in analytical chemistry [56].

15.7 GEOCHEMISTRY

The classification of metal ions into class 'a' and 'b' or hard or soft (see Sections 14.5(ii) and 14.5(iii)) can be used to understand why a particular metal occurs in a particular type of ore. First of all we need to know something about the history of the earth's formation, about which there is no general agreement. However, many geochemists feel that the earth started off as a gas which slowly cooled in three stages:

$$\text{Gas} \xrightarrow{\text{stage 1}} \text{Liquid} \xrightarrow{\text{stage 2}} \text{Solid} \xrightarrow{\text{stage 3}} \text{Solution} \qquad (15.34)$$

Stage 1 led to the formation of three immiscible phases together with an atmosphere; the traditional view, following Goldschmidt, is that these three phases are clearly separated (left-hand side of Fiqure 15.4) whereas a more recent view, following Kuhn and Rittmann, suggests that the three phases are less clearly separated (right-hand side of Figure 15.4) [59]. Of these phases, two are particularly important for the present purpose: the crust, which is siliceous, and the next lower layer which is a sulphide/oxide layer. A separation into three layers can be demonstrated in the laboratory and furthermore the individual metal ions go into sulphide or silicate layers according to the free energy change of Reaction (15.35).

$$\text{Msulphide} + \text{M'silicate} \rightleftharpoons \text{M'sulphide} + \text{Msilicate} \qquad (15.35)$$

ΔG for this reaction closely parallels the electrochemical series. Elements more electropositive than iron (that is, 'hard' or class 'a' metals) occur in the 'hard' silicate phase, whilst the less electropositive 'softer' metals occur in the 'soft' sulphide phase. The very soft metals probably occur in the core, which is thought to be metallic. Thus the elements of the periodic table are distributed as in Figure 15.5.

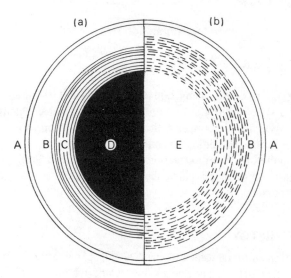

Figure 15.4 – Possible layers of material in the earth's crust: left-hand side (a) after Goldschmidt (Reference [60]); right-hand side (b) after Kuhn and Rittmann (Reference [61]) A = crust, B = silicate layer, C = sulphide layer, D = iron core, E = solar core.

Stage 2, in which rocks were formed, probably occurred in three steps.

(a) In the first crystallisation step ($\sim$1200°C) the heavy refractory oxides containing Fe_3O_4, Cr_2O_3, $FeTiO_3$, Al_2MgO_4, $Ca_5(PO_4)_3F$ and $(FeMg)SiO_4$ sank to the bottom. During this step pyrites (FeS_2) separated out as a liquid phase contaminated with Ni, Cu and the platinum metals, that became trapped in the mass of more refractory crystals.

(b) In the second crystallisation step (1200–500°C) the solvent was molten SiO_2 which contained FeO, MgO, CaO, Al_2O_3, B_2O_3, Na_2O, K_2O, CO_2, SO_2, H_2S, HF and H_2O as solutes. During cooling the metallic elements separated from each other to some extent, although rarely enough to be extracted economically.

(c) The third crystallisation step ($<$500°C) involved water as the main solvent and metal ions that are either too large or too small to fit into any of the lattices so far formed. They are associated with anions such as borate, phosphate, sulphide, niobate and molybdate which were rejected by the silicate lattices.

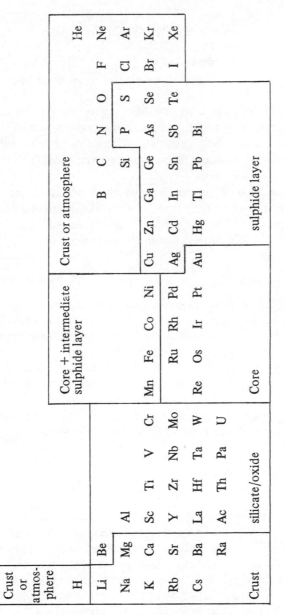

Figure 15.5 – Distribution of the elements of the periodic table within the earth's crust.

This slow cooling allows metal salts to crystallise out stepwise, giving a concentration of individual metal ions in layers around the central crust.

Central crust ⦙ W, Sn ⦙ Bi ⦙ Ag ⦙ Cu, Zn, Pb ⦙ Sb, Hg ⦙

←   →

deposited at   deposited at
higher temperature   lower temperature

Stage 3 in which stage 2 was modified by weathering. Metals such as the alkali and alkaline earth metals, iron and manganese which are the principal elements of life, are selectively extracted by the action of water, carbon dioxide, humic acids, volcanic hydrogen chloride and sulphur dioxide to leave a residue of TiO_2, SiO_2, Fe_2O_3 and clay.

Thus the chemical combinations in which metals are found in the earth's crust are closely related to their 'hard' and 'soft' characteristics. The incipient earth can be considered as a vast, albeit poorly stirred, soup of metals and ligands which slowly formed their preferred complexes.

15.8 PHOTOGRAPHY

With the exception of silver fluoride all the silver halides are sensitive to light. They therefore form the basis of the photographic process. Fine crystals of one or another, or a mixture of the silver halides, particularly the bromide, are spread as gelatin coating onto a film backing. Light from the camera image reacts with the silver ions in the silver halide grains to form silver atoms. Those silver halide grains in which silver atoms have been formed have an enhanced sensitivity to reduction. Thus when the film is exposed to a mild reducing agent such as hydroquinone the silver halide grains that already have silver atoms in them are preferentially completely reduced to silver metal:

$$AgX + \epsilon^-(\text{from reducing agent}) \rightarrow Ag + X^- \tag{15.36}$$

In order to fix the film and prevent the unreacted silver halide grains from reacting on further exposure to light it is essential to dissolve away the unreacted silver halide. This is usually effected by washing with sodium thiosulphate, known to photographers as 'hypo', which is one of the few solutions in which silver halides are soluble. This dissolution depends on the high stability constants of silver with thiosulphate [62] ($\beta_1 = 7.1 \times 10^8$; $\beta_2 = 2.9 \times 10^{13}$; $\beta_3 = 1.9 \times 10^{14}$), which indicate that the silver halide is dissolved principally as the $[Ag(S_2O_3)_2]^{3-}$ complex ion. Once the unreacted silver halide has been removed, the film is quite stable to light and can be handled normally.

REFERENCES

[1] Williams, D. R. (1971). *The Metals of Life*. London: Van Nostrand Reinhold.

[2] Hughes, M. N. (1972). *The Inorganic Chemistry of Biological Processes*. London: Wiley.

[3] Fiabane, A. M. and Williams, D. R. (1977). *The Principles of Bioinorganic Chemistry*, Chemical Society Monographs for Teachers, No. 31, Chemical Society, London.

[4] *An Introduction to Bioinorganic Chemistry* (1976) (ed. Williams, D. R.). Springfield, Illinois: Thomas.

[5] da Silva, J. J. R. F. and Williams, R. J. P. (1976). *Structure and Bonding*, **29**, 67.

[6] Schneider, W. (1975). *Structure and Bonding*, **23**, 123.

[7] Williams, R. J. P. (1970). *Quart Rev.*, **24**, 331.

[8] Chock, P. B. and Titus, E. O. (1973). *Prog. Inorg. Chem.*, **18**, 287.

[9] Frensdorff, H. K. (1971). *J. Amer. Chem. Soc.*, **93**, 600.

[10] Weissbluth, M. (1967). *Structure and Bonding*, **2**, 1.

[11] Smith, D. W. and Williams, R. J. P. (1970). *Structure and Bonding*, **7**, 1.

[12] Wüthrick, K, (1970). *Structure and Bonding*, **8**, 53.

[13] Perutz, M. F. (1970). *Nature*, **228**, 726.

[14] Vallee, B. L. and Williams, R. J. P. (1968). *Proc. Nat. Acad. Sci. USA*, **59**, 498.

[15] Fanelli, A. R., Antonini, E. and Caputo, A. (1964). *Adv. Protein Chem.*, **19**, 73.

[16] Wood, J. M. (1974). *Science*, **183**, 1049.

[17] Luckey, T. D. and Venugopal, B. (1977, Vol. 1; 1978, Vol. 2). *Metal Toxicity in Mammals*. New York: Plenum Press.

[18] Goyer, R. A. and Mehlman, M. A. (1977). *Advances in Modern Toxicology*.

[19] Perrin, D. D. and Agarwal, R. P., Ref. [4] Chapter 20, p. 361.

[20] Perrin, D. D. (1976). *Topics in Current Chemistry*, **64**, 181.

[21] Keberle, H. (1964). *Ann, N.Y. Acad. Sci.*, **119**, 758.

[22] Sarkar, B., Ref. [4], Chapter 18, p. 318.

[23] Lau, S., Kruck, T. P. A., and Sarkar, B. (1974). *J. Biol. Chem.*, **249**, 5878.

[24] Sarkar, B. (1977). 9th Jerusalem Symposium on Quantum Chemistry and Biochemistry, Part 1, 193.

[25] Hepple, P. (ed). *Lead in the Environment*. London: Applied Science.

[26] Shulam, A. and Dwyer, F. P. (1964). In *Chelating Agents and Metal Chelates* (ed. Dwyer, F. P. and Mellor, D. P.) p. 432. New York: Academic Press.

[27] Perrin, D. D. (1976). In *Topics in Current Chemistry. Inorganic Biochemistry*. Berlin: Springer-Verlag.

[28] Perrin, D. D. (1969). *Suomen Kem.*, **42**, (9), 205.

[29] May, P. M., Linder, P. W., and Williams, D. R. (1977). *J. C. S. (Dalton)*, 588.

[30] Perrin, D. D. and Sayce, I. G. (1967). *Talanta*, **14**, 833.

[31] Ingri, N., Kakolowicz, W., Sillén, L. G. and Warnqvist, B. (1967). *Talanta*, **14**, 1261.

[32] Thomson, A. J. (1977). *Platinum Metals Review*, **21**, 2.

[33] Cleare, M. J. (1977). *Platinum Metals Review*, **21**, 56.

[34] Williams, D. R., Ref. [4] Chapter 19, p. 334.

[35] Williams, D. R. (1972). *Chem. Rev.*, **72**, 203.

[36] Rosenberg, B. (1971). *Platinum Metals Review.*, **15**, 42.

[37] Rosenberg, B., Van Camp, L., Trosko, J. E., and Mansour, V. H. (1969). *Nature*, **222**, 385.

[38] Ambrose, E. J., and Roe, F. J. C. (eds.) (1966). *The Biology of Cancer*. London: Van Nostrand (2nd ed. Chichester: Ellis Horwood, 1975).

[39] Johnston, D. O., Netterville, J. T., Wood, J. L., and Jones, M. M. (1973). *Chemistry and the Environment*. Philadelphia: Saunders.

[40] Martell, A. E. (1975). *Pure Appl. Chem.*, **44**, 81.

[41] Berth, P., Jakobi, G., Schmadel, E., Schwuger, M. J., and Krauch, C. H. (1975). *Agnew. Chem. Int. Ed.*, **14**, 94.

[42] Schindler, D. W. (1974). *Science*, **184**, 897.

[43] Martin, D. F. (1974). Proceedings XVI International Conference on Coordination Chemistry, Dublin, paper S.20.

[44] *Modern Electroplating* (1963; 2nd ed.) (ed. Lowenheim, F. A.). New York: John Wiley.

[45] Lowenheim, F. A. (1978). *Electroplating*. New York: McGraw-Hill.

[46] Machu, W. (1978). *Handbook of Electropainting Technology*, Chapter 8. Ayr, Scotland: Electrochemical Publications Ltd.

[47] Skoog, D. A. and West, D. M. (1970). *Fundamentals of Analytical Chemistry*. London: Holt, Rinehart and Winston.

[48] Inczedy, J. (1976). *Analytical Applications of Complex Equilibria*. Chichester: Ellis Horwood.

[49] Schwarzenbach, G. (1957). *Complexometric Titrations* (translated by Irving, H. M. N. H.). New York: Interscience.

[50] Ringbom, A. (1963). *Complexation in Analytical Chemistry*. New York: Interscience.

[51] Reilley, C. N. and Schmid, R. W. (1959). *Anal. Chem.*, **31**, 887.

[52] Snell, F. D. and Snell, C. T. *Colorimetric Methods in Analysis*, 3rd ed., 4 vols. Princeton, N.J.: Van Nostrand.

[53] Marczenko, Z. (1976). *Spectrophotometric Determination of Elements*. Chichester: Ellis Horwood.

[54] Fogg, A. G., Burgess, C., and Burns, D. T. (1971). *Talanta*, **18**, 1175.

[55] Kelly, J. J. and Sutton, D. C. (1966). *Talanta*, **13**, 1573.

[56] Khopkar, A. K. De S. M., and Chalmers, R. A. (1970). *Solvent Extraction of Metals*. New York: Van Nostrand.

[57] Laitinen, H. A. and Harris, W. E. (1975). *Chemical Analysis*, 2nd ed., Chapter 23. New York: McGraw-Hill.

[58] Lacroix, S. (1947). *Anal. Chim. Acta,* **1,** 260.

[59] Gibson, D. T. (1949). *Quart. Rev.,* **3,** 263.

[60] Goldschmidt, V. M. (1922). *Z. Electrochem.,* **28,** 411.

[61] Kuhn, W. and Rittmann, A. (1941). *Geol. Rundschau.,* **32,** 215.

[62] Chateau. H., Pouradier, J., and Berry, C. R. (1966). *The Theory of the Photographic Process,* 3rd ed. (ed. James, T. H.) p. 9. New York: Macmillan.

Notes on Matrix Algebra

This appendix provides examples of a few very basic matrix definitions and concepts. Readers interested in further matrix algebra should consult references [1–5].

I.1 DEFINITION OF A MATRIX

Consider a set of simultaneous equations:

$$ax + by + cz = p$$
$$dx + ey + fz = q \tag{I.1}$$
$$gx + hy + iz = r$$

This can be written in matrix terms as:

$$\begin{bmatrix} a & b & c \\ d & e & f \\ g & h & i \end{bmatrix} \begin{bmatrix} x \\ y \\ z \end{bmatrix} = \begin{bmatrix} p \\ q \\ r \end{bmatrix} \tag{I.2}$$

where the 3 × 3 array of symbols in brackets is termed a matrix of coefficients and the other two bracketed sets of symbols are called column vectors (3 × 1 matrices). Equation (I.2) is more usually written as:

$$\begin{bmatrix} a_{11} & a_{12} & a_{13} \\ a_{21} & a_{22} & a_{23} \\ a_{31} & a_{32} & a_{33} \end{bmatrix} \begin{bmatrix} x_1 \\ x_2 \\ x_3 \end{bmatrix} = \begin{bmatrix} p_1 \\ p_2 \\ p_3 \end{bmatrix} \tag{I.3}$$

or in matrix notation as:

$$\mathbf{A} X = P \tag{I.4}$$

Thus a_{ij} refers to the element in the ith row and j^{th} column of the matrix $\mathbf{A}$.

I.2 TRANSPOSE OF A MATRIX

The transpose of a matrix is that matrix having all its rows and columns inter-
changed. Thus the transpose of **A** is:

$$\begin{bmatrix} a_{11} & a_{21} & a_{31} \\ a_{12} & a_{22} & a_{32} \\ a_{13} & a_{23} & a_{33} \end{bmatrix} \tag{I.5}$$

usually written $\tilde{\mathbf{A}}$.

I.3 INVERSE OF A MATRIX

Matrices are multiplied by forming the products of rows and columns as follows:

$$\begin{bmatrix} a_{11} & a_{12} \\ a_{21} & a_{22} \end{bmatrix} \begin{bmatrix} b_{11} & b_{12} & b_{13} \\ b_{21} & b_{22} & b_{23} \end{bmatrix} =$$
$$\begin{bmatrix} a_{11}b_{11} + a_{12}b_{21} & a_{11}b_{12} + a_{12}b_{22} & a_{11}b_{13} + a_{12}b_{23} \\ a_{21}b_{11} + a_{22}b_{21} & a_{21}b_{12} + a_{22}b_{22} & a_{21}b_{13} + a_{22}b_{23} \end{bmatrix} \tag{I.6}$$

The inverse of matrix **A**, therefore, is that matrix which when premultiplying **A** gives the identity or unit matrix:

$$\mathbf{A}^{-1}\,\mathbf{A} = \mathbf{I} \tag{I.7}$$

I is a matrix with unity on the leading diagonal and zeros on all other elements.

If the matrix **A** has no inverse, it is said to be singular. Such a matrix could
be derived from the simultaneous Equations (I.8), as one equation is a multiple
of the other.

$$\begin{aligned} x_1 + x_2 &= y_1 \\ 2x_1 + 2x_2 &= y_2 \end{aligned} \tag{I.8}$$

Thus the matrix $\begin{bmatrix} 1 & 1 \\ 2 & 2 \end{bmatrix}$ is singular.

I.4 DETERMINANT OF A MATRIX

Consider the matrix $\mathbf{A}$ in (I.9):

$$\mathbf{A} = \begin{bmatrix} a_{11} & a_{12} \\ a_{21} & a_{22} \end{bmatrix} \tag{I.9}$$

The determinant of $\mathbf{A}$ is defined as:

$$\det \mathbf{A} = a_{11} a_{22} - a_{21} a_{12} \tag{I.10}$$

which is usually written as:

$$\det \mathbf{A} = \begin{vmatrix} a_{11} & a_{12} \\ a_{21} & a_{22} \end{vmatrix} \tag{I.11}$$

The determinants of matrices of higher order than 2×2 can be evaluated as follows. If $\mathbf{A}$ is a general $n \times m$ matrix defined as.

$$\mathbf{A} = \begin{bmatrix} a_{11} & \cdots & a_{1m} \\ \vdots & & \vdots \\ a_{m1} & \cdots & a_{nm} \end{bmatrix} \tag{I.12}$$

then the determinant of $\mathbf{A}$ becomes:

$$\det \mathbf{A} = a_{11} M_{11} - a_{21} M_{21} + a_{31} M_{31} - \ldots (-1)^{n+1} a_{n1} M_{n1} \tag{I.13}$$

where the general quantity M_{ij} is the determinant of the submatrix remaining when row i and column j of the matrix have been removed. The determinant of $\mathbf{A}$ can be expanded by using any row or column of $\mathbf{A}$ in this fashion. It is a property of determinants that the same value is obtained. Thus, if $\mathbf{A}$ is the 3×3 matrix,

$$\mathbf{A} = \begin{bmatrix} a_{11} & a_{12} & a_{13} \\ a_{21} & a_{22} & a_{23} \\ a_{31} & a_{32} & a_{33} \end{bmatrix} \tag{I.14}$$

then the value of the determinant can be found from:

$$\det \mathbf{A} = a_{11} M_{11} - a_{12} M_{12} + a_{13} M_{13} \tag{I.15}$$

therefore,

$$\det \mathbf{A} = a_{11} \begin{vmatrix} a_{22}\,a_{23} \\ a_{32}\,a_{33} \end{vmatrix} - a_{12} \begin{vmatrix} a_{21}\,a_{23} \\ a_{31}\,a_{33} \end{vmatrix} + a_{13} \begin{vmatrix} a_{21}\,a_{22} \\ a_{31}\,a_{32} \end{vmatrix} \qquad (\text{I.16})$$

therefore,

$$\det \mathbf{A} = a_{11}\,(a_{22}\,a_{33} - a_{23}\,a_{32}) - a_{12}\,(a_{21}\,a_{33} - a_{31}\,a_{23}) +$$
$$a_{13}\,(a_{21}\,a_{32} - a_{31}\,a_{22})$$
$$(\text{I.17})$$

or from:

$$\det \mathbf{A} = -a_{12}M_{12} + a_{22}M_{22} - a_{32}M_{32} \qquad (\text{I.18})$$

therefore,

$$\det \mathbf{A} = -a_{12} \begin{vmatrix} a_{21}\,a_{23} \\ a_{31}\,a_{33} \end{vmatrix} + a_{22} \begin{vmatrix} a_{11}\,a_{13} \\ a_{31}\,a_{33} \end{vmatrix} - a_{32} \begin{vmatrix} a_{11}\,a_{13} \\ a_{21}\,a_{23} \end{vmatrix} \qquad (\text{I.19})$$

therefore,

$$\det \mathbf{A} = -a_{12}\,(a_{21}\,a_{33} - a_{31}\,a_{23}) + a_{22}\,(a_{11}\,a_{33} - a_{13}\,a_{31}) -$$
$$a_{32}\,(a_{11}\,a_{23} - a_{21}\,a_{13})$$
$$(\text{I.20})$$

It can be seen from the terms in Equations (I.17) and (I.20), that they are identical.

If the reader returns to the matrix defined by Equation (I.8), it is apparent that the determinant is zero:

$$\det \begin{bmatrix} 1 & 1 \\ 2 & 2 \end{bmatrix} = 1 \times 2 - 2 \times 1 = 0 \qquad (\text{I.21})$$

This is a property of all singular matrices (no inverse). The determinant is always zero. For other properties of determinants the reader should consult standard textbooks [1–5].

I.5 SYMMETRIC MATRIX

If a matrix **A** is such that:

$$\tilde{\mathbf{A}} = \mathbf{A} \qquad (\text{I.22})$$

where $\tilde{\mathbf{A}}$ is the transpose of **A**, then **A** is said to be symmetric. For such a matrix $a_{ji} = a_{ij}$.

I.6 NORMALISATION

If a row or column vector X is such that:

$$\tilde{X} X = x_1^2 + x_2^2 + x_3^2 \ldots x_n^2 = 1 \tag{I.23}$$

X is said to be normalised. It is possible for rows or columns of two-dimensional matrices to be normalised, provided that (I.23) is true for that row or column.

I.7 EIGENVALUES AND EIGENVECTORS (MATRIX DIAGONALISATION)

If a matrix A is a square symmetric matrix, it will obey Equation (I.24).

$$A = \tilde{U} V U \tag{I.24}$$

The matrix U is termed the eigenvector matrix, $\tilde{U}$ is the transpose of U and V is the matrix of eigenvalues. The matrix U has the property that each vector (column) of the matrix is normalised and they are also orthogonal [2,4] to each other. V is a diagonal matrix. Only the diagonal elements are non-zero. For this reason when the operation (I.24) is carried out on a matrix it is often said to have been diagonalised.

I.8 RANK OF A MATRIX

The rank of a matrix is defined as the order of the largest non-zero determinant that can be obtained from the matrix. A matrix is singular (that is, its determinant is zero) if its rows or columns are linearly dependent (see (I.21)). However, a single $m \times m$ matrix can have a rank of n where $n < m$ if deleting a row and column results in linearly independent rows or columns.

I.9 TRIANGULARISATION OF A MATRIX

Given a matrix A, it is possible to transform this to a triangular matrix (zeros below the principal diagonal) by performing the following operation on each element except those in the first row:

$$a'_{ij} = a_{ij} - \frac{a_{i1}}{a_{11}} a_{1j} \tag{I.25}$$

If this process is then repeated on all but the second row and so on, a triangular matrix results. This procedure has no effect on the determinant of the matrix.

REFERENCES

[1] Jennings, A. (1978). *Matrix Computation for Engineers and Scientists.* Wiley-Interscience.

[2] Brickell, F. (1972). *Matrices and Vector Spaces.* George Allen and Unwin.

[3] Martin, H. G. (1970). *Mathematics for Engineering, Technology and Computing Science.* Pergamon Press.

[4] Korn, G. A. and Korn, T. M. (1968). *Mathematical Handbook for Scientists and Engineers.* McGraw-Hill.

[5] Coulson, A. E. (1970). *Introduction to Matrices.* Longman.

TRIANG: A Computer Program for Determining the Number of Species in Solution

TRIANG is a Fortran computer program that can be used to analyse spectro-photometric data to determine the number of absorbing species present in solution. The basis of the method has been outlined in Section 2.4. The input data are the absorbances at a number of wavelengths of a series of solutions. This data is then analysed assuming that Beer's law (Equation (8.6)) is valid for each component. Thus,

$$A^\lambda = \sum_{i=1}^{i=m} \epsilon_i^\lambda c_i \tag{II.1}$$

where A^λ = absorbance per unit path length at wavelength λ of a solution containing m absorbing species, ϵ_i^λ is the molar absorptivity of species i, and c_i is the concentration of species i. If n experiments are performed in which the relative values of the concentrations c_i are altered, then Equation (II.1) may be written as a matrix:

$$\mathbf{A} = \mathcal{E}\, C \tag{II.2}$$

in which $\mathbf{A}$ is a $p \times n$ matrix, $\mathcal{E}$ is a $p \times m$ matrix, and C is an $n \times m$ matrix where p = number of wavelengths, n = number of experiments, and m = number of absorbing species. Since the rank of $\mathbf{A}$ is equal to the rank of $\mathcal{E}$ or C, whichever is the smaller, and since the rank of $\mathcal{E}$ and C can be no larger than m, then provided that p and n are equal to or greater than m, it will only be necessary to determine the rank of $\mathbf{A}$ to find the number of absorbing species. As mentioned in Section (2.4), one of the problems of calculating the rank of $\mathbf{A}$ is determining whether elements close to zero would have been truly zero but for the experimental error. Accordingly, TRIANG has the facility for determining the rank of $\mathbf{A}$ for a series of estimated errors. A flowchart of this program is given in Figure II.1.

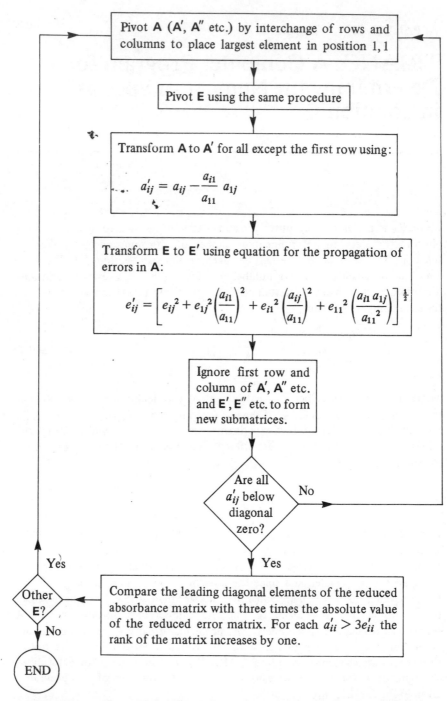

Figure II.1 – Flowchart for TRIANG, a program for determining the number of species in solution.

THE COMPUTER PROGRAM TRIANG

```
C
C       THIS IS A PROGRAM TO EVALUATE THE NUMBER OF ABSORBING SPECIES IN
C       A SET OF SOLUTIONS OF VARYING COMPOSITION.
C       WRITTEN BY R.M.ALCOCK, CHEMISTRY DEPARMENT, UNIVERSITY OF
C       SOUTHAMPTON
C       THE METHOD IS BASED ON THE MATRIX RANK DETERMINATION OF AN 'NWAVE
C       *NSOLN' (SEE BELOW) ABSORBANCE MATRIX. THE RANK IS DETERMINED BY
C       TRIANGULARISING THE MATIX BY THE METHOD OF GAUSSIAN ELIMINATION
C       AND SUBSEQUENT COMPARISON OF THE DIAGONAL ELEMENTS WITH A DERIVED
C       ERROR MATRIX FOR DETAILS SEE 'R.M.WALLACE AND S.M.KATZ J.PHYS.CHEM
C       68 (1964) P.3890' AND ALSO 'L.P.VARGA AND F.C.VEATCH ANAL.CHEM. 39
C       (1967) P.1101'.
C
C       ****************************************************************
C
C       -----------------------CARD (1).-----------------------------
C       PUNCH 'NWAVE', THE NUMBER OF WAVELENGTHS AT WHICH ABSORBANCE MEAS-
C       UREMENTS WERE MADE. (MAX NO. 25) FORMAT I3.
C       PUNCH 'NSOLN', THE NUMBER OF SOLUTIONS ON WHICH 'NWAVE' ABSORBANCE
C       MEASUREMENTS WERE MADE.(MAX NO. 25) FORMAT I3.
C       PUNCH 'NOINCR', THE NUMBER OF DIFFERENT ERROR MATRICES TO BE CALC
C       -ULATED ALONG WITH THE REDUCED ABSORBANCE MATRIX FOR THE PURPOSES
C       OF RANK EVALUATION. FORMAT I3.
C       PUNCH 'FAC', THE FACTOR BY WHICH THE CURRENT ESTIMATED ABSORBANCE
C       ERROR IS TO BE MULTIPLIED TO GENERATE THE NEXT ERROR MATRIX. E.G.
C       IF ABSORBANCE ERRORS OF 0.001, 0.002, 0.004, AND 0.008 ARE TO BE
C       TRIED, 'FAC'=2. FORMAT I3.
C       PUNCH 'ESE', THE ESTIMATED ABSORBANCE ERROR IN THE EXPERIMENTAL
C       READINGS. USUALLY THIS IS NOT KNOWN FOR CERTAIN AND A RANGE OF
C       ERROR MATRICES ARE TRIED BY VIRTUE OF NON-UNITY VALUES FOR 'FAC'
C       AND 'NOINCR'. FORMAT F6.4.
C       -----------------------CARD (2)-CARD (NSOLN+1)-----------------
C       PUNCH NWAVE EXPERIMENTAL ABSORBANCES. FORMAT 16F5.3. NSOLN CARDS
C       IN ALL (EXCEPT FOR NWAVE>16, WHEN THERE ARE 2*NSOLN CARDS).
C       -----------------------CARD (NSOLN+2)-------------------------
C       PUNCH 'DT'. IF THE %TAGE ERROR IN THE TRANSMITTANCE IS KNOWN AN
C       ERROR MATRIX CAN BE GENERATED USING THIS QUANTITY. PUNCHED AS DEC
C       -IMAL SO THAT 1% ERROR IS INPUT AS 0.01. FORMAT F5.3.
C
C       ****************************************************************
C
        LIST(LP)
        PROGRAM(TRIA)
        INPUT 5=CR0
        OUTPUT 6=LP0
        END
        MASTER TRIANG
        INTEGER FAC
        DIMENSION R(25,25),ER(25,25),B(25),BER(25),SR(25,25)
        DT=0.0
        READ(5,71)NWAVE,NSOLN,NOINCR,FAC,ESE
   71   FORMAT(4I3,F6.4)
        DO 72 I=1,NWAVE
   72   READ(5,73)(R(I,J),J=1,NSOLN)
   73   FORMAT(16F5.3)
        DO 53 I=1,NWAVE
        DO 54 J=1,NSOLN
   54   SR(I,J)=R(I,J)
   53   CONTINUE
        WRITE(6,91)
   91   FORMAT(23H1 THE ABSORBANCE MATRIX)
        DO 90 I=1,NWAVE
   90   WRITE(6,89)(R(I,J),J=1,NSOLN)
```

```
      89  FORMAT(/15(2X,F8.6))
          ERR=0.0
          DO 8888 LX=1,NOINCR
          ERR=ERR+ESE*FAC
          DO 75 K=1,NWAVE
          DO 76 L=1,NSOLN
      76  ER(K,L)=ERR
      75  CONTINUE
          GO TO 2
      59  DO 55 I=1,NWAVE
          DO 56 J=1,NSOLN
      56  R(I,J)=SR(I,J)
      55  CONTINUE
    8888  CONTINUE
      94  READ(5,95)DT
      95  FORMAT(F5.3)
          DO 97 I=1,NWAVE
          DO 98 J=1,NSOLN
          ER(I,J)=0.43429*DT*EXP10(SR(I,J))
      98  CONTINUE
      97  CONTINUE
          DO 61 I=1,NWAVE
          DO 62 J=1,NSOLN
      62  R(I,J)=SR(I,J)
      61  CONTINUE
       2  WRITE(6,50)
      50  FORMAT(1H1 THE ERROR MATRIX)
          DO 40 I=1,NWAVE
          WRITE(6,41) (ER(I,J),J=1,NSOLN)
      41  FORMAT(3X,/15(2X,F8.6))
      40  CONTINUE
      96  NI=1
          NJ=1
          NR=1
          NC=1
          AMAX=R(NR,NC)
          GO TO 83
      84  NR=NR+1
          NC=NC+1
          AMAX=R(NR,NC)
C
C         SEEK LARGEST ELEMENT
C
      83  DO 77 I=NI,NWAVE
          DO 78 J=NJ,NSOLN
          IF(ABS(R(I,J)).LT.ABS(AMAX))GO TO 78
          NR=I
          NC=J
          AMAX=R(I,J)
      78  CONTINUE
      77  CONTINUE
C
C         INTERCHANGE ROWS
C
          DO 79 N=1,NSOLN
          B(N)=R(NI,N)
          R(NI,N)=R(NR,N)
          BER(N)=ER(NI,N)
          ER(NI,N)=ER(NR,N)
          ER(NR,N)=BER(N)
      79  R(NR,N)=B(N)
C
C         INTERCHANGE COLUMNS
C
          DO 80 M=1,NWAVE
          B(M)=R(M,NJ)
          R(M,NJ)=R(M,NC)
          BER(M)=ER(M,NJ)
```

```
      ER(M,NJ)=ER(M,NC)
      ER(M,NC)=BER(M)
   80 R(M,NC)=B(M)
      IF(NI.EQ.NWAVE.OR.NJ.EQ.NSOLN)GO TO 85
      IF(DT.GT.0.0)GO TO 101
C
C     GENERATE ERROR MATRIX
C
      DO 99 I=NI+1,NWAVE
      DO 100 J=NJ,NSOLN
  100 ER(I,J)=SQRT(ER(I,J)**2+(ER(NI,J)**2)*((R(I,NJ)/AMAX)**2)+(ER(I,NJ
     1)**2)*((R(I,J)/AMAX)**2)+(ER(NI,NJ)**2)*((R(I,NJ)*R(NI,J)/(AMAX)**
     12)**2))
   99 CONTINUE
C
C     CARRY OUT REDUCTION
C
  101 DO 102 I=NI+1,NWAVE
      RS=R(I,NJ)
      DO 103 J=NJ,NSOLN
  103 R(I,J)=R(I,J)-(RS/AMAX)*R(NI,J)
  102 CONTINUE
      NI=NI+1
      NJ=NJ+1
      GO TO 84
   85 WRITE(6,92)
   92 FORMAT(31H1 THE REDUCED ABSORBANCE MATRIX)
      DO 86 I=1,NWAVE
   86 WRITE(6,87)(R(I,J),J=1,NSOLN)
   87 FORMAT(/15(2X,F8.6))
      WRITE(6,93)
   93 FORMAT(26H1 THE REDUCED ERROR MATRIX)
      DO 88 I=1,NWAVE
   88 WRITE(6,87)(ER(I,J),J=1,NSOLN)
      NOS=0
      NUM=NSOLN
      IF(NSOLN.LT.NWAVE)NUM=NSOLN
      DO 444 J=1,NUM
      IF(ABS(R(J,J)).LT.ABS(3.0*ER(J,J)))GO TO 444
      NOS=NOS+1
  444 CONTINUE
      WRITE(6,4444)NOS
 4444 FORMAT(20H0 NUMBER OF SPECIES=,I4)
      IF(DT.GT.0.0)GO TO 777
      IF (LX.EQ.NOINCR) GO TO 94
      GO TO 59
  777 STOP
      END
      FINISH
```

DALSFEK: A Damped Non-Linear Least-Squares Computer Program for Calculating Stability Constants

III.1 INTRODUCTION

This appendix decribes a non-linear least-squares program (DALSFEK) [1] which we have used [2,3] for the analysis of stability constant data. It is here described for anyone contemplating using it or writing a program of their own. Such a program needs to perform certain tasks, and our methods of performing these tasks are described here for guidance. Our program incorporates one of the best literature algorithms [4] for ensuring convergence (see Section 5.7), but it would be possible for it to be adapted to use another because, as it is written, it would require only the replacement of a subroutine.

It will currently deal with two types of observable (dependent variable), namely absorbance and potentiometric data. Others can easily be added as further subroutines, provided that the observable can be expressed as a function of the concentrations of the species forming the proposed chemical model. The total (analytical) concentrations are assumed to be the independent variables as these can be calculated precisely by weighing, or addition of accurately measured volumes of standard solutions.

A flowchart is given in Figure III.1 and a listing of the program is at the end of this appendix.

III.2 OUTLINE DESCRIPTION

(i) *Master routine*

The master routine reads in the control variables such as the number of parameters to be adjusted, the number of equilibria and their definition. The initial estimates of the stability constants are read in here. This routine will be entered only once in each run.

(ii) *Cycle routine*

This routine controls the use of the magnetic tape backing store, so that, as the

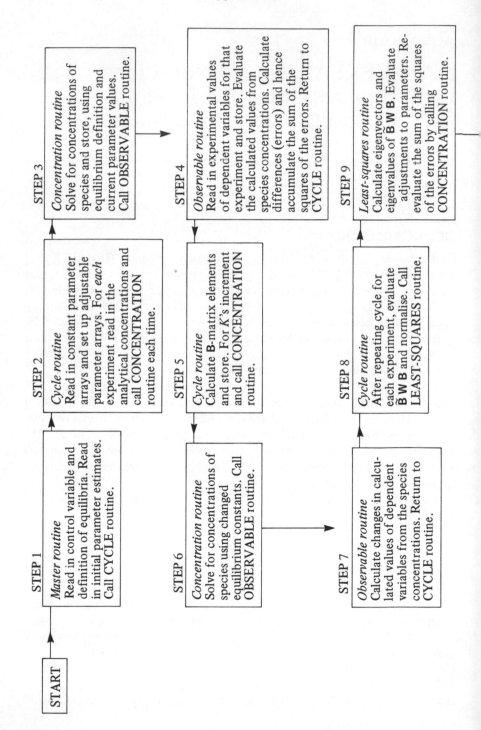

STEP 1

Master routine
Read in control variable and definition of equilibria. Read in initial parameter estimates. Call CYCLE routine.

STEP 2

Cycle routine
Read in constant parameter arrays and set up adjustable parameter arrays. For *each* experiment read in the analytical concentrations and call CONCENTRATION routine each time.

STEP 3

Concentration routine
Solve for concentrations of species and store, using equilibrium definition and current parameter values. Call OBSERVABLE routine.

STEP 4

Observable routine
Read in experimental values of dependent variables for that experiment and store. Evaluate the calculated values from species concentrations. Calculate differences (errors) and hence accumulate the sum of the squares of the errors. Return to CYCLE routine.

STEP 5

Cycle routine
Calculate **B**-matrix elements and store. For K's increment and call CONCENTRATION routine.

STEP 6

Concentration routine
Solve for concentrations of species using changed equilibrium constants. Call OBSERVABLE routine.

STEP 7

Observable routine
Calculate changes in calculated values of dependent variables from the species concentrations. Return to CYCLE routine.

STEP 8

Cycle routine
After repeating cycle for each experiment, evaluate **B̃ W B** and normalise. Call LEAST-SQUARES routine.

STEP 9

Least-squares routine
Calculate eigenvectors and eigenvalues of **B̃ W B**. Evaluate adjustments to parameters. Re-evaluate the sum of the squares of the errors by calling CONCENTRATION routine.

START

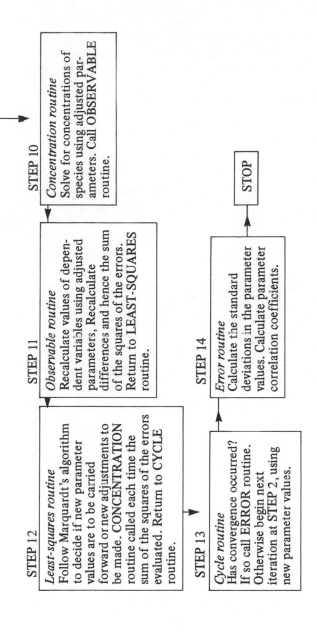

Figure III.1 – Outline flowchart for a non-linear least-squares program for evaluating stability constants – DALSFEK.

program cycles over each experiment[†] (each potentiometric titration or each set of absorbance readings), the total (analytical) concentrations of the components, the experimental readings, and the concentration of each species are stored in a systematic way. The **B**-matrix of differentials (see Chapter 5) are calculated here and the calculations achieved to create $\tilde{B}$ **W B**. If these elements can be obtained analytically, they should be used, but for the stability constants this is not possible. Difference approximations to the derivatives are calculated in DALSFEK according to:

$$\frac{\partial o_i}{\partial K_j} = \frac{\Delta o_i}{\Delta K_j} \tag{III.1}$$

The function Δ, by which the stability constant is incremented, is variable, but we have found 0.001 (0.1%) to be satisfactory. Before calling the iterative least-squares routine, $\tilde{B}$ **W B** is normalised to place values of unity on the diagonal.

(iii) *Concentration routine*

At the start of each iteration the system must be solved for the concentrations of the species. (This must also be done when calculating the difference approximations to the differentials for the stability constants). DALSFEK achieves this with a Gauss-Newton iteration on some 'guessed' concentrations, using the current values of the stability constants and the mass balance information (the total concentrations). Similar procedures have been incorporated into previous programs for the evaluation of solution equilibria [5,6].

Consider m equilibria relating n species in solution. At equilibrium there are m equations of the type:

$$\ln K_i = a_{i1} \ln c_1 + \dots a_{in} \ln c_n \tag{III.2}$$

where $a_{in} > 0$ for a product and < 0 for a reactant. In matrix notation:

$$\ln K = A \ln C \tag{III.3}$$

Also considering the material balance equations gives:

$$t_j = q_{j1} c_1 + \dots q_{jn} c_n \tag{III.4}$$

where t_j is the total (analytical) concentration of component j. The q_{ji} are integers defining the number of atoms of component j in species i. In matrix notation this becomes:

$$T = Q C \tag{III.5}$$

---

† Note that all data sets are fitted simultaneously to the model.

Since **A** and **Q** are fixed in this fashion by the equilibrium definition, then from a knowledge of T and the current values of K, a trial set of C can be adjusted until (III.3) and (III.5) are satisfied.

When the species concentrations have been calculated in this fashion, this program reads in a control parameter which determines which experimental observation routine to enter.

(iv) *Spectrophotometric routine*

One of the two most commonly used methods for studying solution equilibria is spectrophotometry, hence this program has a routine for dealing with this type of dependent variable. On the first iteration the measured absorbances for each experiment are read in and stored, as are the estimates of the molar absorptivities for each species at each wavelength (on the first entry only). On every iteration the calculated absorbances are evaluated from the species concentrations found by the concentration routine, assuming that Beer's' law holds:

$$A^\lambda = \sum_{i=1}^{i=n} \epsilon_i^\lambda c_i l \tag{III.6}$$

where A^λ is the absorbance at wavelength λ, ϵ_i^λ is the molar absorptivity of the species i at wavelength λ, c_i is the concentration, l is the path length and n is the total number of species present. This enables the deviations between the observed and calculated absorbances to be determined, and hence the sum of the squares of the errors.

(v) *Potentiometric routine*

The program DALSFEK also has a routine for potentiometric data, the other most commonly used technique. The routine reads and stores the experimental e.m.f. values and also calculates the e.m.f.'s from the evaluated concentrations, using the Nernst equation. To do this the routine must of course be supplied with information as to which species is being monitored potentiometrically.

(vi) *Variance routines*

These routines can be included if it is desired to calculate weights from estimates of the variances of the residuals. Error propagation rules [7] are used to do this, but the routines require the estimates of the errors in the experimental quantities: the absorbances, e.m.f.'s and total concentrations. Note that the variances depend on the values of the parameters, so they must be recalculated on each iteration.

(vii) *Least-squares algorithm routine*

The program described here (DALSFEK) uses the algorithm of Marquardt [4] to obtain the parameter corrections to be applied to this iteration. This has been found to have been very successful in our work, but other algorithms such as that of Fletcher-Powell could be used. The procedure followed is to obtain the eigenvectors and eigenvalues of $\tilde{B} W B$ (a square symmetric matrix) and calculate the contribution to the parameter correction vector made by each eigenvalue. The corrections are then applied and the concentration and dependent variable routines called to re-evaluate the sum of the squares of the errors to compare with the previous value. Marquardt's algorithm (see Section 5.7) is then followed to decide whether the corrections must be 'damped' or whether the new values of the parameters can be carried through to begin the next iteration. Briefly, the strategy employed is as follows:

On the ith iteration we want ω_i (see Section 5.7) to be such that $S_{i+1} < S_i$, where S is the sum of the squares of the errors. Let ω_{i-1} be the value of ω from the previous iteration (initially this is set to an arbitrary value of 0.01). Let V be a quantity > 1.0 (the choice is again arbitrary). Compute $S(\omega_{i-1})$ and $S(\omega_{i-1}/V)^\dagger$ and then:

(1) If $S(\omega_{i-1}/V) \leqslant S_i$ then let $\omega_i = \omega_{i-1}/V$.

(2) If $S(\omega_{i-1}/V) > S_i$ and $S(\omega_{i-1}) \leqslant S_i$ then let $\omega_i = \omega_{i-1}$.

(3) If $S(\omega_{i-1}/V) > S_i$ and $S(\omega_{i-1}) > S_i$ increase ω by successive multiplication by V until for some smallest n:

$$S(\omega_{i-1} V^n) \leqslant S_i \text{ whereupon let}^\ddagger \ \omega_i = \omega_{i-1} V^n.$$

Usually ω_i may begin at fairly large values, but it often decreases steadily as the minimum is approached.

viii) *Error routine*

This routine is entered on the final iteration to calculate an unbiased estimate of the variance of unit weight, σ^2, (see Equation (4.34)) and the standard deviations of the parameters from the diagonal elements of the variance-covariance matrix Equation (4.33)). Correlation coefficients are also calculated and printed for judgement as to problem conditioning and the precision of the parameter estimates.

If ω_{i-1} is already $\ll 1.0$ compared to the number of significant figures carried, then go on to tests (2) and (3) and ignore comparisons with $S(\omega_{i-1}/V)$.

Where parameters are very badly correlated it is possible for ω to increase to unreasonably large values. In this case a scale factor b_i for the correction vector Δ is used when the angle θ_i, between the correction vector Δ and the steepest descent direction (determined by ω_i), is less than $\pi/4$.

THE COMPUTER PROGRAM DALSFEK

```
C
C    ****************************************************************
C    THIS IS A DAMPED NON-LINEAR LEAST-SQUARES PROGRAM TO CALCULATE
C    STABILITY CONSTANTS FROM MULTI-OBSERVABLE DATA.
C    WRITTEN BY R.M.ALCOCK AND D.E.ROGERS, CHEMISTRY DEPT. UNIVERSITY
C    OF SOUTHAMPTON.
C    THE PROGRAM CLOSELY FOLLOWS MARQUARDTS  ALGORITHM FOR OBTAINING
C    THE OPTIMUM PARAMETER CORRECTIONS ON EACH ITERATION. FOR DETAILS
C    SEE  D.W.MARQUARDT J.SOC.IND.APPL.MATHS. 11 (1963) P.431 .
C    ****************************************************************
C
C    (1)
C    PUNCH THE FOLLOWING CONTROL PARAMETERS, ON A SINGLE CARD.
C    "NOR"  THE NUMBER OF REACTIONS (MAX NO. 6).FORMAT I3.
C    "NOEK"  THE NUMBER OF EQUILIBRIUM CONSTANTS (MAX NO. 6). FORMAT I3
C    "NOS"  THE NUMBER OF SPECIES DEFINING THE SYSTEM (MAX NO. 8). FOR
C    -MAT I3.
C    "NOW". IF SPECTROPHOTOMETRIC DATA IS BEING EVALUATED THIS IS THE
C    TOTAL NUMBER OF WAVELENGTHS AT WHICH ABSORBANCE VALUES HAVE BEEN
C    OBTAINED (MAX NO.20). FORMAT I3.
C    "NOCP"  THE NUMBER OF CONSTANT PARAMETERS. THESE ARE THE NUMBER OF
C    PARAMETERS HOLDING FIXED VALUES IN THE REFINEMENT. (MAX NO.50)
C    FORMAT I3.
C    "NEXP" THE NUMBER OF EXPERIMENTS (SOLUTIONS) ON WHICH DATA HAS BEEN
C    OBTAINED. FORMAT I3.
C    INCR  THE RECIPROCAL OF THE FRACTION BY WHICH THE EQUILIBRIUM
C    CONSTANTS ARE TO BE INCREMENTED WHEN CALCULATING THE NUMERICAL
C    DERIVATIVES. THUS IF THE INCREMENTATION IS TO BE 0.01, INCR=100.
C    FORMAT I4.
C    "NPMAX"  THE MAXIMUM NUMBER OF ITERATIONS. FORMAT I3.
C    "NOT"  THE NUMBER OF ANALYTICAL CONCENTRATIONS(FUNDAMENTAL TYPES).
C    (MAX NO. 8). FORMAT I3.
C    "IFW"  A WEIGHTING OPTION. IF IFW=1 UNIT WEIGHTS ARE USED. IF IFW=0
C    WEIGHTS ARE CALCULATED FROM THE ESTIMATED ERRORS IN THE EXPERI
C    -MENTAL QUANTITIES. FORMAT I3.
C    "IFC"  AN OPTION FOR ADJUSTING FOR ERRORS IN THE ANALYTICAL CONC
C    -ENTRATIONS (SYSTEMATIC ERRORS). IF IFC=1 ERRORS ADJUSTED. IF IFC=
C    0 NO ADJUSTMENT. FORMAT I3. NB* THE NUMBER OF PARAMETERS BEING RE
C    -FINED (CALCULATED IN THE PROGRAM AS NVAR) PLUS NEXP*NOT MUST NOT
C    BE GREATER THAN 80. (60 IN THE ICL 1907A VERSION OF THE PROGRAM)
C    "NDV"  THE TOTAL NUMBER OF DEPENDANT VARIABLES (OBSERVATIONS) PER
C    EXPERIMENT. FOR SPECTROPHOTOMETRIC DATA, NDV=NOW. FORMAT I3.
C    "NOP"  THE TOTAL NUMBER OF PARAMETERS, ADJUSTABLE AND FIXED, IN
C    THE REFINEMENT. FOR SPECTROPHOTOMETRC DATA NOP=NOEK+NOS*NOW. FOR
C    -MAT I3.
C    "IFRITE"  A PRINTOUT OPTION. IF IFRITE=0 ONLY THE CURRENT PARAMETER
C    VALUES ARE WRITTEN OUT, BUT IF IFRITE=1 THE PARAMETER CORRECTIONS
C    ARE ALSO WRITTEN ON EACH PERTURBATION. FORMAT I3.
C    (2)
C    PUNCH THE EQUILIBRIUM DEFINITION. THE REACTANTS, EQUILIBRIUM CONS
C    -TANTS, AND PRODUCTS ARE ASSIGNED INTEGER DIGITS AND THESE ARE
C    PUNCHED FOR EACH REACTION. NOR CARDS IN ALL. E.G. FOR THE TWO EQUI
C    -LIBRIA 2A=B+2C AND B=D+C TWO CARDS ARE PUNCHED,  1  1  1  2  3  3
C    AND  2    2  4  3. FOR THESE CARDS THE FIRST TWO DIGITS ARE THE
C    NUMBERS OF THE FIRST AND SECOND REACTANT RESPECTIVELY (THE SECOND
C    EQUILIBRIUM HAS NO SECOND REACTANT), THE THIRD NUMBER IS THAT OF
C    THE EQUILIBRIUM CONSTANT, AND THE LAST TWO ARE THOSE OF THE FIRST
C    AND SECOND PRODUCTS RESPECTIVELY. FORMAT 6I3.
C    (3)
C    PUNCH THE LOGARITHMS (BASE 10) OF THE ESTIMATED (GUESSED) EQUIL
C    -IBRIUM CONSTANTS. FORMAT 6F10.4.
```

```
C       (4)
C       PUNCH THE INTEGER POWERS TO WHICH THE SPECIES MUST BE RAISED TO
C       DEFINE THE EQUILIBRIUM CONSTANTS. NOEK CARDS IN ALL. E.G. FOR THE
C       ABOVE EQUILIBRIA TWO CARDS ARE PUNCHED, -2  1  2  0 AND 0 -1  1  1
C       FORMAT 8I3.
C       (5)
C       PUNCH THE NUMBERS OF THE CONSTANT PARAMETERS. FOR SPECTROPHOTO
C       -METRIC DETERMINATIONS ASSUME THE EQUILIBRIUM CONSTANTS FORM THE
C       PARAMETERS, 1....NOEK, AND THE EXTINCTION COEFFICIENTS PARAMETERS
C       NOEK+1....NOP. THE EXTINCTION COEFFICIENTS ARE STORED E(1),E(2)...
C       E(NOS) FOR WAVELENGTH 1, E(1),E(2)...E(NOS) FOR WAVELENGTH 2 ETC.
C       E.G. FOR A TWO WAVELENGTH DETERMINATION OF AN A=B EQUILIBRIUM IN
C        WHICH THE THE EXTINCTION COEFFICIENTS OF A ARE TO BE FIXED PUNCH,
C        2  4. FORMAT 26I3.
C       (6)
C       PUNCH THE ANALYTICAL CONCENTRATIONS OF THE COMPONENTS IN EXPERI
C       -MENT (SOLUTION) 1. FORMAT 7E10.4.
C       (7)
C       PUNCH THE NUMBERS OF ATOMS OF THE COMPONENT IN EACH SPECIES. NOT
C       CARDS IN ALL, EACH CARD HOLDING NOS INTEGERS. E.G. FOR THE SYSTEM
C       A+2B=AB2 THE TWO CARDS WOULD BE  1  0  1 AND  0  1  2. FORMAT 8I3.
C       FOR THIS FIRST EXPERIMENT ONLY, PUNCH A SET OF ,GUESSED, CONCENTR
C       -ATIONS (THESE NEED NOT BE VERY ACCURATE). NOS NUMBERS, FORMAT
C       8D7.3.
C       (8)
C       PUNCH "IFOBS" AN INTEGER NUMBER TO INDICATE WHICH OF THE OBSERVN
C       SUBROUTINE(S) ARE TO BE ENTERED. E.G. IF BOTH SPECTROPHOTOMETRIC
C       AND POTENTIOMETRIC DATA IS TO BE INPUT FOR EACH EXPERIMENT, PUNCH
C       12 OR 21, BUT IF THE FORMER THE SPECTROPHOTOMETRIC DATA MUST PRE
C       -CEDE THE POTENTIOMETRIC AND IF THE LATTER THIS ORDER MUST BE REV
C       -VERSED. FORMAT I3.
C       (9)
C       IF IFOBS=1, PUNCH THE WAVELENGTH, FOLLOWED BY THE EXTINCTION
C       COEFFICIENTS (NOS OF THEM). NOW CARDS IN ALL. FORMAT F5.1, 6E10.4.
C       (THIS IS FOR THE FIRST EXPERIMENT ONLY)
C       PUNCH THE NOW ABSORBANCES. FORMAT 16F5.3. (THE DECIMAL POINT IS INS
C       -ERTED WITHIN THE PROGRAM)
C       (10)
C       PUNCH THE ESTIMATED ABSORBANCE ERROR (ABSOLUTE VALUE), AND THE
C       ESTIMATED ERRORS IN THE ANALYTICAL CONCENTRATIONS EXPRESSED AS DEC
C       -IMAL PERCENTAGES. FORMAT 10F6.3.
C       (11)
C       IF IFOBS=2, PUNCH THE NERNST CONSTANT, THE NUMBER OF THE SPECIES
C       BEING MONITORED (THE NUMBER ASSIGNED TO THAT SPECIES IN THE EQUIL
C       -IBRIUM DEFINITION),AND THE NUMBER OF THE ANALYTICAL COMPONANT
C       USED IN THE REFERENCE ELECTRODE. FORMAT (F7.4, 2I3)
C       (12)
C       PUNCH THE ESTIMATED E.M.F. ERROR (ABSOLUTE VALUE), AND THE ESTIMAT
C       -ED ERRORS IN THE ANALYTICAL CONCENTRATIONS EXPRESSED AS DECIMAL
C       PERCENTAGES. FORMAT 9F6.3.
C       (13)
C       THEN CONTINUE ASSEMBLING DATA DECK IN THE ORDER, ANALYTICAL CONC
C       -ENTRATIONS, IFOBS, EXPERIMENTAL DATA (ABSORBANCES AND/OP E.M.FS)
C       FOR A TOTAL OF NEXP CARDS OF EACH.
C       (14)
C       FINALLY PUNCH IN THE FOLLOWING CARD HOLDING THE QUANTITIES ,5, (A
C       CONTROL VARIABLE)  "CORREC" THE MAXIMUM PERMITTED CORRECTION,
C       "CONV"  THE CRITERION FOR CONVERGENCE, AND "SCALF" ALL EXPRESSED
C       AS FRACTIONS OF THE PARAMETERS. FORMAT I3, 3E12.4.
C       ****************************************************************
        PROGRAM DALS(INPUT,OUTPUT,TAPE5=INPUT,TAPE6=OUTPUT,TAPE1)
        INTEGER A
        REAL LE
        DIMENSION NR1(6),NR2(6),NK(6),NP1(6),NP2(6),NP3(6),LE(6),A(6,8),X(
       180),E(6),P(100)
        COMMON/SET1/P
```

```
      COMMON/SET6/X,A
      EQUIVALENCE (P(1),E(1))
C
C     READ IN CONTROL PARAMETERS.
C
      READ(5,2)NOR,NOEK,NOS,NOW,NOGP,NEXP,INCR,NPMAX,NOT,IFW,IFC,NDV,NOP
     1,IFRITE
    2 FORMAT(6I3,I4,7I3)
      WRITE(6,3)NOR,NOEK,NOS,NOW
    3 FORMAT(22H NUMBER OF REACTIONS =,I3/34H NUMBER OF EQUILIBRIUM CONS
     1TANTS =,I3/20H NUMBER OF SPECIES =,I3/24H NUMBER OF WAVELENGTHS =,
     1I3)
C
C     READ IN EQUILIBRIUM DEFINITION.
C
      READ(5,4)(NR1(I),NR2(I),NK(I),NP1(I),NP2(I),NP3(I),I=1,NOR)
    4 FORMAT(6I3)
      WRITE(6,6)
    6 FORMAT(///23H EQUILIBRIUM DEFINITION)
      WRITE(6,5)
    5 FORMAT(120H ---------------------------------------------------------
     1---------------------------------------------------------------)
      WRITE(6,7)
    7 FORMAT(48H REACTANTS          EQUILIBRIUM CONSTANT        PRODUCTS)
      DO 8 I=1,NOR
      J=NR1(I)
      K=NR2(I)
      L=NP1(I)
      M=NP2(I)
      N=NP3(I)
      IF(K)9,9,10
    9 IF(M)11,11,12
   11 WRITE(6,13)(NR1(I),NK(I),NP1(I))
   13 FORMAT(2X,I3,20X,I3,13X,I3)
      GO TO 8
   12 IF(N)14,14,15
   14 WRITE(6,16)(NR1(I),NK(I),NP1(I),NP2(I))
   16 FORMAT(2X,I3,18X,I3,14X,I3,1H,,I3)
      GO TO 8
   15 WRITE(6,17)(NR1(I),NK(I),NP1(I),NP2(I),NP3(I))
   17 FORMAT(2X,I3,18X,I3,9X,I3,1H,,I3,1H,,I3)
      GO TO 8
   10 IF(M)18,18,19
   18 WRITE(6,20)(NR1(I),NR2(I),NK(I),NP1(I))
   20 FORMAT(1X,I3,1H,,I3,18X,I3,13X,I3)
      GO TO 8
   19 IF(N)21,21,22
   21 WRITE(6,23)(NR1(I),NR2(I),NK(I),NP1(I),NP2(I))
   23 FORMAT(1X,I3,1H,,I3,18X,I3,12X,I3,1H,,I3)
      GO TO 8
   22 WRITE(6,24)(NR1(I),NR2(I),NK(I),NP1(I),NP2(I),NP3(I))
   24 FORMAT(1X,I3,1H,,I3,15X,I3,12X,I3,1H,,I3,1H,,I3)
    8 CONTINUE
      WRITE(6,5)
C
C     READ IN ESTIMATED EQUILIBRIUM CONSTANTS IN ORDER IN WHICH THEY
C     APPEAR IN DEFINITION.
C     ALSO READIN IN INTEGER POWERS FOR SPECIES APPEARING IN EQUILIBRIUM
C     CONSTANT EQUATIONS.
C
      READ(5,25)(LE(I),I=1,NOEK)
   25 FORMAT(6F10.4)
      WRITE(6,28)(I,LE(I),I=1,NOEK)
   28 FORMAT(///26H EQUILIBRIUM CONSTANT LIST/(I3,5X,E10.4))
      WRITE(6,5)
      DO 39 K=1,NOEK
```

```
   39 E(K)=EXP(ALOG(10.0)*LE(K))
      DO 37 I=1,NOR
   37 READ(5,38)(A(I,J),J=1,NOS)
   38 FORMAT(12I3)
      CALL CYCLE(NEXP,NOP,NOEK,NOCP,INCR,NOS,NPMAX,NOW,NOT,NOR,IFW,IFC,N
     1DV,IFRITE)
      STOP
      END
      SUBROUTINE CYCLE(NFXP,NOP,NOEK,NOCP,INCR,NOS,NPMAX,NOW,NOT,NOR,IFW
     1,IFC,NDV,IFRITE)
      DOUBLE PRECISION ERR,SSQER,SUMSLIN,SC,DC,GC
      REAL MSUMSQ
      INTEGER BI
      DIMENSION NPAR(100),KP(50),P(100),ERR(20),NCODE(100),NR(200),NC(20
     10),S(80,80),Y(80),B(200),SIGMA(80),T(8),VAR(20),BI(8,8),DVAR(20),D
     1C(8,4),SC(8),GC(8)
      COMMON/SET1/P
      COMMON/SET2/GC,SC,DC
      COMMON/SET3/DVAR
      COMMON/SET4/S,Y,NPAR,NCODE,SIGMA
      COMMON/SET5/ERR,ABS
      COMMON/SET7/T,VAR,MSUMSQ,FAC,BI
      COMMON/SET11/SSQER
      NSPMAX=NPMAX
      IF(NOCP.EQ.0)GO TO 230
C
C     READ IN CONSTANT PARAMETER LIST.
C
      READ(5,2)(KP(I),I=1,NOCP)
    2 FORMAT(26I3)
C
C     ASSIGN PARAMETER CODES AND VARIABLE NUMBERS TO ARRAY ,P,
C
  230 K=0
      DO 216 J=1,NOEK
      DO 217 I=1,NOCP
      IF(J.EQ.KP(I))GO TO 216
  217 CONTINUE
      K=K+1
      NCODE(K)=2
      NPAR(K)=J
  216 CONTINUE
      IF(NOEK.EQ.NOP)GO TO 120
      NZ=NOEK+1
      DO 214 J=NZ,NOP
      DO 215 I=1,NOCP
      IF(J.EQ.KP(I))GO TO 214
  215 CONTINUE
      K=K+1
      NCODE(K)=1
      NPAR(K)=J
  214 CONTINUE
  120 NVAR=K
      NP=1
      IFAC=0
      MSUMSQ=0.0
      FAC=0.0
      NTC=1
      JU=1
  222 REWIND 1
  233 NT=1
      DO 224 I=1,80
      Y(I)=0.0
      DO 224 J=1,80
  224 S(I,J)=0.0
      SSQER=0.0
```

```
C
C       CYCLING OVER THE TOTAL NUMBER OF EXPERIMENTS, THE OBSERVABLES
C       ARE CALCULATED AND HENCE "SSQER"   THE SUM OF THE SQUARES OF THE
C       ERRORS.
C
        DO 201 K=1,NEXP
        IF(NP.GT.1.AND.NPMAX.NE.0)GO TO 256
        WRITE(6,236)K,NP
  236 FORMAT(12H0 EXPERIMENT,2X,I2,5X,13H PERTURBATION,I3//)
  256 NO1=2
        IF(NP.EQ.1)GO TO 271
        GO TO 219
  271 NO1=1
        READ(5,246)(T(M),M=1,NOT)
  246 FORMAT(7E10.4)
        IF(JU.GT.1)GO TO 220
        DO 4 I=1,NOT
    4 READ(5,231)(BI(I,J),J=1,NOS)
  231 FORMAT(20I3)
  220 DO 121 N=1,NOT
        P(NOP+NTC)=T(N)
        NPAR(NVAR+NTC)=NOP+NTC
        NCODE(NVAR+NTC)=3
        NTC=NTC+1
  121 CONTINUE
        WRITE(1)(T(M),M=1,NOT)
        GO TO 221
  219 READ(1)(T(M),M=1,NOT)
        IF(IFAC.NE.1)GO TO 221
        DO 122 I=1,NOT
        T(I)=P(NOP+NT)
        NT=NT+1
  122 CONTINUE
C
C       CALCULATE THE CONCENTRATIONS OF ALL THE SPECIES.
C
  221 CALL CONC(NO1,0,NOP,NOEK,NOS,NOR,NOT,JU,NOW,IFW,NPMAX,NVAR,NEXP,ND
     1V,1,NT,IFAC)
C
C       CALCULATE B-MATRIX ELEMENTS AND NORMALISE
C
        NOT1=0
        NOB=0
        DO 301 I=1,NVAR
        IF(NCODE(I).NE.1)GO TO 302
        NOB=NOB+1
        L=1+(NPAR(I)-1-NOFK)/NOS
        N=NPAR(I)
        NR(NOB)=L
        NC(NOB)=N
        B(NOB)=SC(NPAR(I)-NOS*(L-1)-NOEK)
        GO TO 301
  302 IF(NCODE(I).NE.2)GO TO 310
        NOB=NOB+1
        J=NPAR(I)
        P(J)=P(J)+P(J)/INCR
        CALL CONC(3,1,NOP,NOEK,NOS,NOR,NOT,JU,NOW,IFW,NPMAX,NVAR,NEXP,NDV,
     11,NT,IFAC)
        P(J)=P(J)*INCR/(INCR+1)
        L=1
  304 NR(NOB)=L
        NC(NOB)=J
        B(NOB)=DVAR(L)*INCR/P(J)
        IF(L.EQ.NDV)GO TO 301
        L=L+1
        NOB=NOB+1
        GO TO 304
```

```
  310 IF(NCODE(I).NE.3)GO TO 303
      NOT1=NOT1+1
      IF(NOT1.GT.NOT)GO TO 307
      NOB=NOB+1
      J=NPAR(I+NT-NOT-1)
      P(J)=P(J)+P(J)/TNCR
      T(NOT1)=P(J)
      CALL CONC(3,1,NQP,NOEK,MOS,NOR,NOT,JU,NOW,IFW,NPMAX,NVAR,NEXP,NDV,
     11,NT,IFAC)
      P(J)=P(J)*INCR/(INCR+1)
      T(NOT1)=P(J)
      L=1
  308 NR(NOB)=L
      NC(NOB)=J
      B(NOB)=DVAR(L)*INCR/P(J)
      IF(L.EQ.NDV)GO TO 301
      L=L+1
      NOB=NOB+1
      GO TO 308
  301 CONTINUE
  307 IF(NPMAX.NE.0)GO TO 291
      WRITE(6,208)
  208 FORMAT(////27H NON-ZERO B-MATRIX ELEMENTS)
      WRITE(6,5)
      WRITE(6,209)(NR(M),NC(M),B(M),M=1,NOB)
  209 FORMAT(5(I3,2X,I3,3X,F10.4,2X))
      WRITE(6,5)
C
C     RENUMBER B-MATRIX ELEMENTS
C
  291 DO 200 I=1,NOB
      DO 200 L=1,NVAR
      IF(NPAR(L).NE.NC(I))GO TO 200
      NC(I)=L
  200 CONTINUE
      GO TO 258
  303 WRITE(6,306)
  306 FORMAT(76H VARIABLE UNDEFINED AS EITHER EXTINCTION COEFFICIENT OR
     1EQUILIBRIUM CONSTANT)
      GO TO 211
C
C     CALCULATE THE MATRICES "B-TRANSPOSE B"  AND "B-TRANSPOSE E"
C
  258 DO 213 M=1,NOB
      I=NC(M)
      DO 213 N=M,NOB
      J=NC(N)
      IF(NR(M).NE.NR(N))GO TO 213
      S(I,J)=S(I,J)+(B(N)*B(N))/VAR(NR(M))
      S(J,I)=S(I,J)
  213 CONTINUE
      DO 210 I=1,NOB
  210 Y(NC(I))=Y(NC(I))+(B(I)*ERR(NR(I)))/VAR(NR(I))
      IF(K.NE.NEXP)GO TO 201
      WRITE(6,290)SSQFR
  290 FORMAT(/10H SUMSQERR=,D10.4)
  201 CONTINUE
      IF(NPMAX.EQ.0)GO TO 237
      DO 259 K=1,NVAR
  259 SIGMA(K)=SQRT(S(K,K))
C
C     NORMALISE S AND Y
C
      DO 253 I=1,NVAR
      DO 254 J=1,NVAR
  254 S(I,J)=S(I,J)/(SIGMA(I)*SIGMA(J))
```

```
    253 CONTINUE
        DO 255 I=1,NVAR
    255 Y(I)=Y(I)/SIGMA(I)
        NO1=1
        IF(NP.GT.1)NO1=2
C
C       CALCULATE CORRECTIONS TO PARAMETERS.
C
        CALL LEASTSQ(NVAR,NP,NPMAX,NEXP,NOP,NOS,NOEK,NOW,NOT,NOP,NO1,NDV,N
       1T,IFAC,IFW,IFRITE)
        IF(NPMAX.EQ.-1)GO TO 211
        GO TO 222
    237 CFAC=0.0
        DO 261 J=1,NVAR
        DO 262 I=1,NVAR
    262 CFAC=CFAC+P(NPAR(I))*S(I,J)*P(NPAR(J))
    261 CONTINUE
C
C       CALCULATE ERRORS IN THE PARAMETERS (STANDARD DEVIATIONS).
C
        CALL ERROR(NVAR,NEXP,NDV)
        WRITE(6,223)
    223 FORMAT(44H NEW VALUES OF PARAMETERS AND STD DEVIATIONS)
        WRITE(6,5)
      5 FORMAT(120H ------------------------------------------------------------
       1------------------------------------------------------------)
        WRITE(6,225)(P(NPAR(K)),SIGMA(K),K=1,NVAR)
    225 FORMAT(8(/1X,F10.4,4X,E10.4))
        WRITE(6,5)
C
C       CALCULATE QUANTITIES TO ESTIMATE GOODNESS OF FIT.
C
        RF=DSQRT(SSQER/FAC)
        RL=SQRT(MSUMSQ/FAC)
        WRITE(6,257)MSUMSQ
    257 FORMAT(//43H MAXIMUM PROBABLE SUM OF SQUARES OF ERRORS=,F10.6)
        WRITE(6,248)RF
    248 FORMAT(//19H HAMILTON R-FACTOR=,F10.6)
        WRITE(6,249)RL
    249 FORMAT(//25H HAMILTON R-LIMIT FACTOR=,F10.6)
        SUMSLIN=FAC-CFAC
        WRITE(6,250)SUMSLIN
    250 FORMAT(//23H LINEAR SUM OF SQUARES=,F10.6)
        IF(IFC.NE.1)GO TO 211
        IF(NPMAX.EQ.0.AND.IFAC.EQ.1)GO TO 211
        NPMAX=NSPMAX
        IFAC=1
        NVAR=NVAR+NEXP*NOT
        GO TO 222
    211 RETURN
        END
        SUBROUTINE CONC(NO1,NE,NOP,NOFK,NOS,NOR,NOT,JU,NOW,IFW,NPMAX,NVAR,
       1NEXP,NDV,JJ,NT,IFAC)
C
C       THIS ROUTINE CALCULATES THE CONCENTRATIONS OF ALL THE SPECIES IN
C       THE SYSTEM BY A GAUSS-NEWTON ITERATION ON A SET OF GUESSED
C       CONCENTRATIONS. USES MASS BALANCE AND EQUILIBRIUM CONSTANT
C       EQUATIONS.
C
        INTEGER BI,A,SIFOBS
        DOUBLE PRECISION GC,SC,ERR,LC,TERR,DC,SSQER,SSC
        DIMENSION GC(8),TABS(20),SC(8),B(8,8),SS(80,80),SY(8),ERR(14),A(6,
       18),BI(8,8),T(8),LC(8),E(6),X(80),TERR(6),DC(8,4),TC(8),PC(8),VAR(2
       10),SSC(8),P(100)
        COMMON/SET1/P
        COMMON/SET2/GC,SC,DC
```

```
      COMMON/SET6/X,A
      COMMON/SET7/T,VAR,MSUMSQ,FAC,BI
      COMMON/SET8/SS,SY
      COMMON/SET12/SSC
      GO TO (2,116,119),NO1
    2 IF(JU.GT.1)GO TO 119
      READ(5,6)(GC(K),K=1,NOS)
    6 FORMAT(10(D7.3))
      IV=0
      GO TO 118
  116 IF(JJ.EQ.1)GO TO 114
      READ(1)(T(K),K=1,NOT)
      IF(IFAC.NE.1)GO TO 114

      DO 112 I=1,NOT
      T(I)=P(NOP+NT)
      NT=NT+1
  112 CONTINUE
  114 READ(1)(SC(K),K=1,NOS)
  119 DO 47 K=1,NOS
   47 GC(K)=SC(K)
      IV=0
      GO TO 118
  117 IF(IV.GT.NOT)GO TO 77
      T(IV)=T(IV)+T(IV)/100
  118 DO 10 K=1,NOS
      IF(GC(K).LT.0.0)GO TO 41
      GO TO 10
   41 GC(K)=(GC(K)-X(K))/2
   10 LC(K)=DLOG10(GC(K))
C
C     CALCULATE ERRORS
C
      DO 51 I=1,NOR
   51 E(I)=0.0
      DO 11 I=1,NOR
      DO 12 J=1,NOS
   12 E(I)=A(I,J)*LC(J)+E(I)
   11 CONTINUE
      DO 13 I=1,NOR
      TERR(I)=P(I)-EXP(ALOG(10.0)*E(I))
   13 ERR(I)=ALOG10(P(I))-E(I)
      DO 52 I=1,NOT
   52 TC(I)=0.0
      DO 15 I=1,NOT
      DO 14 J=1,NOS
   14 TC(I)=TC(I)+BI(I,J)*GC(J)
   15 CONTINUE
      DO 16 I=1,NOT
   16 ERR(NOR+I)=T(I)-TC(I)
      SSQER=0.0
      DO 48 I=1,NOR
   48 SSQER=SSQER+(TERR(I)*TERR(I))/(P(I)*P(I))
      DO 26 I=1,NOT
   26 SSQER=SSQER+(ERR(NOR+I)*ERR(NOR+I))/(T(I)*T(I))
      IF(IV.GT.0.AND.SSQER.LT.5.0E-08)GO TO 113
      IF (SSQER.LT.5.0E-08) GO TO 30
C
C     OBTAIN B-MATRIX ELEMENTS
C
      DO 17 I=1,NOR
      DO 18 J=1,NOS
   18 B(I,J)=A(I,J)/GC(J)
   17 CONTINUE
      DO 19 I=1,NOT
      DO 20 J=1,NOS
   20 B(I+NOR,J)=BI(I,J)
```

```
   19 CONTINUE
C
C     CONSTRUCT S AND Y
C
      NAC=NOR+NOT
   96 DO 224 K=1,NOS
      SY(K)=0.0
      DO 224 I=1,NOS
  224 SS(K,I)=0.0
      DO 23 K=1,NOS
      DO 21 I=1,NOS
      DO 22 J=1,NAC
   22 SS(K,I)=SS(K,I)+B(J,K)*B(J,I)
   21 CONTINUE
   23 CONTINUE
      DO 24 K=1,NOS
      DO 25 I=1,NAC
   25 SY(K)=SY(K)+B(I,K)*ERR(I)
   24 CONTINUE
      CALL LEASTCO(SSQER,NOS)
      DO 27 I=1,NOS
   27 GC(I)=GC(I)+X(I)
      GO TO 118
   30 DO 33 I=1,NOS
   33 SSC(I)=GC(I)
      IF(NE.EQ.1)GO TO 31
      DO 28 I=1,NOS
   28 SC(I)=GC(I)
      IF(NO1.GT.1)GO TO 115
      WRITE(1)(SC(K),K=1,NOS)
      GO TO 111
  113 T(IV)=T(IV)*100/101
      DO 61 I=1,NOS
      DC(I,IV)=(GC(I)-SC(I))*100/T(IV)
   61 GC(I)=SC(I)
  111 IV=IV+1
      GO TO 117
   31 DO 32 I=1,NOS
   32 GC(I)=GC(I)-SC(I)
      GO TO 77
  115 IF(NPMAX.NE.0)GO TO 77
C
C     ON FINAL PERTURBATION WRITE DISTRIBUTION OF SPECIES AS PERCENTAGES
C     OF ANALYTICAL CONCENTRATIONS.
C
      DO 81 I=1,NOT
      WRITE(6,83)I
   83 FORMAT(//6H TYPE ,I3)
      DO 82 J=1,NOS
      IF(BI(I,J).EQ.0)GO TO 82
      PC(J)=(GC(J)/T(I))*100.0
      WRITE(6,84)J,PC(J)
   84 FORMAT(9H SPECIES ,I3,12H %TAGE CONC ,F6.3)
   82 CONTINUE
   81 CONTINUE
   77 GO TO (78,71,76),NO1
   78 READ(5,246)IFOBS
  246 FORMAT(I3)
      SIFOBS=IFOBS
      WRITE(1)IFOBS
      GO TO 76
   71 READ(1)IFOBS
      SIFOBS=IFOBS
C
C     CALCULATE OBSERVABLES FROM EVALUATED CONCENTRATIONS OF SPECIES.
C
```

```
   76 ND=1
      DO 42 I=1,3
      NUM=IFOBS/(10**(3-I))
      IF(NUM.LE.0)GO TO 42
      GO TO (219,220,221),NUM
  219 CALL OBSERV1(NO1,NOS,NOW,NOEK,JU,NEXP,JJ,IFW,NPMAX,NOT,NOP,ND)
      ND=ND+NOW
      GO TO 161
  220 CALL OBSERV2(NO1,NOS,NOEK,JU,NOT,JJ,NPMAX,IFW,ND)
      ND=ND+1
      GO TO 161
  221 CALL OBSERV3(NO1,NOP,NOS,NOW,NOEK,JU,NP,NVAR)
  161 IFOBS=IFOBS-(10**(3-I))*NUM
   42 CONTINUE
      IFOBS=SIFOBS
      JU=2
      RETURN
      END
      SUBROUTINE LEASTCO(SSQER,NOS)
C
C     THIS ROUTINE CALCULATES CORRECTIONS TO THE CONCENTRATION VECTOR.
C
      DIMENSION SS(80,80),SY(8),V(80,80),R(8),XK(8),X(80),A(6,8)
      COMMON/SET6/X,A
      COMMON/SET8/SS,SY
      COMMON/SET9/V
      DET=1.0
      IEGEN=0
      NR=0
C     DIAGONALISE S
      CALL HDIAG(SS,NOS,IEGEN,V,NR)
      ROOT=1.0E-08
      DO 8 K=1,80
    8 X(K)=0.0
      DO 19 K=1,NOS
      R(K)=SS(K,K)
      IF(R(K).LT.ROOT)GO TO 19
      RVY=0.0
      DO 9 J=1,NOS
    9 RVY=RVY+(V(J,K)*SY(J))/R(K)
      DO 16 I=1,NOS
      XK(I)=V(I,K)*RVY
   16 X(I)=X(I)+XK(I)
   19 CONTINUE
  999 RETURN
      END
      SUBROUTINE HDIAG(H,N,IEGEN,U,NR)
      DIMENSION H(80,80),U(80,80),XX(80),IQ(80)
C
C     THIS SUBROUTINE DIAGONALISES A SQUARE SYMMETRIC MATRIX.
C     IF IEGEN = 0 THE ORTHOGONAL EIGENVECTORS ARE ALSO CALCULATED.
C
      IF (IEGEN) 15,10,15
   10 DO 14 I=1,N
      DO 14 J=1,N
      IF(I-J)12,11,12
   11 U(I,J)=1.0
      GO TO 14
   12 U(I,J)=0.0
   14 CONTINUE
   15 NR = 0
      IF (N-1) 1000,1000,17
C     SCAN FOR LARGEST OFF DIAGONAL ELEMENT IN EACH ROW
C     XX(I) CONTAINS LARGEST ELEMENT IN  ITH ROW
C     IQ(I) HOLDS SECOND SUBSCRIPT DEFINING POSITION OF ELEMENT
   17 MNI1=N-1
```

```
        NMI1=MNI1
        DO 30 I=1,NMI1
        XX(I)=0.0
        IPL1=I+1
        DO 30 J=IPL1,N
        IF(XX(I)-ABS(H(I,J))) 20,20,30
20      XX(I)=ABS(H(I,J))
        IQ(I)=J
   30 CONTINUE
C     SET INDICATOR FOR SHUT-OFF.RAP=2**-27,NR=NO.OF ROTATIONS
        RAP=.745058059E-08
        HDTEST=1.0E38
C     FIND MAXIMUN OF XX(I)S FOR PIVOT ELEMENT AND
C     TEST FOR END OF PROBLEM
   40 DO 70 I=1,MNI1
        IF (I-1) 60,60,45
   45 IF(XMAX-XX(I))60,60,70
60      XMAX=XX(I)
        IPIV=I
        JPIV=IQ(I)
   70 CONTINUE
C     IS MAX.XX(I) EQUAL TO ZERO,IF LESS THAN HDTEST,REVISE HDTEST
        IF (XMAX) 1000,1000,80
   80 IF( HDTEST) 90,90,85
   85 IF (XMAX - HDTEST) 90,90,148
   90 HDIMIN = ABS( H (1,1) )
        DO 110 I=2,N
        IF (HDIMIN - ABS( H (I,I))) 110,110,100
  100 HDIMIN=ABS(H(I,I))
  110 CONTINUE
        HDTEST = HDIMIN*RAP
C     RETURN IF MAX.H(I,J)LESS THAN(2**-27)ABSF(H(K,K)-MIN)
        IF (HDTEST-XMAX) 148,1000,1000
  148 NR= NR+1
C     COMPUTE TANGENT, SINE AND COSINE,H(I,I),H(J,J)
        XDIF=H(IPIV,IPIV)-H(JPIV,JPIV)
        IF(XDIF)9151,9150,9151
 9150 XO=2.0*H(IPIV,JPIV)
        GO TO 9152
 9151 XO=SIGN(2.0,XDIF)*H(IPIV,JPIV)
 9152 XS=XDIF**2+4.0*H(IPIV,JPIV)**2
        IF(XS)150,9153,150
 9153 TANG=1.0
        GO TO 9154
  150 TANG=XO / (ABS(XDIF)  + SQRT(XS))
 9154   COSINE=1.0/SQRT(1.0+TANG**2)
        SINE=TANG*COSINE
        HII=H(IPIV,IPIV)
        H(IPIV,IPIV)=COSINE**2*(HII+TANG*(2.0*H(IPIV,JPIV)+TANG*H(JPIV,JPI
     1V)))
        H(JPIV,JPIV)=COSINE**2*(H(JPIV,JPIV)-TANG*(2.0*H(IPIV,JPIV)-TANG*H
     1 II))
        H(IPIV,JPIV)=0.0
C     PSEUDO RANK THE EIGENVALUES
C     ADJUST SINE AND COS FOR COMPUTATION OF H(IK) AND U(IK)
        IF ( H(IPIV,IPIV) - H(JPIV,JPIV)) 152,153,153
  152 HTEMP = H(IPIV,IPIV)
        H(IPIV,IPIV) = H(JPIV,JPIV)
        H(JPIV,JPIV) =HTEMP
C     RECOMPUTE SINE AND COS
        HTEMP = SIGN(1.0, -SINE) * COSINE
        COSINE =ABS(SINE)
        SINE =HTEMP
  153 CONTINUE
C     INSPECT THE IQS BETWEEN I+1 AND N-1 TO DETERMINE
C     WHETHER A NEW MAXIUM VALUE SHOULD BE COMPUTE SINCE
```

```
C      THE PRESENT MAXIMUM IS IN THE I OR J ROW.
       DO 350 I=1,NMI1
       IF(I-IPIV)210,350,200
  200  IF (I-JPIV) 210,350,210
  210  IF(IQ(I)-IPIV) 230,240,230
  230  IF(IQ(I)-JPIV) 350,240,350
  240  K=IQ(I)
  250  HTEMP=H(I,K)
       H(I,K)=0.0
       IPL1=I+1
       XX(I)=0.0
C      SEARCH IN DEPLETED ROW FOR NEW MAXIMUM
       DO 320 J=IPL1,N
       IF (XX(I) -ABS( H(I,J)) ) 300,300,320
  300  XX(I)=ABS(H(I,J))
       IQ(I)=J
  320  CONTINUE
       H(I,K)=HTEMP
  350  CONTINUE
       XX(IPIV)=0.0
       XX(JPIV)=0.0
C      CHANGE THE ORDER ELEMENTS OF H
       DO 530 I=1,N
       IF (I-IPIV) 370,530,420
  370  HTEMP = H(I,IPIV)
       H(I,IPIV)= COSINE*HTEMP + SINE*H(I,JPIV)
       IF (XX(I)- ABS( H(I,IPIV)) )380,390,390
  380  XX(I)=ABS(H(I,IPIV))
       IQ(I) = IPIV
  390  H(I,JPIV) = - SINE*HTEMP + COSINE*H(I,JPIV)
       IF (XX(I) - ABS( H(I,JPIV)) ) 400,530,530
  400  XX(I)= ABS(H(I,JPIV))
       IQ(I) = JPIV
       GO TO 530
  420  IF(I-JPIV) 430,530,480
  430  HTEMP = H(IPIV,I)
       H(IPIV,I) = COSTNE*HTEMP + SINE*H(I,JPIV)
       IF (XX(IPIV) - ABS(H(IPIV,I)) ) 440,450,450
  440  XX(IPIV)= ABS(H(IPIV,I))
       IQ(IPIV) = I
  450  H(I,JPIV) = - SINE*HTEMP + COSINE*H(I,JPIV)
       IF (XX(I)- ABS(H(I,JPIV)) ) 400,530,530
  480  HTEMP = H(IPIV,I)
       H(IPIV,I) = COSINE*HTEMP + SINE*H(JPIV,I)
       IF (XX(IPIV) - ABS( H(IPIV,I)) ) 490,500,500
  490  XX(IPIV)= ABS(H(IPIV,I))
       IQ(IPIV) = I
  500  H(JPIV,I) = - SINE*HTEMP + COSINE*H(JPIV,I)
       IF (XX(JPIV) - ABS( H(JPIV,I)) )510,530,530
  510  XX(JPIV)= ABS(H(JPIV,I))
       IQ(JPIV) = I
  530  CONTINUE
C      TEST FOR COMPUTATION OF EIGENVECTORS
       IF(TEGEN) 40,540,40
  540  DO 550 I=1,N
       HTEMP=U(I,IPIV)
       U(I,IPIV)=COSINE*HTEMP+SINE*U(I,JPIV)
  550  U(I,JPIV)= -SINE*HTEMP+COSINE*U(I,JPIV)
       GO TO 40
 1000  RETURN
       END
       SUBROUTINE OBSERV1(NO1,NOS,NOW,NOFK,JU,NEXP,JJ,IFW,NPMAX,NOT,NOP,N
      1D)
C
C      THIS ROUTINE CALCULATES ABSORBANCE VALUES AT UP TO 20 WAVELENGTHS
C      FROM THE SPECIES DISTRIBUTION CALCULATED IN CONC.
```

```
C
      INTEGER BI
      DOUBLE PRECISION ERR,SC,DC,GC,SSQER
      DIMENSION DVAR(20),ABS(20),GC(8),P(100),ERR(20),WAVEL(20),XT(80),N
     1CODE(100),NPAR(100),S(80,80),Y(80),SC(8),T(8),VAR(20),DC(8,4),SIGM
     2A(80),BI(8,8),IABS(20)
      COMMON/SET1/P
      COMMON/SET2/GC,SC,DC
      COMMON/SET3/DVAR
      COMMON/SET4/S,Y,NPAR,NCODE,SIGMA
      COMMON/SET5/ERR
      COMMON/SET7/T,VAR,MSUMSQ,FAC,BI
      COMMON/SET11/SSQER
      GO TO (250,252,222),NO1
  250 IF(JU.GT.1)GO TO 221
      DO 26 L=1,NOW
      NOE=(L-1)*NOS
      NEZ=NOE+1
      NOZ=NOE+NOS
   26 READ(5,27)WAVEL(L),(XT(I),I=NEZ,NOZ)
   27 FORMAT(F5.1,6E10.4)
      WRITE(6,29)
   29 FORMAT(//24H EXTINCTION COEFFICIENTS)
      WRITE(6,5)
      WRITE(6,30)(I,I=1,NOS)
   30 FORMAT(8H SPECIES,6(13X,I3))
      WRITE(6,5)
      WRITE(6,31)
   31 FORMAT(11H WAVELENGTH)
C
C     READ IN EXTINCTION COEFFICIENTS.
C
      DO 32 L=1,NOW
      NOE=(L-1)*NOS
      NEZ=NOE+1
      NOZ=NOE+NOS
   32 WRITE(6,33)WAVEL(L),(XT(I),I=NEZ,NOZ)
   33 FORMAT(2X,F5.1,2HNM,9X,E10.4,5(6X,E10.4))
      WRITE(6,5)
      DO 47 L=1,NOW
      NOE=(L-1)*NOS
      NEZ=NOE+1
      NOZ=NOE+NOS
      DO 46 I=NEZ,NOZ
   46 P(NOEK+I)=XT(I)
   47 CONTINUE
      GO TO 221
  252 READ(1)(ABS(L),L=1,NOW)
      GO TO 222
C
C     READ IN EXPERIMENTAL ABSORBANCES.
C
  221 READ(5,220)(ABS(L),L=1,NOW)
  220 FORMAT(16F5.3)
      WRITE(1)(ABS(L),L=1,NOW)
  222 IF(NO1.GT.1)GO TO 404
      WRITE(6,402)(GC(K),K=1,NOS)
  402 FORMAT(8(3X,D12.6))
C
C     CALCULATE ABSORBANCES.
C
  404 DO 401 L=ND,NOW
      DVAR(L)=0.0
      NQ=(L-ND)*NOS+1
      NT=(L-ND)*NOS+NOS
      DO 403 K=NQ,NT
```

```
  403 DVAR(L)=DVAR(L)+GC(K-(L-ND)*NQS)*P(NOEK+K)
  401 CONTINUE
      GO TO (240,217,218),NO1
C
C        CALCULATE WEIGHTS AND "R-LIMIT" FACTOR.
C
  240 CALL VARIAN1(NOT,JU,NOS,NOW,NOP,NOEK,NO1,IFW,ND)
      IF(IFW.NE.1)GO TO 253
      DO 254 L=ND,NOW
  254 VAR(L)=1.0
      WRITE(1)(VAR(L),L=ND,NOW)
  253 DO 219 L=ND,NOW
  219 FAC=FAC+(ABS(L+1-ND)*ABS(L+1-ND))/VAR(L)
      GO TO 233
  217 READ(1)(VAR(L),L=ND,NOW)
C
C        CALCULATE ERROR VECTOR.
C
  233 DO 203 L=ND,NOW
      ERR(L)=ABS(L+1-ND)-DVAR(L)
  203 IF(ABS(L+1-ND).EQ.0.0)ERP(L)=0.0
      IF(JJ.EQ.2)GO TO 234
      IF(NPMAX.NE.0)GO TO 234
C
C        ON FINAL PERTURBATION WRITE OUT CALCULATED AND OBSERVED
C        ABSORBANCES WITH RESIDUALS.
C
      WRITE(6,204)
  204 FORMAT(////12H ABSORBANCES)
      WRITE(6,5)
    5 FORMAT(120H ------------------------------------------------------------
     1------------------------------------------------------------------------)
      WRITE(6,205)
  205 FORMAT(51H WAVELENGTH(NM)    OBSERVED    CALCULATED    ERRORS)
      WRITE(6,5)
      DO 206 L=1,NOW
  206 WRITE(6,207)WAVEL(L),ABS(L),DVAR(ND+L-1),ERR(ND+L-1)
  207 FORMAT(3X,F5.1,12X,F5.3,8X,F5.3,7X,F6.4)
      WRITE(6,5)
C
C        CALCULATE THE SUM OF THE SQUARES OF THE ERRORS.
C
  234 DO 2061 L=ND,NOW
 2061 SSQER=SSQER+(ERR(L)*ERR(L))/VAR(L)
  218 RETURN
      END
      SUBROUTINE VARIAN1(NOT,JU,NOS,NOW,NOP,NOEK,NO1,IFW,ND)
C
C        THIS ROUTINE WILL CALCULATE WEIGHTS FOR THE OBSERVED ABSORBANCES
C        USING ERROR PROPAGATION RULES. ALSO HAMILTON "R-LIMIT" FACTOR IS
C        EVALUATED.
C
      REAL MSUMSQ,MPER
      DOUBLE PRECISION GC,SC,DC
      DIMENSION DC(8,4),MPER(20),VAR(20),P(100),T(8),EEC(8),GC(8),SC(8),
     1BI(8,8)
      COMMON/SET1/P
      COMMON/SET2/GC,SC,DC
      COMMON/SET7/T,VAR,MSUMSQ,FAC,BI
      GO TO(13,12),JU
C
C        READ IN ESTIMATED ERRORS IN THE EXPERIMENTAL QUANTITIES.
C        (ABSORBANCES AND ANALYTICAL CONCENTRATIONS)
C
   13 READ(5,1)EAF,(EEC(I),I=1,NOT)
    1 FORMAT(10F6.3)
```

```
   12 DO 239 L=ND,NOW
      MPER(L)=0.0
  239 VAR(L)=0.0
      DO 3 L=ND,NOW
      NP=(L-ND)*NOS
      DO 4 K=1,NOS
      DO 5 J=1,NOT
    5 MPER(L)=MPER(L)+DABS(P(NOEK+NP+K)*DC(K,J)*(T(J)*EEC(J)))
    4 CONTINUE
      MPER(L)=MPER(L)+EAE
    3 CONTINUE
C
C     CALCULATE WEIGHTS.
C
      IF(IFW.EQ.1)GO TO 16
      DO 8 L=ND,NOW
      NP=(L-ND)*NOS
      DO 9 K=1,NOS
      DO 10 J=1,NOT
   10 VAR(L)=VAR(L)+((P(NOEK+NP+K)**2)*(DC(K,J)**2))*((T(J)*EEC(J))**2)
    9 CONTINUE
      VAR(L)=VAR(L)+EAE*EAE
    8 CONTINUE
      DO 11 L=ND,NOW
   11 MSUMSQ=MSUMSQ+(MPER(L)*MPER(L))/VAR(L)
      WRITE(1)(VAR(L),L=ND,NOW)
      GO TO 14
   16 DO 15 L=ND,NOW
   15 MSUMSQ=MSUMSQ+(MPER(L)*MPER(L))
   14 RETURN
      END
      SUBROUTINE OBSERV2(NO1,NOS,NOEK,JU,NOT,JJ,NPMAX,IFW,ND)
C
C     THIS ROUTINE CALCULATES POINT BY POINT E.M.F. VALUES FOR A
C     POTENTIOMETRIC TITRATION, USING THE SPECIES DISTRIBUTION EVALUATED
C     IN CONC.
C
      INTEGER BI
      REAL NERNST
      DOUBLE PRECISION ERR,SC,DC,GC,SSQFR,SSC
      DIMENSION DVAR(20),GC(8),P(100),ERR(20),SC(8),T(8),VAR(20),DC(8,4)
     1,BI(8,8),SSC(8)
      COMMON/SET1/P
      COMMON/SET2/GC,SC,DC
      COMMON/SET3/DVAR
      COMMON/SET5/ERR
      COMMON/SET7/T,VAR,MSUMSQ,FAC,BI
      COMMON/SET10/NERNST,KN,KT
      COMMON/SET11/SSQER
      COMMON/SET12/SSC
      GO TO (250,252,253),NO1
  250 IF(JU.GT.1)GO TO 221
      NM=ND
C
C     READ IN NERNST CONSTANT VALUE AND CONCENTRATION NUMBER.
C
      READ(5,27)NERNST,KN,KT
   27 FORMAT(F7.4,2I3)
      WRITE(6,241)NERNST
  241 FORMAT(/8H NERNST=,F5.2)
      GO TO 221
  252 READ(1)EMF
      GO TO 222
C
C     READ IN EXPERIMENTAL E.M.F. VALUES.
C
```

```
    221 READ(5,220)EMF
    220 FORMAT(F7.3)
        WRITE(1)EMF
C
C       CALCULATE E.M.F. VALUES.
C
    222 SEMF=NERNST*DLOG10(T(KT)/GC(KN))
        GO TO (230,231),NO1
    230 CALL VARIAN2(NOT,JU,NOS,NO1,IFW,ND,NM)
        IF(IFW.NE.1)GO TO 242
        DO 202 I=ND,NM
    202 VAR(I)=1.0
        WRITE(1)(VAR(I),I=ND,NM)
    242 DO 243 I=ND,NM
    243 FAC=FAC+(EMF*EMF)/VAR(I)
        GO TO 203
    231 READ(1)(VAR(I),I=ND,NM)
C
C       CALCULATE ERROR VECTOR AND THE SUM OF THE SQUARES OF THE ERRORS.
C
    203 DO 204 I=ND,NM
        ERR(I)=EMF-SEMF
    204 SSQER=SSQER+(FRR(I)*ERR(I))/VAR(I)
        IF(JJ.EQ.2)GO TO 218
        IF(NPMAX.NE.0)GO TO 218
C
C       ON FINAL PERTURBATION WRITE OUT CALCULATED AND OBSERVED E.M.F.
C       VALUES WITH RESIDUALS.
C
        WRITE(6,201)
    201 FORMAT(///9H EMF DATA)
        WRITE(6,5)
      5 FORMAT(120H ---------------------------------------------------------
       1---------------------------------------------------------------)
        WRITE(6,205)
    205 FORMAT(36H   OBSERVED    CALCULATED     ERRORS)
        WRITE(6,5)
        DO 225 I=ND,NM
    225 WRITE(6,207)EMF,SEMF,ERR(I)
    207 FORMAT(4X,F7.4,6X,F7.4,3X,F10.8)
        WRITE(6,5)
        GO TO 218
    253 CEMF=NERNST*DLOG10(T(KT)/SSC(KN))
        DO 232 I=ND,NM
    232 DVAR(I)=CEMF-SEMF
    218 RETURN
        END
        SUBROUTINE VARIAN2(NOT,JU,NOS,NO1,IFW,ND,NM)
C
C       THIS ROUTINE WILL CALCULATE WEIGHTS FOR THE OBSERVED E.M.F. VALUES
C       USING ERROR PROPOGATION RULES. ALSO HAMILTON "R-LIMIT" FACTOR IS
C       EVALUATED.
C
        REAL MPER,MSUMSO,NERNST,NEW
        DOUBLE PRECISION DC,SC,GC
        DIMENSION DC(8,4),VAR(20),T(8),EEC(8),GC(8),SC(8),BI(8,8)
        COMMON/SET2/GC,SC,DC
        COMMON/SET7/T,VAR,MSUMSQ,FAC,BI
        COMMON/SET10/NERNST,KN,KT
        GO TO (1,2),JU
C
C       READ IN THE ESTIMATED ERRORS IN THE EXPERIMENTAL QUANTITIES (E.M.F
C       AND ANALYTICAL CONCENTRATIONS)
C
      1 READ(5,3)EEE,(EFC(I),I=1,NOT)
      3 FORMAT(9F6.3)
```

```
      NEW=2.3026/WERNST
    2 DO 4 I=ND,NM
      MPER=0.0
    4 VAR(I)=0.0
      MPER=MPER+EEE+ABS(EEC(KT)/NEW)
      K=1
    6 IF(K.EQ.KT)GO TO 5
      MPER=MPER+DABS((DC(KN,K)*T(K)*EEC(K))/(NEW*GC(KN)))
    5 K=K+1
      IF(K.LE.NOT)GO TO 6
      IF(IFW.EQ.1)GO TO 7
C
C     CALCULATE WEIGHTS.
C
      K=1
    9 IF(K.EQ.KT)GO TO 8
      DO 11 I=ND,NM
   11 VAR(I)=VAR(I)+EEE*EEE+(EEC(KT)*EEC(KT))/(NEW*NEW)
      DO 12 I=ND,NM
   12 VAR(I)=VAR(I)+(DC(KN,K)/(NEW*GC(KN)))*(DC(KN,K)/(NEW*GC(KN)))*EEC(
     1K)*T(K)*EEC(K)*T(K)
    8 K=K+1
      IF(K.LE.NOT)GO TO 9
      WRITE(1)(VAR(K),K=ND,NM)
      DO 13 I=ND,NM
   13 MSUMSQ=MSUMSQ+(MPER*MPER)/VAR(I)
      GO TO 10
    7 MSUMSQ=MSUMSQ+MPER*MPER
   10 RETURN
      END
      SUBROUTINE LEASTSQ(NVAR,NP,NPMAX,NEXP,NOP,NOS,NOEK,NOW,NOT,NOR,NO1
     1,NDV,NT,IFAC,IFW,IFRITE)
C
C     THIS ROUTINE CALCULATES THE CORRECTIONS TO THE PARAMETERS.
C
      REAL LAMDA
      DOUBLE PRECISION SSQER
      DIMENSION S(80,80),Y(80),P(100),NPAR(100),V(80,80),R(80),XK(80),X(
     180),A(6,8),XK1(80),NCODE(100),SIGMA(80)
      COMMON/SET1/P
      COMMON/SET4/S,Y,NPAR,NCODE,SIGMA
      COMMON/SET6/X,A
      COMMON/SET9/V
      COMMON/SET11/SSQER
      IF(NO1.GT.1)GO TO 27
      LAMDA=0.01
      VEE=5.0
   27 PROD=1.0
      NIT=0
      DIV=0.0
      DO 33 J=1,NVAR
   33 DIV=DIV+Y(J)*Y(J)
      IF(LAMDA.GT.156.25)LAMDA=0.01
      DO 1 I=1,NVAR
    1 PROD=PROD*S(I,I)
      DET=1.0
      IEGEN=0
      NR=0
C
C     DIAGONALISE S
C
      CALL HDIAG(S,NVAR,IEGEN,V,NR)
      WRITE(6,101)NR
  101 FORMAT(///I6,10H ROTATIONS)
      IF(NP.GT.1)GO TO 29
C
```

```
C      READ IN CONVERGENCE CRITERIA, SCALE FACTOR, AND MAXIMUM PERMITTED
C      PARAMETER CORRECTION.
C
       READ(5,102)IND,CORREC,CONV,SCALE
  102 FORMAT(I3,3E12.4)
       IF(IND.EQ.5)GO TO 4
       WRITE(6,103)NOPROB
  103 FORMAT(///9H   PROBLEM,I7,46H TERMINATED,ERROR IN PERTURBATION CONT
      1ROL CARD)
       GO TO 999
  4    IF(CORREC.NE.0)GO TO 5
       CORREC=0.1
  5    IF(CONV.NE.0)GO TO 6
       CONV=1.0E-02
  6    IF (SCALE.NE.0)GO TO 7
       SCALE=1.0
  7 WRITE(6,104)CORREC,CONV,SCALE
  104 FORMAT(/66H MAXIMUM PERMITTED CORRECTION EXPRESSED AS FRACTION OF
      1 PARAMETER =,E12.4/58H TEST FOR CONVERGENCE EXPRESSED AS FRACTION
      2 OF PARAMETER =,E12.4/23H CORRECTIONS SCALED BY,,E12.4,45H IF THE
      3ANGLE IS LESS THAN FORTY-FIVE DEGREES)
  29 TEST=SSQER
C
C      COMPUTE CORRECTIONS
C
       DO 8 K=1,80
  8    X(K)=0.0
       MARQ=0
       GO TO 34
  35 LAMDA=LAMDA/VEE
       MARQ=MARQ+1
  38 DO 28 K=1,NVAR
  28 X(K)=0.0
  34 DET=1.0
       CO=0.0
       SH=0.0
       DO 19 K=1,NVAR
       DET=DET*R(K)
       R(K)=S(K,K)+LAMDA
C
C      ADD IN THE CONTRIBUTION FROM EACH EIGENVALUE.
C
  117 RVY=0.0
       DO 9 J=1,NVAR
  9    RVY=RVY+(V(J,K)*Y(J))/R(K)
       CO=CO+RVY*RVY
       DO 16 I=1,NVAR
       XK(I)=V(I,K)*RVV
  16 X(I)=X(I)+XK(I)
       SQSH=0.0
       DO 30 N=1,NVAR
  30 SQSH=SQSH+V(N,K)*Y(N)
       SH=SH+(SQSH*SQSH)/R(K)
       IF(K.NE.NVAR)GO TO 19
       DO 63 N=1,NVAR
  63 X(N)=X(N)/SIGMA(N)
  19 CONTINUE
       ALPHA=ACOS(SH/(SQRT(CO)*SQRT(DIV)))
       IF(IFRITE.EQ.0)GO TO 199
       RATIO=DET/PROD
       WRITE(6,105)NP
  105 FORMAT(14H0 PERTURBATION,I6)
       WRITE(6,106)(R(I),I=1,K)
  106 FORMAT(7H  ROOTS/(5E12.4))
       WRITE(6,107)(NPAR(I),X(I),I=1,NVAR)
       WRITE(6,108)NP,DET,PROD,RATIO
```

```
  107 FORMAT(///27H  CORRECTIONS TO PARAMETERS/(3X,5(I3,2X,E12.4,4X)))
  108 FORMAT(14H0 PERTURBATION,I4,13H DETERMINANT=,E12.4/12X,19H PRODUCT
     1 OF S(I,I)=,E12.4/24X,7H RATIO=,E12.4)
  199 WRITE(6,99)ALPHA
   99 FORMAT(//11H THE ANGLE=,F10.6)
      WRITE(6,198)LAMDA
  198 FORMAT(//7H LAMDA=,F7.4)
C
C     TEST FOR REASONABLE PERTURBATION
C
      DO 10 I=1,NVAR
      XK(I)=X(I)
      IF((ABS(P(NPAR(I)))*CORREC).GT.ABS(X(I)))GO TO 10
   81 IF((ABS(P(NPAR(I)))*CORREC).LT.ABS(X(I)*SCALE))GO TO 11
   10 CONTINUE
      GO TO 12
   11 WRITE(6,109)NP
  109 FORMAT(14H0 PERTURBATION,I4,34H TOO LARGE,PROBLEM IS BEING DAMPED)
      IF(MARQ.EQ.0)GO TO 61
   62 LAMDA=LAMDA*(VEE*VEE)
      GO TO 64
   61 LAMDA=LAMDA*VEE
   64 NIT=NIT+1
      MARQ=MARQ+1
      IF(NIT.GT.5)GO TO 39
      GO TO 38
   39 NPMAX=-1
      GO TO 999
   12 DO 17 I=1,NVAR
      IF((ABS(P(NPAR(I)))*CORREC).LT.ABS(X(I)))XK(I)=XK(I)*SCALE
   17 P(NPAR(I))=P(NPAR(I))+XK(I)
   73 REWIND 1
      NT=1
      JU=2
      SSQER=0.0
      IO=1
   18 CALL CONC(2,0,NOP,NOEK,NOS,NOR,NOT,JU,NOW,IFW,NPMAX,NVAR,NEXP,NDV,
     12,NT,IFAC)
      IO=IO+1
      IF(IO.LE.NEXP)GO TO 18
      WRITE(6,75)SSQER
   75 FORMAT(/10H SUMSQERR=,D10.4)
C
C     TEST THE SUM OF THE SQUARES OF THE ERRORS AND ALTER LAMDA ACCORD
C     -ING TO MARQUARDTS CRITERIA.
C
      NIF=1
      IF(LAMDA.LT.1.0E-06.AND.SSQER.LT.TEST)GO TO 45
      IF(MARQ.EQ.0)GO TO 41
      IF(SSQER.LT.TEST)GO TO 45
      IF(ALPHA.LT.0.7855)GO TO 71
      IF(MARQ.GT.1)GO TO 56
      IF(MARQ.EQ.1.AND.NIT.EQ.1)GO TO 56
      IF(SUMS1.LT.TEST)GO TO 43
      LAMDA=LAMDA*(VEE*VEE)
      GO TO 58
   56 LAMDA=LAMDA*VEE
   58 MARQ=MARQ+1
      DO 57 I=1,NVAR
   57 P(NPAR(I))=P(NPAR(I))-XK(I)
      GO TO 34
   41 SUMS1=SSQER
   20 DO 23 I=1,NVAR
      XK1(I)=XK(I)
   23 P(NPAR(I))=P(NPAR(I))-XK(I)
      GO TO 35
```

```
   71 DO 72 M=1,NVAR
      P(NPAR(M))=P(NPAR(M))-XK(M)
      XK(M)=XK(M)*SCALE
   72 P(NPAR(M))=P(NPAR(M))+XK(M)
      GO TO 73
C
C     CALCULATE NEW VALUES OF PARAMETERS.
C
   43 DO 44 I=1,NVAR
   44 P(NPAR(I))=P(NPAR(I))-XK(I)+XK1(I)
      LAMDA=LAMDA*VEE
      NIF=2
   45 WRITE(6,31)
   31 FORMAT(//29H CURRENT VALUES OF PARAMETERS)
      WRITE(6,88)
   88 FORMAT(120H ----------------------------------------------------------
     1----------------------------------------------------------------)
      WRITE(6,225)(P(NPAR(K)),K=1,NVAR)
  225 FORMAT(5(5X,E10.4))
      WRITE(6,88)
C
C     TEST FOR CONVERGENCE
C
      GO TO(52,51),NIF
   52 IF(SSQER.LT.1.0E-06)GO TO 25
      DO 21 I=1,NVAR
      IF((ABS(P(NPAR(I)))*CONV).LT.ABS(XK(I)))GO TO 22
   21 CONTINUE
   25 NPMAX=0
      NP=NP+1
      GO TO 999
   51 DO 2 I=1,NVAR
      IF((ABS(P(NPAR(I)))*CONV).LT.ABS(XK1(I)))GO TO 22
    2 CONTINUE
      NPMAX=0
   22 NP=NP+1
      IF(NP.GT.NPMAX)NPMAX=0
  999 RETURN
      END
      SUBROUTINE ERROR(NVAR,NEXP,NDV)
C
C     THIS ROUTINE CALCULATES THE STANDARD DEVIATIONS IN THE PARAMETERS
C     AND CORRELATION COEFFICIENTS.
C
      COMMON/SET1/P
      COMMON/SET4/S,Y,NPAR,NCODE,SIGMA
      COMMON/SET9/V
      COMMON/SET11/SSQER
      DIMENSION S(80,80),Y(80),V(80,80),NPAR(100),CM(80,80),SIGMA(80),NC
     1ODE(100),P(100)
      F=SSQER/(NEXP*NDV-NVAR)
      DO 14 I=1,80
      DO 13 J=1,80
   13 CM(I,J)=0.0
   14 CONTINUE
      IEGEN=0
      NR=0
      CALL HDIAG(S,NVAR,IEGEN,V,NR)
      DO 1 I=1,NVAR
      DO 11 J=1,NVAR
      DO 2 K=1,NVAR
    2 CM(I,J)=CM(I,J)+(F*V(I,K)/S(K,K))*V(J,K)
   11 CONTINUE
    1 CONTINUE
      DO 3 K=1,NVAR
    3 SIGMA(K)=SQRT(CM(K,K))
```

```
C
C        CALCULATE CORRELATION COEFFICIENTS
C
         DO 6 K=1,NVAR
         DO 7 N=1,NVAR
      7  CM(K,N)=CM(K,N)/(SIGMA(K)*SIGMA(N))
      6  CONTINUE
         WRITE(6,8)
      8  FORMAT(///25H CORRELATION COEFFICIENTS)
         DO 10 K=1,NVAR
     10  WRITE(6,9)(CM(K,N),N=K,NVAR)
      9  FORMAT(10(2X,F5.2))
         RETURN
         END
```

REFERENCES

[1] Alcock, R. M., Hartley, F. R., and Rogers, D. E. (1978). *J.C.S. (Dalton)*, 115.

[2] Alcock, R. M., Hartley, F. R., Rogers, D. E., and Wagner, J. L. (1975). *J.C.S. (Dalton)*, 2189.

[3] Alcock, R. M., Hartley, F. R., Rogers, D. E., and Wagner, J. L. (1975). *J.C.S. (Dalton)*, 2194.

[4] Marquardt, D. W. (1963). *J. Soc. Ind. Appl. Maths.*, **11**, 431.

[5] Perrin, D. D., and Sayce, I. G. (1967). *Talanta.*, **14**, 833.

[6] Ting-Po, I., and Nancollas, G. H. (1972). *Anal. Chem.*, **44**, 1940.

[7] Lansbury, R. C., Price, V. E., and Smeeth, A. G. (1965). *J. Chem. Soc. (A)*, 1896.

Index

Personal names are only given when they are referred to in the main body of the text.

Principal Symbols Used

PRINCIPAL SYMBOLS USED (to avoid an unnecessarily long list, symbols that apply to a single section have been omitted).

(i) *Alphabetical symbols*

A	absorbance
A^λ	absorbance of a solution at wavelength λ
a_{ij}	absorbance at wavelength i of solution j
A	absorbance matrix
α_c	degree of formation (Section 3.2(ii))
B	B-matrix (Section 5.3)
β_n	overall stoichiometric stability constant for ML_n (Section 1.5)
$\beta_n^{\ominus}$	overall thermodynamic stability constant for ML_n (Section 1.5)
β_n'	conditional overall stability constant for ML_n (Section 7.5)
β_{nm}	overall stoichiometric stability constant for $M_m L_n$ (Section 6.6)
c	concentration
C	concentration matrix
C	correlation coefficient matrix
∂	partial differential
ΔG	free energy change
ΔH	enthalpy change
ΔH_{dil}	enthalpy of dilution
ΔH_{solv}	solvation enthalpy change
ΔS	entropy change
ΔS_{solv}	solvation entropy change
e_i	error associated with the ith component
E	error-matrix
E	observed potential (e.m.f.)
E^o	standard potential
$E_{\frac{1}{2}}$	half-wave potential (polarography)
ϵ	molar absorptivity
$\mathbf{\varepsilon}$	molar absorptivity matrix
$F(L)$	Leden's function (Section 3.7(i))

$\mathcal{F}$ Faraday

ϕ degree of complex formation (Section 3.2(iii))

γ activity coefficient

k_f forward rate constant

k_r reverse rate constant

K stoichiometric stability constant

$K^{\ominus}$ thermodynamic stability constant

K_n stepwise stoichiometric stability constant

L   ligand

λ wavelength

ln   logarithm to base e

log   logarithm to base 10

m number of metal atoms in a polynuclear complex (sometimes used with a local definition in specific sections)

M   metal

μ ionic strength

ML_n mononuclear complex

M_mL_n polynuclear complex

n number of ligands in a complex (somtimes used with a local definition in specific sections)

$\bar{n}$ complex formation function (Section 3.2(i))

N maximum number of ligands per metal ion

o experimental observation

O   vector of observations

Π product

pX $-\log_{10}[X]$

Q   heat absorbed or liberated

r_x residual of x

R (in association with T) gas constant
(not in association with T) Hamilton R-factor (Section 5.4)

$R_{\lim}$ limiting Hamilton R-factor (Section 5.4)

S sum of squares of residuals (Sections 4.5 and 11.4)

σ_x standard deviation of x

σ_x^2 variance of x

Σ sum

T absolute temperature

T   variance-covariance matrix

$\bar{v}$ average number of ligands per metal ion (Sections 3.7(i) and 11.4)

V   vector of residuals

w_x weight of an observation of x (Section 4.3)

W   weight matrix

x mole fraction (except in Section 3.5 where x = spreading factor)

X(L)   Fronaeus' function (Section 3.7(ii))

z number of electrons; ionic charge

(ii) *Non-alphabetical symbols*

{}   activity

[]   equilibrium concentration

[]$_T$ total concentration

~   transpose

⌢   best fit values